Indie Press Guide
2nd edition

The Mslexia guide to small and independent
book publishers and literary magazines in the
UK and the Republic of Ireland

First published 2018 by Mslexia Publications Ltd

PO Box 656, Newcastle upon Tyne NE99 1PZ
www.mslexia.co.uk

ISBN 978-0-9955250-2-3

Editorial Director: Debbie Taylor
Editor and Production Manager: Françoise Harvey
Reviewers: Lisanne Buijze, Kay Hadden, Charlea Harrison,
Françoise Harvey, Martha Lane, Emily Owens, Emma Whitehall
Production assistants: Kay Hadden, Charlea Harrison, Emily Owens
Advertising: Laura Steven

Printed and bound in the UK by TJ International
Designed by Juliette Boisseau, www.outlinedesign.co.uk

Supported using public funding by
**ARTS COUNCIL
ENGLAND**

Contents

Welcome to the second edition of the *Indie Press Guide*.

Researching the first edition of our Guide was a mammoth task that involved weeks trawling the internet, sorting through hundreds of questionnaires, and sending thousands of emails as we chased up samples and checked details.

The project, supported by Arts Council England (thank you!), took an entire year to complete and left us frazzled and exhausted – but also very proud to have actually done what no other organisation had even attempted for two decades. It was rather humbling too, to find out how very (very) many indie presses there are out there, and to discover the amazing diversity of the work they are producing. Some combine original art with text; or text and digital media. There are magazines on expensive paper, and rough-and-ready stapled pamphlets; exquisite hand-finished artisan volumes and stylish e-books.

As Mslexia Editor Debbie Taylor wrote in her introduction two years ago: 'We created *Indie Presses* as a resource for writers, but we hope it will also act as a calling card for all the independent presses represented here too. Because they need, and deserve, our support.'

When the first edition was eventually published back in 2016, the reaction was everything we hoped it would be. Within weeks we began to receive emails from readers telling us they had at last found homes for their difficult-to-place novels; that their poems were being published for the first time; that they'd discovered a magazine that published exactly the kind of idiosyncratic stories they wrote – work so 'out there' they feared it would never appear in print.

'I'd exhausted my list of agents and larger publishing houses and was feeling pretty low,' Helen Young told us. 'Then I summoned what courage I had left and went through the Guide, submitting my novel to every relevant press. That was over a month ago – since then I've been offered publication, which I've accepted.'

Messages like this make all those long days huddled over spreadsheets worthwhile.

We had similar reactions from many of the editors whose presses and magazines appeared in the first edition – delighted that someone had taken on such a daunting task and excited about all the new writers they might discover as a result.

When we sent that edition to press two years ago, we were confident we had included every significant indie press in the UK and Republic of

Ireland – at that time.

But life doesn't stand still in the indie press sector. The ink was hardly dry when we began to hear about lots of exciting new start-ups, and presses who had maintained such a low profile we hadn't found them the first time around. And in the intervening years, of course, many of the presses have changed their submission guidelines or the kinds of material they published – and, sadly, a few have ceased operation altogether.

We have had to update much of the information in the Guide to take account of these changes. The results await you.

We've divided the Guide into clear sections: book publishers, magazines and journals (including e-zines), and script publishers and producers who are prepared to look at submissions. Subsections divide the book publishers and magazines into those focusing on prose (including fiction, memoir, biography, etc.) and those focusing on poetry. Book publishers that produce both are listed in both sections, while magazines have been divided into poetry only, prose only and mixed form (prose, poetry, graphics and more).

Where a publisher didn't respond to our approaches, we checked to ensure they were still operating, and included them as a 'stub' entry, consisting of contact details and as much information as we could glean from their websites.

Where we did received information from the publisher, we have generated entries that include much of the following information:

- The type of publications they produce. Please note that 'e-books' does not always mean *only* e-books – most also produce print books.
- Contact details (including where possible a postal address, a phone number, an email address and a website) and the name of the editor(s).
- The year the press was established (to give you some idea of their longevity), and where their publications are available (bookshops, online, or both) so that you, the writer, have an idea of where your work might end up. We've also tried to include details of any awards the press might have won.
- The genres published, where relevant.
- How to submit and where you can find further guidelines; any restrictions on eligibility; how long you can expect to wait for a response; whether the editor(s) can offer feedback – and the all-important payment policy.
- A ☆ symbol indicates that the press also runs one or more writing competitions – flip to the Competitions section on p283 for more information.
- References to any wider publishing activity – if a book publisher also runs a magazine, for example, we will direct you to the correct page.
- Some presses have also chosen to include an image – a logo or a sample book cover – and have taken the opportunity to describe

their aims, aesthetics and the kind of writing they are looking for under 'They say'.

• There is an Index at the end of the book if you want to look up a particular publisher (p299).

There is also a section entitled 'We say' included with many of the entries, in which we provide our reviewers' perspective on the quality of production and what to expect from the press in question. In order to compile this, we asked publishers to provide a sample of their output: in print, as a PDF, or as an online link. Not every press was able to oblige, but where possible we've tried to fill in the gaps with our own research. If there is no 'We say' under an entry for a poetry publisher, say, do check to see whether the press is listed in the prose section, where our review might be included.

Some presses state they they do not accept 'unsolicited submissions'. This does not necessarily mean their doors are closed to you. It usually means that the editors' policy is to approach writers whose work they have seen elsewhere, often in a literary magazine – another indication, if one were needed, of how important it is to get your work out there.

We hope this information will set you firmly on the way to being able to find an indie publisher or magazine that will be a good fit for your work. But remember, our 'We say' opinion may not match yours, and guidelines may change – again! – so we strongly urge you to research the presses yourself before sending your work. Visit their websites, check their backlists. Better yet, buy a publication or two.

Part 1:
Book publishers

authices

[auth(or) + (serv)ices]
format - ms critique - story coach -
marketing - query help - copywriting -
indie publish package

lizzieharwood.com

Indie publishers: an introduction

There are pros and cons to approaching an independent press with your work. On the plus side, indie presses are often more willing to take a chance on experimental writing – indeed many were launched precisely because their founders were frustrated that work they admired was being ignored by big publishers. An open submission policy is another bonus; unlike with big publishers, you rarely need to have ensnared an agent before a small press editor is willing to consider your manuscript. And because editors are more personally invested and passionate about the books they publish, they have a reputation for working more closely with the authors they take on. That passionate risk-taking approach has certainly paid off: for example Salt Publishing's *The Many* by Wyl Menmuir was longlisted for the Man Booker Prize, while Unbound produced the seminal work *The Good Immigrant*, the best-selling essay anthology on race and racism in the UK. And there's plenty of love for short stories amongst the indies. Where larger presses tend to shy away, the independents are happy to wave the flag for short fiction – yes, even flash fiction.

What about the cons? Well, not surprisingly, small presses often lack the clout of the bigger publishers when it comes to marketing a book. So you may need to get involved in the marketing and publicity yourself, possibly including contacting distributors to try and get your book into bookshops.

The production values (design, proofing, paper quality, etc.) are also worth keeping an eye on – not because indie presses are lax, but because less money means that it's not always possible to get the materials they want at a reasonable price. If you can, examine other titles published by the press you're considering approaching, and make sure you're happy with their production values. In our 'We Say' comments we have tried to give you an idea of what to expect, but these are only a starting point. Putting time into researching your options can save a lot of heartache later.

So here are some basic guidelines to bear in mind when submitting:

- First, do your research. We've given you enough information to help you shortlist the right press for you, but you should also check the websites, research books they've published, and establish that your work is the kind of thing they are looking for. It's a waste of your time and theirs if you send a sci-fi manuscript to a romance publisher.
- Second, make sure the publisher offers what you're looking for. You don't want your manuscript to be accepted only to discover

that the look and feel of the resulting book is not how you
envisioned your work appearing – or that you've been taken on
by an e-book-only publisher when you harbour dreams of ink and
perfect binding.

- Third, though we have tried very hard to ensure that no vanity
presses are listed here, do double check. It is incredibly exciting
when a publisher is interested in your work, but keep your head. If a
contract seems dodgy, do not sign it. Approach a body such as the
Society of Authors for advice.
- Fourth, don't submit your manuscript until it is finished, by which
we mean redrafted and redrafted (and redrafted) and polished
to a high gleam. No publisher will be interested in reading three
chapters of an unfinished book, or a hastily written first draft.
- Fifth, check whether your work is eligible. Several publishers in
this section also run literary magazines, which can mean that any
anthology they publish is compiled from work submitted to or
published in the magazine. So do check whether you need to have
been published in the magazine before a book manuscript can be
considered.
- Sixth, follow the submission instructions. Most publishers have
guidelines on their website, and they will all be slightly different
from each other. You will irritate the editor if you don't follow the
instructions carefully. Don't send more than the stated word limit;
don't submit outside the submissions window if there is one; don't
send your manuscript if they have asked for a query email first;
don't email if they specify post, or post your only copy if they
specify email. However good your work, it's not good enough for
you to ignore the guidelines.
- Finally, be patient. Most presses will probably receive a lot of
submissions, but won't have many people to assess them. Check
in the Guide for their usual response time, and don't even think
of chasing up your submission until that's elapsed. At that point, if
you still haven't heard, check their website or social media to see
if there's a reason for the delay. Then, and only then, send a polite
reminder. To reiterate: be polite. These people are considering
working closely with you, so any spikiness on your part will affect
their decision. And bear in mind that the world of indie presses is
small. If one publisher declines your work, thank them for reading
it, and move on. Do not reply in anger. Editors talk to each other,
and they remember the writers who have been rude.

Good luck!

Some of the publishers listed here cannot really be considered 'small' at all – Bloodaxe Books, for example, have been established for decades, publish many titles every year, and have an enormous backlist. However, because most specialist poetry publishers are open to submissions by poets without agents, we felt it important to include them all.

Bear in mind that most publishers of poetry collections do expect you to have a history of publication in magazines and anthologies. So if you don't yet have a track record for publishing single poems, skip to page p175 and check out the magazine listings.

Also listed in this section are a number of presses that publish both poetry and prose. In these cases we have indicated, where appropriate, what their dominant area of publishing is.

ACUMEN PUBLICATIONS
COLLECTIONS AND
CHAPBOOKS/PAMPHLETS
info@acumen-poetry.co.uk
www.acumen-poetry.co.uk
Editor: Patricia Oxley
Established 1985. Publications
available direct from publisher
website, by post and email order,
at local literary events and through
Amazon.
Award-winning publishers.
SUBMISSIONS: Open to all, but
publication history required (must
have been published in *acumen
Literary Journal* for pamphlet
publication). Submit by post (6 The
Mount, Higher Furzeham Road,
Brixham, South Devon TQ5 8QY)
or by email (patriciaoxley6@gmail.
com). Guidelines at www.acumen-
poetry.co.uk. Usually responds
within four weeks. May occasionally
provide feedback on submissions,
but only on request. Authors
receive free copies of their book,
no fee or royalties.
WE SAY: We looked at poetry
pamphlet *Dragon Child*, by
Marina Sanchez: a slim, 32-page
pamphlet, with stiff, matt, dark
pink cover with a photographic
image of a dragon sculpture. It's a
well-produced publication, with the
poems carefully ordered to tell a
chronological story.
**See also: *acumen Literary Journal*
(poetry magazine) p237**

AGENDA EDITIONS
COLLECTIONS
The Wheelwrights, Fletching Street,
Mayfield, East Sussex TN20 6TL
editor@agendapoetry.co.uk
www.agendapoetry.co.uk
Editor: Patricia McCarthy
Established 1959
SUBMISSIONS: See *Agenda* (p237).
**For a fuller description of this press,
see *Agenda* (poetry magazine) p237**

ALBA PUBLISHING
COLLECTIONS, ANTHOLOGIES
AND CHAPBOOKS/PAMPHLETS
PO Box 266, Uxbridge UB9 5NX
01895 832444
info@albapublishing.com
www.albapublishing.com
Editor: Kim Richardson
Established 1990. Also publishes
some prose (see p87). Publications
available by post and email order;
and from Amazon.
A title from Alba Publishing
was shortlisted for the Haiku
Foundation Touchstone
Distinguished Book Award 2013.
GENRES: Spirituality and beliefs.
SUBMISSIONS: Publication history
required. Submit by post
(PO Box 266, Uxbridge UB9 5NX)
or by email (info@albapublishing.
com). Usually responds within four
weeks, with submission feedback
only if requested. Authors
contribute to editorial/publication/
marketing costs.
WE SAY: We looked at a PDF
proof of *Initial Response* by Maeve
O'Sullivan, a 33-page perfect-
bound pamphlet. The cover has
a striking red and black design
of scribbled calligraphy, which
will look lovely in print, and the
collection comprises 'an a-z of
haiku moments'. Each letter of

the alphabet has a title ('A is for Autumn', 'B is for Birds & Berries', etc.) and a six-haiku poem across a double-page spread, with some black, splashed-ink illustrations on the second half of their spreads. It's an uncluttered, eye-catching design.
See also: prose publisher p87

ALLARDYCE, BARNETT, PUBLISHERS
COLLECTIONS AND MIXED-FORM COLLECTIONS AND ANTHOLOGIES
14 Mount Street, Lewes, East Sussex BN7 1HL
www.abar.net
Editor: Anthony Barnett
Also publishes prose (see p88). Publications available direct from publisher website; by direct mail and email orders; from independent bookshops; from Amazon; and from SPD in the US.
SUBMISSIONS: By invitation only.
See also prose publisher p88 and *Snow Lit Rev* (mixed-form magazine) p222

AND OTHER STORIES
COLLECTIONS
Central Library, Surrey Street, Sheffield S1 1XZ
nichola@andotherstories.org
www.andotherstories.org
Editors: Tara Tobler, Stefan Tobler, Sophie Lewis
Established 2010. Mainly publishes fiction (see p89). Publications available in chain bookshops nationwide; in independent bookshops; at local literary events; and from Amazon and other bookshop websites. Plans are in place for purchase direct from the publisher. Also offers a subscription: £20, £35 or £50 per

year for two, four or six books per year.
And Other Stories was shortlisted for the 2013 IPG Newcomer Award. Its authors have also been shortlisted for and won awards.
SUBMISSIONS: Open to all, but submitters are required to show proof of purchase from the press. Submit by post to Central Library, Surrey Street, Sheffield S1 1XZ. Guidelines at www.andotherstories. org/about/contact-us. Usually responds within one to three months. A standard rejection may occasionally include unsolicited feedback. Author payment is an advance/fee plus royalties.
For a fuller description of this press, see prose publisher p89

ANIMA POETRY PRESS
COLLECTIONS, ANTHOLOGIES AND CHAPBOOKS/PAMPHLETS
www.animapoetry.uk
Editor: Marcus Sly
Established 2014. Publications available direct from publisher website.
GENRES: Spirituality and beliefs.
SUBMISSIONS: Open to all. Submit through Submittable at anima. submittable.com/submit. Usually responds within four to six months. Rejection may occasionally include unsolicited feedback. Authors receive royalties.
For a fuller description of this press, see *Anima* (poetry magazine) p237

AQUIFER BOOKS
COLLECTIONS / MIXED-GENRE
aquiferbooks@gmail.com
www.aquiferbooks.co.uk
Publishes poetry with an experimental edge, as well as mixed-genre writing (bringing writers together with practitioners

in other areas) and writing from the 'in-between places' (notebooks, letters, email exchanges). Not currently accepting unsolicited submissions.

ARACHNE PRESS ☆
COLLECTIONS AND ANTHOLOGIES
100 Grierson Road, London SE23 1NX
020 8699 0206
www.arachnepress.com
Editor: Cherry Potts
Established 2012. Mainly publishes fiction (see p90) but also some poetry. Publications available direct from publisher website; by post and email order; at chain bookshops and independent bookshops nationwide; at local literary events; and from Amazon and other bookshop websites, including distributor www.inpressbooks.co.uk.
SUBMISSIONS: Particularly welcome from all women, and D/deaf writers. During submissions windows, submit through Submittable at arachnepress. submittable.com/submit. Guidelines at www.arachnepress. com/submissions. Usually responds within one to three months. Provides feedback on submissions where the editor thinks it would be useful to the author, unless explicitly asked not to. Authors receive royalties and/or free copies of their book.
WE SAY: We looked at the 96-page, less-than-A5 *With Paper for Feet* by Jennifer A. McGowan. With white pages and a matt cover, McGowan's poetry collection considers folklore and frailties, often from a woman's perspective; most memorably in 'Lady Macbeth in Palliative Care', Shakespeare's

antagonist did not die by her own hand, but slowly declines, pinning flies to the wall with her stainless hooks.
For a further description of this press, see the extended prose publisher entry p90

ARC PUBLICATIONS
COLLECTIONS, ANTHOLOGIES, CHAPBOOKS/PAMPHLETS AND E-BOOKS
Nanholme Mill, Shaw Wood Road, Todmorden OL14 6DA
01706 812338
info@arcpublications.co.uk
www.arcpublications.co.uk
Editors: Tony Ward, Angela Jarman
Established 1969. Publications available direct from publisher website; by post and email order; at chain and independent bookshops nationwide; at national and local literary events; and from Amazon and other bookshop websites.
Shortlisted for the Griffin Poetry Prize 2015.
SUBMISSIONS: Publication history required. Submit by email to info@arcpublications.co.uk (hard copy submissions not accepted). Guidelines at www.arcpublications. co.uk/submissions. Usually responds within four to six months. Rejections may occasionally include unsolicited feedback. Authors are paid an advance/fee plus royalties, and receive free copies of their book.
WE SAY: We looked at *Indelible, Miraculous*, the collected poems of Julia Darling edited by Bev Robinson. This is a posthumous collection from a much-loved poet. The print quality is high – a matt cover with a faded image of a hand print on a window. The

poems have been selected from an archive and the book includes a preface explaining that process and an introduction by poet Jackie Kay. The 168 pages span work across Darling's lifetime, beautifully presented and divided into chapters. The final poem, 'Entreaty', is a perfect sign off for both the book and for Darling. A well-made tribute from the heart.

ARETÉ BOOKS
COLLECTIONS AND E-BOOKS
8 New College Lane, Oxford OX1 3BN
01865 289193
aretebooks@gmail.com
www.aretemagazine.com
Editor: Craig Raine
Book awards include *A Scattering* by Christopher Reid winning the 2009 Costa Prize, which was also shortlisted for The Forward Prize and the T S Eliot prize in the same year. Writers receive royalties only.
For a fuller description of this press, see *Areté Magazine* (mixed-form magazine) p185

ASLS
COLLECTIONS
7 University Gardens, Glasgow
G12 8QH
0141 330 5309
office@asls.org.uk
www.asls.org.uk
Established 1970. Publications available direct from publisher website; by post and email order; at chain bookshops; at independent bookshops; at national and local literary events; and from Amazon and other bookshop websites.
For a fuller description of this press, see *New Writing Scotland* (mixed-form literary magazine) p213 and prose publisher p91

AS YET UNTITLED
ARTISTS' BOOKS
5 Veales Rd, Kingsbridge, Devon
TQ7 1EX
admin@asyetuntitled.org
www.asyetuntitled.org
Editor: Rosie Sherwood
Established 2012. Mixed form: artists' books. Publications available direct from publisher website; from selected/local chain bookshops; from independent bookshops; at local literary events; and at Artists' Book Fairs (national), and the Small Publishers Fair.
SUBMISSIONS: As Yet Untitled does not take submissions. Artists and writers are invited to collaborate with the press.
For fuller descriptions of this press, including what They Say, see prose publisher p91 and *Elbow Room* (mixed-form magazine) p193

AUGUR PRESS
COLLECTIONS AND ANTHOLOGIES
info@augurpress.com
www.augurpress.com
Established 2004. Books with an emphasis on enabling the reader 'to reflect, and to look beyond ... that which is immediately apparent'. Includes translated collections.
See also: prose publisher p92

AWEN PUBLICATIONS
COLLECTIONS
www.awenpublications.co.uk
Awen looks for 'writing that is imaginative, boundary-pushing, eco-conscious, enchanting, and challenging of received wisdoms'. The majority of Awen's authors are skilled performers, whether as poets or storytellers.
See also: prose publisher p93

BACKLASH PRESS
COLLECTIONS
www.backlashpress.com
Publisher: Gretchen Heffernan
Dedicated to releasing work that
'narrates a contemplated resistance
to obedience and trend'. Looks for
experimental, yet enduring poetry
collections.
**See also: prose publisher (p93) and
Backlash Journal (poetry magazine)
p239**

BARE FICTION ☆
COLLECTIONS AND
CHAPBOOKS/PAMPHLETS
177 Copthorne Road, Shrewsbury
SY3 8NA
info@barefiction.co.uk
www.barefictionmagazine.co.uk
Editor: Robert Harper
Established 2013. Publications
available direct from publisher
website; by post and email order;
and from independent bookshops.
SUBMISSIONS: Currently collection
publication is through the Bare
Fiction Début Poetry Collection
competition, see p288. Writers
receive royalties and free copies of
their book.
WE SAY: The first full collection
from Bare Fiction is Zelda
Chappel's *The Girl in the
Dogtooth Coat*, which is a 72-
page paperback. Bare Fiction have
used the magazine's style (font
choice etc) with this book and the
transition works well. The cover is
matt, with a striking, ghostly, black-
and-white image, the title font
nodding to art-deco. The poems
are well presented, and the quality
of print high.
**For a fuller description of this press,
see also *Bare Fiction Magazine*
(mixed-form magazine) p186**

BARQUE PRESS
CHAPBOOKS AND
PERFECT-BOUND BOOKS
www.barquepress.com
Barque Press was founded
by Andrea Brady and Keston
Sutherland in 1995. Check the
website for details of whether
submissions are being accepted.
Do read publications by the press
before approaching.
**See also: *Quid* (poetry magazine)
p251**

BIRLINN PRESS
COLLECTIONS AND
ANTHOLOGIES
West Newington House,
10 Newington Road, Edinburgh
EH9 1QS
info@birlinn.co.uk
www.birlinn.co.uk
Managing director: Hugh Andrews
Poetry published under the
Polygon imprint. Mixed form:
also publishes fiction and
non-fiction.
See also: prose publisher p94

BLACKHEATH BOOKS
CHAPBOOKS/PAMPHLETS
grunt.blackheath@virgin.net
www.blackheathbooks.org.uk
'A home for literary outsiders.' A
very small press which hand-prints
books using vintage equipment.
Publications are limited print
runs, with signed and numbered
editions. A long waiting list for
poetry publication.
See also: prose publisher p95

BLACK LIGHT ENGINE ROOM, THE
COLLECTIONS, ANTHOLOGIES
AND CHAPBOOKS/PAMPHLETS
theblacklightenginedriver@hotmail.co.uk
Editor: p.a. morbid

Established 2010. Subscription: two Dark Matter chapbooks per year £12 (UK), £16 (Europe), £20 (rest of the world). Publications available by post and email order; and at local literary events. **SUBMISSIONS:** Open to all. Submit by email to theblacklightenginedriver@hotmail.co.uk. Usually responds within one to three months. No feedback offered with rejections. Authors receive copies of their book.
For a fuller description of this press, see *The Black Light Engine Room* (poetry magazine) p239

BLACK PEAR PRESS ☆
COLLECTIONS AND ANTHOLOGIES
office@blackpear.net
www.blackpear.net
Editors: Rod Griffiths, Polly Robinson, Tony Judge
Established 2013. Publications available direct from publisher website; by post and email order; at local literary events; and from Amazon and other bookshop websites.
SUBMISSIONS: Usually by invitation only, but with occasional short submission windows open to all, which are advertised on the website. Usually responds within one to three months. Rejections may occasionally include unsolicited feedback. Authors receive royalties, plus discounted copies of their books.
For a fuller description of this press, see prose publisher p96

BLOODAXE BOOKS
COLLECTIONS, ANTHOLOGIES, E-BOOKS WITH AUDIO, BOOKS WITH VIDEO DVDS AND AUDIO CDS
Eastburn, South Park, Hexham, Northumberland NE46 1BS
01434 611581
admin@bloodaxebooks.com
www.bloodaxebooks.com
Editor: Neil Astley
Established 1978. Publications available direct from publisher website; by post and email order; from chain bookshops nationwide; from independent bookshops; at national literary events; and from Amazon and other bookshop websites.
Bloodaxe is a multi-award-winning press: awards won by its poets in the past ten years include the Nobel Prize in Literature, T S Eliot Prize, Griffin International Poetry Prize, Queen's Gold Medal for Poetry, Pulitzer Prize (USA), National Book Award (USA), Somerset Maugham Award, Geoffrey Faber Memorial Prize, Edwin Morgan Poetry Award, Roland Mathias Poetry Award, Corneliu M. Popescu Prize for European Translation, Criticos Prize, Bernard Shaw Prize, and Cholmondeley Award – to name just a few.
SUBMISSIONS: Publication history required. Submit by post to Submissions, Bloodaxe Books, Eastburn, South Park, Hexham, Northumberland NE46 1BS. A sample of up to a dozen poems is preferable to a full manuscript, and don't forget to include return postage. Usually responds within one to three months. Usually no feedback if rejected, but very occasionally a standard rejection may include unsolicited feedback. Authors receive an advance/fee, plus royalties.

WE SAY: Bloodaxe is a major indie publisher with open submissions, a long history of successfully taking risks on poets, and beautifully produced publications. With their high-gloss covers and instantly recognisable black spine and logo, Bloodaxe books are quality products. Most collections have an uncluttered layout on bright white paper, but the press also stretches to thick shiny paper and a square format for Frieda Hughes' poems and paintings book *Alternative Values*, which wouldn't be out of place on a coffee table.

BURNING EYE BOOKS
COLLECTIONS, ANTHOLOGIES AND CHAPBOOKS/PAMPHLETS
15 West Hill, Portishead, Bristol BS20 6LG
07904 191394
infodata@burningeye.co.uk
www.burningeye.co.uk
Editors: Jenn Hart, Clive Birnie
Established 2012. Publications available direct from publisher website and can be ordered to bookstores internationally. Burning Eye Books won the Saboteur Award for Most Innovative Publisher 2016.
SUBMISSIONS: Submit only during submissions windows (via Submittable), otherwise by invitation only. Guidelines at burningeyebooks.wordpress.com/about/submit. Sometimes charges a reading fee. Usually responds within one to three months. No feedback offered with rejection. Authors are paid royalties.
WE SAY: We looked at three digital samples of books from Burning Eye. For the most part, the books all contain prose poems, but the design style varies – showcasing

Burning Eye's range. *All Damn Day* by Jemima Foxtrot has a simple but satisfying layout, with a serif, left-aligned type and spacious pages. The poems are abstract, and all have dedications. *Letters I Never Sent To You* by Paula Varjack has a straight, sans-serif font, left aligned, and is less experimental. *The Fire Eater's Lover* by Sophia Blackwell has a beautifully illustrated cover.

BUTCHER'S DOG
ANTHOLOGIES
c/o New Writing North, 3 Ellison Place, Newcastle upon Tyne NE1 8ST
submissions@butchersdogmagazine.com
www.butchersdogmagazine.com
Editors: Degna Stone, Luke Allan, Sophie F Baker, Jake Campbell, Amy Mackelden, Andrew Sclater
Established 2012. Publications available direct from publisher website; at selected/local chain bookshops; at independent bookshops; and at national and local literary events.
Butcher's Dog was selected for The Pushcart Prize 2016.
GENRES: Includes prose poetry.
SUBMISSIONS: Butcher's Dog is currently on hiatus while the editorial team makes plans. Keep checking their website for further news.
For a fuller description of this press, including what They Say, see *Butcher's Dog Poetry Magazine* p240

CANDLESTICK PRESS
COLLECTIONS, ANTHOLOGIES AND CHAPBOOKS/PAMPHLETS
Diversity House, 72 Nottingham Road, Arnold, Nottingham NG5 6LF
01159 674455

info@candlestickpress.co.uk
www.candlestickpress.co.uk
Editors: Di Slaney, Katharine Towers
Established 2008. Also publishes
prose (see p98). Publications
available direct from publisher
website; by direct mail and email
orders; from chain bookshops
nationwide; from independent
bookshops; at national and local
literary events; and from Amazon
and other bookshop websites.
GENRES: None specified.
SUBMISSIONS: By invitation
only. Feedback not offered with
rejections. Authors are paid a flat
fee and receive free copies of the
book.
WE SAY: Well-presented anthology
chapbooks that can be sent
as gifts, as Candlestick Press
say, 'instead of a card'. The A5
chapbook comes complete with
envelope, sticker and bookmark.
We looked at *Ten Poems on the
Telephone* (Candlestick covers
many different topics): a quality
product printed on thick textured
paper with a bright cover and
simple illustrations. Perfect as a
light read for readers who enjoy
quality over quantity.
See also: prose publisher p98

CARCANET PRESS
COLLECTIONS AND
ANTHOLOGIES
4th Floor, Alliance House,
30 Cross Street, Manchester M2 7AQ
0161 834 8730
info@carcanet.co.uk
www.carcanet.co.uk
Publisher: Michael Schmidt
One of the UK's major poetry
publishing houses, founded in the
1960s. Includes several imprints,
and publishes a comprehensive
and diverse list of modern and
classic poetry in English and in
translation.
SUBMISSIONS: Open to all. Hard-
copy submissions only, which
should include six to ten pages of
work and an SAE – see the website
for full details. Decisions usually
taken within eight weeks. Please
familiarise yourself with Carcanet's
books before submitting.
**See also: *PN Review* (poetry
magazine) p247**

CB EDITIONS
COLLECTIONS
146 Percy Road, London W12 9QL
020 8743 2467
info@cbeditions.com
www.cbeditions.com
Editor: Charles Boyle
Established 2007. Publishes
poetry, and short fiction and other
prose (see p99). Publications
available direct from publisher
website; at chain and independent
bookshops nationwide; at national
and local literary events; and from
Amazon and other bookshop
websites.
A multi-award-winning publisher:
titles have won the Aldeburgh First
Collection Prize (2009, 2011, 2013);
the Scott Moncrieff Translation
Prize (2014) and the McKitterick
Prize (2008), as well as being
shortlisted for the Goldsmiths Prize
(2014) and the *Guardian* First Book
Award (2014).
SUBMISSIONS: Currently publishing
only a small number of titles;
please email (info@cbeditions.com)
before submitting. No feedback
offered with rejection. Authors are
paid an advance/fee plus royalties,
and receive free copies of the
book.
WE SAY: We looked at Dan
O'Brien's *War Reporter*, a 134-

CINNAMON PRESS ☆

COLLECTIONS, ANTHOLOGIES,
AND CHAPBOOKS/PAMPHLETS
Meirion House, Glan yr afon, Blaenau
Ffestiniog, Gwynedd LL41 3SU
01766 832112
jan@cinnamonpress.com
www.cinnamonpress.com
Editors: Jan Fortune, Adam Craig

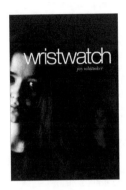

Established 2005. Mixed form:
alongside poetry, also publishes
novels, short stories and creative
non-fiction (p100). Cinnamon Book
Club: £40 per annum for six brand-
new books. Publications available
direct from publisher website; at
chain and independent bookshops
nationwide; at local literary events;
from Amazon and from Inpress
Books. Titles from Cinnamon Press
have won Scottish Arts Best First
Book of the Year; Wales Book of
the Year; and Wales Book of the
Year Readers' Vote. Also shortlisted
for Wales Book of the Year and
the Forward Prize for Best First
Collection.

SUBMISSIONS: Submit only during
submissions periods. See www.
cinnamonpress.com/index.php/
about-cinnamon-press/submissions
for full details. Usually responds
within one to three months.
Submissions that came close to
publication may receive some
feedback with rejection. Authors
are paid royalties only.

WE SAY: Gail Ashton's perfect-
bound collection *What Rain Taught
Us*, from the Liquorice Fish imprint,
is wrapped in a black and white,
psychedelic paperback cover. The
poems follow a mind fracturing. On
the off-white pages, there is the
sense that the text layout is

They say

Cinnamon Press is in its
12th year and committed to
keeping alive the passion
that got us this far. We're a
small, independent publisher
based in North Wales and the
Midlands. We select books
that we feel passionate about
and aim to be innovative,
publishing fiction, poetry and
selective non-fiction that is
not defined by genre, but by
unique voices with something
to say something. Our authors
come from all over the world
and we aim to remain outward
looking. In addition to books
we run mentoring, courses,
competitions and literary
events. Join our mailing list at
www.cinnamonpress.com.

devolving, with lines trailing away
in waves or making sharp turns
vertically down the page. Order is
restored against a background of
geometric shapes.

**See also: prose publisher p100 and
Envoi Poetry Journal p241**

page paperback, printed on high quality materials. The cover design adheres to the CB brand, which is a textured grey/brown background, with another single colour (red in this case) accenting the design. The text (long-line poems, based on interviews, conversations and transcripts) is well laid out.

CIRCAIDY GREGORY PRESS
COLLECTIONS
Creative Media Centre, 45 Robertson Street, Hastings, East Sussex TN34 1HL
sales@circaidygregory.co.uk
www.circaidygregory.co.uk
A mixed form 'independent publisher for independent readers'. As well as poetry, this press also publishes a range of prose.
See also: prose publisher p100

CLINIC
COLLECTIONS AND CHAPBOOKS/PAMPHLETS
clinicpresents@gmail.com
www.clinicpresents.com
Established 2009. Publishes pamphlets, anthologies, and occasionally on its website. Also runs popular poetry events.

CLUTAG PRESS
COLLECTIONS AND CHAPBOOKS/PAMPHLETS
PO Box 154, Thame OX9 3RQ
info@clutagpress.com
www.clutagpress.com
Publishes poetry and memoir with 'a marked but not exclusive interest in the margins and the marginal, in nature and place, in the British and Irish Archipelago'. Not currently accepting unsolicited manuscripts.
See also: *Archipelago Magazine* (poetry magazine) p185

COLUMBA PRESS
MIXED-FORM COLLECTIONS AND ANTHOLOGIES
23 Merrion Square North, Dublin 2, Ireland
garry@columba.ie
www.columba.ie
Editor: Garry O'Sullivan
Established 1985. Mainly publishes prose (see p101). Publications available direct from publisher website; by direct mail and email orders; from chain bookshops nationwide; from independent bookshops; at local literary events; and from Amazon and other bookshop websites.
SUBMISSIONS: Open to all. Submit by email to garry@columba.ie. Usually responds within four weeks. Rejections may occasionally include unsolicited feedback. Authors are paid an advance/fee plus royalties and receive free copies of the book.
See also: prose publisher p101

CRATER PRESS, THE
COLLECTIONS, ANTHOLOGIES, CHAPBOOKS/PAMPHLETS AND E-BOOKS
3 Kennington Park House, Kennington Park Place, London SE11 4JT
richie_fire@hotmail.com
www.craterpress.co.uk
Editor: Richard Parker
Established 2009. Offers a subscription of £55 for ten books. Publications available direct from publisher website; from independent bookshops; and from Amazon.
In 2011 The Crater Press won the Michael Marks Publishers' Award for British poetry pamphlet publisher of the year.
SUBMISSIONS: By invitation only. Rejections may occasionally

include unsolicited feedback. Authors receive free copies of the book.

CULTURED LLAMA
COLLECTIONS AND ANTHOLOGIES
Cultured Llama Publishing, INTRA, 337-341 High Street, Rochester
ME1 1DA
07800 522724
info@culturedllama.co.uk
www.culturedllama.co.uk
Editors: Maria C McCarthy, Bob Carling
Established 2011. Mixed form: poetry, short fiction and cultural non-fiction (see p104). Publications available direct from publisher website; at national and local literary events; and from Amazon and other bookshop websites.
SUBMISSIONS: Publication history required. Poetry submissions are not always open – check the guidelines at www.culturedllama. co.uk/publishing/submission to find out when and how to submit your work. Usually responds within one to three months. A rejection may occasionally include unsolicited feedback, but usually not. Authors are paid royalties only and receive free copies of the book.
For a fuller description of this press, see prose publisher p104

CURRACH PRESS
ANTHOLOGIES AND MIXED-FORM COLLECTIONS AND ANTHOLOGIES
23 Merrion Square North, Dublin 2, Ireland
garry@columba.ie
www.currach.ie
Editor: Garry O'Sullivan
Established 2003. Mixed form:

also publishes prose (see p105). Publications available direct from publisher website; by direct mail and email orders; from chain bookshops nationwide; from independent bookshops; at local literary events; and from Amazon and other bookshop websites.
SUBMISSIONS: Open to all. Submit by email to garry@columba.ie. Usually responds within four weeks. Rejections may occasionally include unsolicited feedback. Authors are paid an advance/fee plus royalties and receive free copies of the book.
See also: prose publisher p105

DAHLIA PUBLISHING ☆
ANTHOLOGIES
shaikhf@hotmail.com
www.dahliapublishing.co.uk
Editor: Farhana Shaikh
Established 2010. Mainly publishes fiction (see p105). Publications available direct from publisher website; by direct mail and email orders; from chain bookshops nationwide; and from independent bookshops.
SUBMISSIONS: Open to all. Submit by email (submissions@ dahliapublishing.co.uk) or by post (6 Samphire Close, Hamilton, Leicester LE5 1RW). Also accepts a Twitter pitch to @farhanashaikh. Guidelines at www.dahliapublishing.co.uk/submission-guidelines. Usually responds within four to six months. Rejections may occasionally include unsolicited feedback. Authors are paid royalties only and receive free copies of the book.
For further information, see also prose publisher p289

DEDALUS PRESS
COLLECTIONS AND
ANTHOLOGIES
13 Moyclare Road, Baldoyle,
Dublin D13 K1C2, Ireland
+35 318 392034
www.dedaluspress.com
office@dedaluspress.com
Editor: Pat Boran
Established 1985. Publications
are available direct from publisher
website; chain bookshops
nationwide; at independent
bookshops; at local literary
events; and from Amazon and
other online booksellers.
GENRES: Poetry (mostly Irish, some
translation).
SUBMISSIONS: Submissions
open to all, but only during
submission windows (see
Submission Guidelines on website).
Submissions via Submittable
only. Usually responds within
three months. Rejections may
occasionally include feedback.
Authors are paid royalties only,
although an advance may be
offered in particular cases.
WE SAY: The three books we

DEMPSEY & WINDLE ☆
COLLECTIONS, ANTHOLOGIES
AND CHAPBOOKS/PAMPHLETS
01483 571164
janice@dempseyandwindle.co.uk
www.dempseyandwindle.co.uk
Editor: Janice Dempsey

Publications sold direct from
publisher website; at local
literary events; on amazon.co.uk
and by ordering through any
bookshop.
SUBMISSIONS: Open to all,
during submissions windows.
Submit by email to janice@
dempseyandwindle.co.uk.
Guidelines are posted
on the website (www.
dempseyandwindle.co.uk).
Usually responds within
four weeks. Rejections may
occasionally include unsolicited
feedback. Authors must
contribute to production costs
by agreeing to buy 50 copies
of their book at 50% of RRP.
Authors sign an agreement

DEMPSEY & WINDLE PUBLISHING

setting out the rate of commission
due from sales through publishers'
distribution channels and within
four to six months. Rejections may
occasionally include unsolicited
feedback. Authors are paid
royalties only, and receive free
copies of the book.
WE SAY: We saw *A Talent for Hats*
by Fiona Sinclair, a perfect-bound
collection with a bright image on
the white, glossy cover. The poems
cover moments in life for a variety
of characters, from a bride whose
aunt can't share a nice word; to a
group of female teachers getting
ready for a night out.

looked at (*Geomantic* by Paula Meehan, *Clasp* by Doireann Ní Ghríofa, and *Transmissions* by Elaine Cosgrove) all have a matt finish and illustrated cover – Meehan's showing stylised landscapes within a large white border, and Ni Ghríofa's featuring a green-toned scene of Eve reaching for the apple. However, the cover for Cosgrove's book is the most striking: it appears to be a purple flower on a black background, but on closer look, the image is made of geometric shapes. All three collections are under 100 pages. Meehan's poetry seems to have a more uniform style, while Ní Ghríofa and Cosgrove experiment with form slightly more.

DIAMOND TWIG
COLLECTIONS
9 Eversley Place,
Newcastle upon Tyne NE6 5AL
0191 276 3770
www.diamondtwig.co.uk
diamond.twig@virgin.net
Editor: Ellen Phethean
Established 1992. Predominantly publishes poetry, but also publishes short story collections (see p107). Publications available direct from publisher website, and by post and email order.
Diamond Twig title *The Ropes: poems to hold on to*, an anthology of poems for teenagers, was shortlisted for the 2009 CLPE Poetry Award (Centre for Literacy in Primary Education) (www.clpe.co.uk).
SUBMISSIONS: Submissions for book publication are by invitation only. Usually decides within one to three months. Rejection may include occasional unsolicited feedback. Authors are paid a flat

fee and receive free copies of the book.
WE SAY: Though the A6-sized collections we saw, *Colours/Colors* by Angela Readman and *Inviolate* by Sara Park, are small, these perfect-bound collections are of a good quality. With glossy black covers bearing a single black and white image, both were printed on white paper; but *Inviolate*'s pages are of a much thicker stock, making the collection a bit harder to peruse. The font size is comparable to most larger-sized prints, making these books fairly easy to read.
See also: prose publisher p107 and *Diamond Twig* (poetry e-zine) p241

DIRT PIE PRESS
ANTHOLOGIES
editors@riptidejournal.co.uk
www.riptidejournal.co.uk
Editors: Dr Virginia Baily, Dr Sally Flint
Established 2006. Mainly fiction (see p107), but also some poetry. Publications available direct from publisher website; by post and email order; from independent bookshops; and at local literary events. All stockists are listed on the website.
SUBMISSIONS: Open to all, guidelines on the website. Submit by email to editors@riptidejournal.co.uk. Usually responds within four to six months. No feedback offered with rejections. Contributors receive a flat fee.
For a fuller description of this press see *Riptide Journal* (mixed-form magazine) p219. See also prose publisher p107

DOG HORN PUBLISHING ☆
COLLECTIONS, ANTHOLOGIES AND CHAPBOOKS/PAMPHLETS
45 Monk Ings, Birstall, Batley

28

WF17 9HU
01924 466853
editor@doghornpublishing.com
www.doghornpublishing.com
Editor: Adam Lowe
Established 2005. Also publishes
prose (short stories, non-fiction,
novels), see p108. Publications
available direct from publisher
website; by post and email order;
from chain bookshops nationwide;
from independent bookshops; at
national and local literary events;
and from Amazon and other
bookshop websites, including Lulu.
Titles from Dog Horn have won the
Guardian First Book Award (reader
nomination); the Noble (not Nobel)
Book Prize; and have had multiple
honourable mentions in the Year's
Best Horror.
SUBMISSIONS: Submissions
by invitation only. If invited,
submit by email to editor@
doghornpublishing.com.
Guidelines at www.
doghornpublishing.com/
wordpress/about. Usually responds
in over six months. Rejections may
occasionally include unsolicited
feedback. Authors are paid
royalties only and receive free
copies of the book.
See also: prose publisher p108

DOIRE PRESS
COLLECTIONS AND
ANTHOLOGIES
Aille, Inverin, County Galway, Ireland
+353 091 593290
www.doirepress.com
Editor: John Walsh
Established 2007. Publishes poetry
and short stories equally (see p108).
Publications available direct
from publisher website; from
independent bookshops; at
national literary events; and from

Amazon and www.kennys.ie.
Doire Press title *Waiting for the
Bullet* by Madeleine D'Arcy won
the 2015 Edge Hill Readers' Prize
and Breda Wall Ryan's *In a Hare's
Eye* won the 2016 Shine/Strong
Prize.
SUBMISSIONS: Only open to
writers living in Ireland, and not
actively seeking submissions
(though open to being approached
by writers familiar with Doire's
books who are sure their work will
be a good fit). Submit by post
(Aille, Inverin, County Galway,
Ireland) or by email (doirepress@
gmail.com). Guidelines at www.
doirepress.com/submissions.
Usually responds within one to
three months. No feedback offered
with rejections. Book deals vary:
authors may be paid royalties only;
may be paid an advance/fee plus
royalties; and/or may receive free
copies of book – the deal depends
on grant funding received.
WE SAY: *The Woman on the Other
Side* by Stephanie Conn is an
80-page poetry collection. Perfect
bound, with prize credentials
proud on the cover above the
title and set over the image of a
snowy path. The book features
pale blue end papers, which are a
lovely touch, while the main block
is made up of thick cream pages.
The poetry, largely free verse,
explores feelings of alienation in
language, place and relationships.
Well designed, with well-ordered
poems that conduct the reader on
a journey through the Netherlands.
See also: prose publisher p108

DOSTOYEVSKY WANNABE
COLLECTIONS, ANTHOLOGIES
AND CHAPBOOKS/PAMPHLETS
dostoyevskywannabe@gmail.com

www.dostoyevskywannabe.com
Editors: Victoria Brown, Richard Brammer
Established 2014. Also publishes prose and mixed-form anthologies (see p109). Publications available from Amazon and The Poetry Library, South Bank, London.
SUBMISSIONS: Open to all. Submit by email to dostoyevskywannabe@gmail.com. Guidelines at www.dostoyevsky.com/submit. Usually responds within four weeks. Authors are given two choices regarding royalties which are outlined in the submission guidelines.
For more information, see also prose publisher p109 and *The All-New Swimmers Club* (mixed-form magazine) p182

EARLYWORKS PRESS ☆
ANTHOLOGIES, INC.
MIXED-FORM ANTHOLOGIES
Creative Media Centre,
45 Robertson St, Hastings, TN34 1HL
kay@earlyworkspress.co.uk
www.earlyworkspress.co.uk
Editor: Kay Green
Established 2005. Mixed form. As well as poetry, Earlyworks publishes prose, as well as mixed-form anthologies (see p109). Most books are anthologies of work by authors from the publisher's competition shortlists. Publications available direct from publisher website; at independent bookshops; at local literary events; and from Amazon. Discounted books are available to club members and competition shortlisted authors.
GENRES: Any.
SUBMISSIONS: As Earlyworks Press is a club for authors and illustrators – running writing competitions,

producing winners' anthologies and some other books – please submit via competition initially (www.earlyworkspress.co.uk/Competitions.htm, see p290). The press often invites shortlisted authors to join in other publishing projects.
WE SAY: The 66-page A5 collection we saw, *This is a book about Alice*, contained the press' 2012 competition winners' works. Perfect-bound, with a colour photograph on its glossy cover, the included poems range from funny to ruthless. In one piece that stands out, 'Snegurochka', a sarafan and kokoshnik-clad girl performs for the General in the balcony, filled with silent rage as she thinks of the bones that protrude from the 'ruddied mortar' of walled cemetaries.
See also: prose publisher p109

EGG BOX PUBLISHING
COLLECTIONS, ANTHOLOGIES AND CHAPBOOKS/PAMPHLETS
ueapubsoc@gmail.com
www.eggboxpublishing.com
Advisor: Nathan Hamilton
Established 2006, working in partnership with UEA students. Publications available direct from publisher website; by post and email order; from chain bookshops nationwide; from independent bookshops; at national literary events; and from Amazon and other bookshop websites.
See also: prose publisher p110

ENITHARMON PRESS
COLLECTIONS, ANTHOLOGIES, CHAPBOOKS/PAMPHLETS, ART BOOKS AND E-BOOKS
10 Bury Place, London, WC1A 2JL
020 7430 0844

EMMA PRESS, THE

COLLECTIONS FOR CHILDREN, ANTHOLOGIES AND CHAPBOOKS/ PAMPHLETS
16-26 Hylton Street, Jewellery Quarter, Birmingham, B18 6HQ
queries@theemmapress.com
www.theemmapress.com
Editors: Emma Wright, Rachel Piercey, Richard O'Brien

Established 2012. Also publishes prose (see p110). Publications available direct from publisher website; from chain bookshops nationwide; from independent bookshops; at national and local literary events; and from Amazon and other bookshop websites. In 2016, The Emma Press won the Michael Marks award for Poetry Pamphlet Publishers.
SUBMISSIONS: Open to all, during submission windows. Submit online at www.theemmapress.com/about/submissions. Usually responds within four to six months. Rejections may occasionally include unsolicited feedback. Submitters are required to buy a book from the press. Authors are paid royalties only and receive free copies of the book.
WE SAY: We looked at anthology *Slow Things*, a slightly smaller than A5 paperback, 53 pages long. Made from quality materials, with a lovely, quirky cover that has an illustration of a sloth having a picnic, and blue end papers. A clean layout, plenty of biog space and illustrated with sketches.
See also: prose publisher p110

They say

The Emma Press is an independent publisher dedicated to producing beautiful, thought-provoking, often illustrated books. The founder, Emma Wright, caught the publishing bug while working at Orion Publishing Group and originally started the press to share the poetry of Rachel Piercey. Five years later, the Emma Press has retained its initial principles of openness and accessibility and published over 50 titles, including 31 single-author pamphlets and forays into translated poetry, children's poetry and prose. *Moon Juice*, by Katie Wakeling, with illustrations by Elīna Braslina, won the 2017 CLiPPA, the Centre for Literacy in Primary Education's award for children's poetry books.

info@enitharmon.co.uk
www.enitharmon.co.uk

Established 1967. Publishes art and poetry. Publications available direct from publisher website; by post and email order; from chain bookshops nationwide; from independent bookshops; and from Amazon.

SUBMISSIONS: Submissions by invitation only.

WE SAY: Enitharmon Press have had 40 years of experience publishing poetry – longevity achieved by the production of first-rate publications. The quality of materials used remains high. Recent poetry collections favour bold, uncluttered graphic cover designs. We are particular fans of Maureen Duffy's *Pictures from an Exhibition*, which features different coloured eyes staring out from a dark blue background.

ERBACCE-PRESS
COLLECTIONS, ANTHOLOGIES AND CHAPBOOKS/PAMPHLETS
erbacce@blueyonder.co.uk
www.erbacce-press.com
Editor: Dr Alan Corkish
Co Editor: Dr Andrew Taylor
Established 2004. Publications available direct from publisher website; by post and email order; from independent bookshops; at national and local literary events; on and from Amazon. Note: erbacce is a cooperative, all profits are used exclusively to produce new books.

SUBMISSIONS: Open to all. Submit by post (Dr Andrew Taylor, 5 Farrell Close, Melling, Liverpool L31 1BU) or by email (erbacce@ hotmail.com). Guidelines are on the website. Usually responds within 48hrs. Authors are paid 20% royalties and receive free copies of the book and a discount on further copies.

WE SAY: The A5, 96-page perfect-bound collection we saw by Mudnakudu Chinnaswamy, *Before It Rains Again*, had a glossy cover showing a textured painting. Chinnaswamy, a prominent Dalit poet based in Bengaluru, India, was first being translated by Rowena Hill in 2002, before his collection was picked up by erbacce-Press. *Before It Rains Again* explores the social mores of touch and taboo in Hinduism, digging into two thousand years of history.

See also: *erbacce* (poetry magazine) p242

ESC ZINE
SHORT FICTION AND POETRY ANTHOLOGIES
escpeople@gmail.com
esczine.wordpress.com
Editors: Jessica Maybury, Aine Belton
Established 2011. Mixed form: fiction (see p111) and poetry. Publications available direct from publisher website; and at national and local literary events.

GENRES: Literary fiction; slipstream, experimental; art, fashion and photography.

SUBMISSIONS: During submissions windows, submit by email to escpeople@gmail.com. Guidelines at esczine.wordpress.com/ submissions. Usually responds within four weeks. Rejections may occasionally include unsolicited feedback. Contributors receive print copies.

See also: prose publisher p111 and *ESC zine* (mixed-form magazine) p194

ETRUSCAN BOOKS
COLLECTIONS AND
ANTHOLOGIES
Flat 2, 9 Maze Hill,
St Leonards-on-Sea, East Sussex
TN38 0BA
01424 433412
etruscanpublishing@gmail.com
www.llpp.ms11.net/etruscan/index2.
html

Primarily a poetry publisher,
though now looking at expanding
into prose. Publications include
visual and verbal poems and
translated works.

EYEWEAR PUBLISHING ☆
COLLECTIONS, ANTHOLOGIES
AND CHAPBOOKS/PAMPHLETS
Suite 333, 19-21 Crawford Street,
Marylebone, London W1H 1PJ
info@eyewearpublishing.com
www.eyewearpublishing.com
Editors: Todd Swift, Rosanna Hildyard,
Alexandra Payne

Established 2012. Also publishes
prose (see p112). Publications
available direct from publisher
website; from chain bookshops
nationwide; from independent
bookshops; and from Amazon and
other bookshop websites.
Eyewear Publishing title *Psalmody*
by Maria Apichella was shortlisted
for the Felix Dennis Prize (aka
The Forward Prize for Best First
Poetry Collection). *Weemoed* by
Tim Dooley and *Mr Universe* by
Rich Goodson have also been PBS
recommendations.
SUBMISSIONS: Open to all.
Submit by email to info@
eyewearpublishing.com.
Usually responds within one to
three months. Rejections may
occasionally include unsolicited
feedback. A reading fee is
sometimes required. Authors are
paid royalties only.
WE SAY: We saw titles from
the Lorgnette Series, a set of
20 limited-edition pamphlets
chosen and edited by Todd Smith
from open submissions to the
press. These A5 perfect-bound
collections feature around 30-
40 pages wrapped in vibrantly
patterned, matt covers. Rose
Rouse's *Tantric Goddess* moves
from Tantric modalities for older
people to the evolution of her
relationship with her Alzheimer's-
suffering mother. In 'Reborn', while
everything she hated has been
'emptied out', the image of the
two giggling as the writer trims
her mother's toenails, trying not to
make her bleed, is moving.
See also: prose publisher p112

FAIR ACRE PRESS ☆
COLLECTIONS, ANTHOLOGIES
AND CHAPBOOKS/PAMPHLETS
Primrose Cottage, Sweeney Mountain,
Oswestry SY10 9EZ
01691 239466
fairacrepress@gmail.com
www.fairacrepress.co.uk
Editor: Nadia Kingsley

Established 2011. Also publishes
prose (see p113). Publications
available direct from publisher
website; from chain bookshops
nationwide; from independent
bookshops; at local literary events;
and from Amazon.
*I Once Knew a Poem Who Wore
a Hat*, a Fair Acre Press children's
poetry book by Emma Purshouse
and Catherine Pascall Moore, won
the Rubery Award for Poetry in
2016.
GENRES: Nature writing; wildlife
photography; poetry pamphlets.
SUBMISSIONS: By invitation only.
Guidelines at www.fairacrepress.

co.uk/about. Authors are paid royalties only and receive free copies of the book.

WE SAY: Emma Purshouse's A5, 112-page perfect-bound collection of silly poems *I Once Knew a Poem Who Wore a Hat* isn't just for drawing kids' attention or making them laugh. Throughout the book, Figment (of the Imagination) pops up with suggestions for how to perform and memorise poetry. With fun illustrations by Catherine Pascall Moore, the collection won the Rubery Book Award in 2016.

See also: prose publisher p113

FAR HORIZONS PRESS ☆
MIXED-FORM COLLECTIONS AND ANTHOLOGIES
info.far.horizons@gmail.com
farhorizonsmagazine.wordpress.com
Editors: Peter Sutton,
Kimberly Nugent
Established 2014. Mainly publishes prose (see p113). Publications available at local literary events and from Amazon.

SUBMISSIONS: Open to all. Submit by email to info.far.horizons@gmail.com. Guidelines at farhorizonmagazine.wordpress.com/about. Usually responds within four weeks. Rejections may occasionally include unsolicited feedback. Authors are paid royalties only and receive free copies of the book.

See also: prose publisher p113 and *Far Horizons* **(mixed-form magazine) p194**

FINE PRESS POETRY
COLLECTIONS
andrewmoorhouse@me.com
www.finepresspoetry.com
Editor: Andrew Moorhouse
Established 2014. Publications

available direct from publisher website.

SUBMISSIONS: By invitation only. Submit by email to andrewmoorhouse@me.com. Usually responds within four weeks. Rejections include reason for decision and suggestions of alternative publishers. No feedback offered with rejections. Payment to author is individually arranged.

WE SAY: We were unable to see a full publication from Fine Press Poetry, but we did view some photos of the books, which are hard back and clothbound with plenty of texture. The title and author appear framed on white paper, embedded in the cover. The inner pages look delicate and well designed, featuring detailed ink drawings and a pleasing serif font, and the paper appears to be thick and textured.

FISH PUBLISHING ☆
ANTHOLOGIES
Durrus, Bantry, Co. Cork, Ireland
info@fishpublishing.com
www.fishpublishing.com
Editors: Clem Cairns, Jula Walton, Mary-Jane Holmes
Established 1994. Poetry is published only as part of mixed-content anthologies, alongside short stories and memoir. Please see p114 (prose publisher) for more details.

For a fuller description of this press, including what They Say, see prose publisher p114

FITZCARRALDO EDITIONS ☆
COLLECTIONS
243 Knightsbridge, London SW7 1DN
info@fitzcarraldoeditions.com
www.fitzcarraldoeditions.com
Editor: Jacques Testard

Established 2014. Mixed-form publisher: primarily publishes literary fiction and non-fiction/ essays (see p114). Publications available direct from publisher website; by post and email order; from chain bookshops and independent bookshops nationwide; at national and local literary events; and from Amazon. Offers a books subscription: £70 for eight books, £35 for four. Fitzcarraldo title *My Documents*, by Alejandro Zambra, was shortlisted for the 2015 Frank O'Connor Short Story Award.

SUBMISSIONS: Open to all. Usually responds within one to three months. Rejections may occasionally include unsolicited feedback. Authors are paid an advance/fee plus royalties.

For a fuller description of this press see prose publisher p114

FIVE LEAVES PUBLICATIONS

COLLECTIONS, ANTHOLOGIES AND CHAPBOOKS/PAMPHLETS

14a Long Row, Nottingham NG1 2DH

0115 837 3097

bookshop@fiveleaves.co.uk

www.fiveleaves.co.uk

Editor: Ross Bradshaw

Established 1995. Mainly publishes prose (see p115). Publications available direct from publisher website; by direct mail and email orders; from chain bookshops nationwide; from independent bookshops; at local literary events; and from Amazon and other bookshop websites.

SUBMISSIONS: By invitation only. No feedback offered with rejections. Author payment varies between books but a no contribution is required.

WE SAY: We looked at the digital copy of *Staring Directly at the Eclipse* by Henry Normal, an 80-page collection which features two blocky, stylised figures on the cover. The medium of the cover image looks like acrylic paint, thickly applied – almost like a child's painting, which reflects the author's focus on themes of family and connection in the poetry within, which is tenderly written. The design of the inner pages is clean and professional, with a narrow san-serif font used for the poem titles.

See also: prose publisher p115

FLAPJACK PRESS

PAPERBACKS, E-BOOKS, COLLECTIONS AND ANTHOLOGIES

6 Chiffon Way, Salford, Greater Manchester M3 6AB

mail@flapjackpress.co.uk

www.flapjackpress.co.uk

Editor: Paul Neads

Established 2008. Publications available direct from publisher website; by post and email order; at independent bookshops; at local literary events; and from Amazon and other bookshop websites. Flapjack poets include Rosie Garland, Henry Normal, Dominic Berry (Best Spoken Word Performer winner, Saboteur Awards), Jackie Hagan (Creative Future Literary Award winner & Best Spoken Word Show winner, Saboteur Awards), Ben Mellor (Radio 4 Slam Champion), Gerry Potter and Tony Walsh. Flapjack Press title *Selkie Singing at the Passing Place* by Sarah Miller and Melanie Rees was runner-up for Best Collaborative Work, Saboteur Awards 2015. Children's collection *We Are Poets!* by Helên

Thomas won the Book of the Month Award from The Poetry Kit, 2008.

SUBMISSIONS: Priority is for northwest-based performance poetry and début collections. Currently closed to unsolicited submissions. Usually responds within one to three months. No feedback offered with rejection. Authors receive a flat fee or advance plus royalties, and free copies of the book.

WE SAY: The less-than-A5 perfect-bound paperbacks we saw, *As in Judy* by Rosie Garland and *Travelling Second Class Through Hope* by Henry Normal, both featured pictures of the poets on the matt covers. Not all books by the press are so designed though, and the cover on Normal's collection also differed as a French-flap style. Poem titles in both are underscored by a line the width of the text area. The final section of Garland's collection was inspired by the 1913 attack on paintings in Manchester Art Gallery by three suffragettes. One of the paintings, 'Syrinx' by Arthur Hacker, depicts Ovid's story of a woman who was transformed into reeds to escape the satyr Pan's advances; Pan fashioned pipes from the reeds, so he could forever press his lips to them and keep Syrinx strung around his neck.

FLARESTACK POETS
CHAPBOOKS/PAMPHLETS
flarestackpoets@gmail.com
www.flarestackpoets.co.uk
Editors: Jacqui Rowe, Isabel Palmer
Established 2009. Publications available direct from publisher website; at independent bookshops; and at national and local literary events.

Flarestack Poets has won numerous awards, including Publisher of the Year and Pamphlet of the Year for Gaud by David Clarke in 2013.

SUBMISSIONS: Open to all, during submissions windows. Submit by email to flarestackpoets@gmail.co.uk. Guidelines on the website. Usually responds within one to three months. No feedback offered with rejections. Authors receive free copies of the book, and are able to buy more copies at 33% discount. Pamphlets are promoted: sent to an extensive review list, plus a limited number of places nominated by the writer; submitted to PBS for Pamphlet Choice; and entered for the Michael Marks Award.

WE SAY: Wendy Pratt's A5 sized, saddle-stitched poetry pamphlet *Lapstrake* is bound in a thick, green cover, with pale pink inner covers. At the bottom of many of the cream-coloured pages are explanations of various references to Norse mythology; 'lapstrake' is a method of boat building where the edges of hull planks overlap, and as such the poems are interconnected. The collection considers the movement and what Pratt calls 'the changing emotions of the sea' in relation to loss.

FLIPPED EYE PUBLISHING
COLLECTIONS, ANTHOLOGIES AND CHAPBOOKS/PAMPHLETS
Free Word Centre, 60 Farringdon Road, London, EC1R 3GA
books@flippedeye.net
www.flippedeye.net
Established 2001. Predominantly publishes poetry, but also some fiction (see p115). Publications available direct from publisher

website; from selected/local chain bookshops; from independent bookshops; from Amazon; and at book launches and readings. Titles from Flipped Eye have won the PBS Pamphlet Choice award (2015) and been shortlisted for the Michael Marks Award (2014).
SUBMISSIONS: Submit by email to newwork@flippedeye.net. Guidelines at www.flippedeye.net/blog/2009/08/thesubs. A response is not guaranteed, but may be sent within one to three months. Rejections may occasionally include unsolicited feedback. Authors are paid royalties only and receive free copies of the book.
WE SAY: We saw *A Suburb of Heaven* by Pnina Shinebourne, a 48-page A5 paperback pamphlet with a matt cover, and winner of the 2014 Venture Pamphlet Award. On off-white paper, the first section of the collection is based on Stanley Spencer's work, known for its depiction of Biblical scenes placed in rural settings such as Cookham; the second on the part-imagined life of Anna O, patient zero of psychoanalysis.
See also: prose publisher p115

FOR BOOKS' SAKE
ANTHOLOGIES
www.forbookssake.net
Mixed-form publisher. Publishes poetry but also a lot of fiction and non-fiction prose (see p115 and p196). Publications available direct from publisher website; from selected/local chain bookshops; from independent bookshops; and at national and local literary events. For Book's Sake title *Furies: A Poetry Anthology of Women Warriors* was runner-up for the Best Anthology prize at the 2015 Saboteur Awards.
SUBMISSIONS: Open to self-identifying women, and especially encouraged from women of colour, disabled women, queer women, trans women and women from low-income backgrounds. Submit, during submissions windows only, via Submittable (forbookssake.submittable.com/submit – guidelines at same address). Usually responds within four weeks.
WE SAY: We checked out *Furies: A Poetry Anthology of Women Warriors*, which is one of a handful of For Books' Sake's cherry-picked titles. A perfect-bound hardcover with a sleek black and silver design, the collection has a luxurious feel – made edgy and current by the content itself. A fierce product for a fierce campaign: the collection raised money for the charity Rape Crisis. We approve.
See also: *For Books' Sake* (mixed-form e-zine) p196 and prose publisher p115

FOX SPIRIT BOOKS
COLLECTIONS / MIXED-FORM ANTHOLOGIES
adele@foxspirit.co.uk
www.foxspirit.co.uk
Editor: Adele Wearing
Established 2012. Mainly fiction publisher (see p116), but does publish some poetry collections, and prose/poetry anthologies. Publications available from Amazon and at select events.
Fox Spirit Books won the 2015 British Fantasy Society award for Best Small Press.
SUBMISSIONS: Submit only during submissions windows. See submissions guidelines at www.foxspirit.co.uk/sample-page/submissions for full instructions

and details of author renumeration. Feedback not usually offered with rejections. Will try to provide feedback on request, but this is not always possible.
See also: prose publisher p116

FREIGHT BOOKS
COLLECTIONS AND ANTHOLOGIES
49/53 Virginia Street, Glasgow G1 1TS
info@freightbooks.co.uk
www.freightbooks.co.uk
Editor: Henry Bell
Established 2011. Mainly publishes fiction, but also some non-fiction (see p116) and poetry. Publications available direct from publisher website; from chain bookshops nationwide; from independent bookshops; at national and local literary events; and from Amazon and other bookshop websites. Shortlisted for The Saltire Society's Scottish Publisher of the Year Award (2013, 2014).
SUBMISSIONS: No unsolicited poetry manuscripts. Authors are paid an advance/fee plus royalties. Guidelines on the website. Usually responds in over six months, with feedback only if requested.
For a fuller description of this press see *Gutter Magazine* (mixed-form literary magazine) p198. See also prose publisher p116

FROGMORE PAPERS, THE ☆
PRINT AND E-ZINE
21 Mildmay Road, Lewes, East Sussex BN7 1PJ
frogmorepress@gmail.com
www.frogmorepress.co.uk
Editor: Jeremy Page
Established 1983. Poetry, reviews, interviews. Subscription £10 per year. Available by post and email order. All online content is available to all.
GENRES: Poetry.
SUBMISSIONS: During submissions windows, submit by post to The Frogmore Papers, 21 Mildmay Road, Lewes BN7 1PJ. Usually responds within one to three months, no feedback offered with rejection. Contributors receive a print copy.

GALLERY PRESS, THE
COLLECTIONS
Loughcrew, Oldcastle, County Meath, Ireland
+353 49 854 1779
gallery@indigo.ie
www.gallerypress.com
Established in 1970 to publish the work of young Irish poets, with many of those poets becoming established, leading figures, and continues to look for new poets. Submit hard copy only, and ensure you are familiar with previous publications.
See also: script publisher (p279)

GATEHOUSE PRESS
COLLECTIONS AND CHAPBOOKS/PAMPHLETS
32 Grove Walk, Norwich, NR1 2QG
admin@gatehousepress.com
www.gatehousepress.com
Editors: Meirion Jordan, Andrew McDonnell, Julia Webb
Established 2006. Mainly publishes poetry, but also some fiction (short stories and novellas – see p117).
Publications available direct from publisher website; from selected/local chain bookshops; from independent bookshops; at national and local literary events; and from bookshop websites.
SUBMISSIONS: Submit during submissions windows. Usually

responds within one to three months. No feedback offered with rejections. Writer payment/ remuneration varies according to publication.

For a fuller description of this press, see *Lighthouse* **(mixed-form magazine) p204. See also prose publisher p117**

GIRASOL PRESS

CHAPBOOKS/PAMPHLETS
girasolpressuk@gmail.com
www.girasolpress.com
A very small press that seeks to explore connections and disconnections between Spanish and English. Prints work which explores language in all its forms, in exchange between these two (or more) languages.

GRAFT POETRY

COLLECTIONS AND ANTHOLOGIES
Frizingley Hall, Frizinghall Road, Bradford BD9 4LD
01274 541015
nicholas.bielby@talktalk.net
www.graftpoetry.co.uk
Editor: Nicholas Bielby
Established 2008. Publications available direct from publisher website; by direct mail and email orders; at local literary events; and from Amazon and other bookshop websites.
SUBMISSIONS: By invitation only. Usually responds within one to three months. Authors receive free copies of the book with further copies offered at half-price.
See also: *Pennine Platform* **(poetry magazine) p245**

GREEN BOTTLE PRESS

COLLECTIONS AND
CHAPBOOKS/PAMPHLETS
83 Grove Avenue, London N10 2AL
jennifer@greenbottlepress.com
www.greenbottlepress.com
Editor: Jennifer Grigg
Established 2014. Publications available direct from publisher website; from selected/local chain bookshops; and from independent bookshops.
SUBMISSIONS: During submissions windows. Publication history required – must have a record of publishing in magazines and journals. Submit by post to 83 Grove Avenue, London, N10 2AL, or via the submissions form at www.greenbottlepress.com/ submission-guidelines (guidelines at the same address). Usually responds within one to three months. The press will provide comments and feedback as part of rejection letters, but only on request. Authors are paid royalties only and receive free copies of the book.
WE SAY: Green Bottle Press arrived with a bang. The pamphlet *The Withering Room* by Sarah Sibley was named as the *London Review of Books*' pamphlet of the year. Containing 20 (mostly short) poems, this is a disconcerting collection, a feeling echoed in the beautiful cover image, which features lovely wallpaper with mould creeping across it. The layout is clear and uncluttered and the production values very high indeed. Any poet would be proud to have a pamphlet produced by this press.

GRIST

MIXED-FORM ANTHOLOGIES
www.mhm.hud.ac.uk/grist
Grist is the publishing branch of the University of Huddersfield, and

39

produces acclaimed anthology Grist, which includes poetry and short prose. Submissions are through competitions. Also publishes some single-author books.
See also: prose publisher p119

GUG PRESS
COLLECTIONS, ANTHOLOGIES AND CHAPBOOKS/PAMPHLETS
frogsandjays@gmail.com
www.gugpress.com
Editor: Francis Byrne
Established 2016. Mixed form: also publishes prose (see p119). Publications available direct from publisher website; by direct mail and email orders; and from independent bookshops.
SUBMISSIONS: Open to all. Submit by email to info@gugpress.com. Usually responds within one to three months. Rejections may occasionally include unsolicited feedback. Authors receive free copies of the book.
See also: prose publisher p119

HAFAN BOOKS (REFUGEES WRITING IN WALES)
ANTHOLOGIES AND CHAPBOOKS/PAMPHLETS
c/o Tom Cheesman, Dept of Languages, Swansea University SA2 8PP
t.cheesman@swansea.ac.uk
sbassg.wordpress.com
Editors: Tom Cheesman, Jeni Williams
Established 2003. Mixed form: publishes poetry and prose, and various refugee-related books and booklets (see p119). Publications available direct from publisher website; by post and email order; at local literary events; and from Amazon.
SUBMISSIONS: By invitation only,

depending on the publication. Author contributions needed. Submit by email to t.cheesman@swansea.ac.uk. Usually responds within four weeks. Rejections may occasionally include unsolicited feedback. Authors receive free copies of the book; no fee or royalties.
WE SAY: Hafan Books is part of local community efforts to support asylum seekers and refugees. All proceeds from sales go to Swansea Bay Asylum Seekers Support Group.
See also: prose publisher p119

HALF MOON BOOKS
PAMPHLETS/CHAPBOOKS
Half Moon House, 9B Westgate, Otley, West Yorkshire LS21 3AT
books@owfpress.com
www.owfpress.com
Half Moon Books is part of the OWF Press Community Interest Company, and an active member of the poetry community in Otley.

HAPPENSTANCE PRESS ☆
COLLECTIONS, ANTHOLOGIES AND CHAPBOOKS/PAMPHLETS
nell@happenstancepress.com
www.happenstancepress.com
Editor: Helena Nelson
Established 2005. Subscription available for £12.50 which includes one free pamphlet, discount on all titles and feedback on poems sent in during reading windows. Publications available direct from publisher website; by direct mail and email orders; from independent bookshops; at national and local literary events; and from Amazon. HappenStance Press was shortlisted in 2016 for the Michael Marks Award for Pamphlet Publishing.

SUBMISSIONS: During submission windows only; publication history required. Submit by post to 21 Hatton Green, Glenrothes, Fife. Guidelines at www.happenstancepress.com/index.php/poetry-submission/submitting-to-happenstance. Usually responds within four weeks. Rejections include a personal letter with feedback. Authors receive at least 12 free copies of their book, plus ongoing support.

WE SAY: We saw Charlotte Gann's *Noir*, a slightly-larger-than-A5, 76-page collection featuring a cover with a matt finish. The title is displayed in a yellow text, inside a yellow box, which contrasts nicely with the black and grey cityscape that makes up the rest of the front. The pages feel thicker than normal, which makes the collection easy to peruse. *Noir* is a collection of prose poetry with a focus on darkness, obsession, and a sense of place – specifically, an urban setting.

HEARING EYE
COLLECTIONS
Box 1, 99 Torriano Avenue, London NW5 2RX
020 7482 0044
info@hearingeye.org
www.hearingeye.org
Editors: Susan John, Emily Johns, David Floyd
Established 1987 and publishes poetry ranging from haiku to epic translations. Its poets are often guest readers at Torriano Meeting House. Rarely publishes unsolicited collections.

HERCULES EDITIONS
CHAPBOOKS/PAMPHLETS
07949 211740
tamar@herculeseditions.com
www.herculeseditions.com
Editor: Tamar Yoseloff
Established 2012. Publishes poetry combined with visual imagery. Publications sold direct from publisher website; at local literary events and from independent bookshops. Their first publication, *Formerly*, was shortlisted for the Ted Hughes Award in 2012.

SUBMISSIONS: Open to all, but accept very few unsolicited submissions. Submit by query only by email to tamar@herculeseditions.com. Usually responds within four weeks. Rejections may occasionally include unsolicited feedback. Authors are paid royalties only.

WE SAY: We looked at the available catalogue on the Hercules Editions website, where we found some very eye-catching books (Sean O'Brien's *Hammersmith* is particularly beautiful) which blend poetry and art together to create coffee-table-style collections. The site itself is very easy to use, and full of information without being over cluttered – worth a browse to see if Hercules is a fit for you.

HIGH WINDOW PRESS, THE
COLLECTIONS AND ANTHOLOGIES
submissions@thehighwindow.uk
www.thehighwindowpress.com/the-press
Editor: David Cooke
Established 2015.
GENRES: Contemporary verse.
SUBMISSIONS: Submitters must have a publication history. Usually responds within one to three months. Rejections may occasionally include unsolicited feedback. Authors can by 50

copies of their book at 50% cover price.

For a fuller description of this press, see also *The High Window* poetry magazine p242

HI VIS PRESS
COLLECTIONS AND ANTHOLOGIES
contact@hi-vispress.com
www.hi-vispress.com
Editors: Sophie Pitchford, Jim Gibson, Ben Williams
Established 2016. Also publishes prose (see p120). Publications available direct from publisher website; from selected/local chain bookshops; from independent bookshops; and at national literary events.
SUBMISSIONS: During submission windows only. Submit by email to contact@hi-vispress.com. Usually responds within one to three months, with feedback only if requested. Authors are paid royalties only and receive free copies of the book.
See also: prose publisher p120 and *Low Light Magazine* (mixed-form magazine) p206

HOLLAND PARK PRESS ☆
COLLECTIONS AND ANTHOLOGIES
46 Baskerville, Malmesbury SN16 9BS
publishing@hollandparkpress.co.uk
www.hollandparkpress.co.uk
Established 2009. Mixed form: also publishes prose (see p121). Publications available direct from publisher website; by direct mail and email orders; from chain bookshops nationwide; from independent bookshops; at national and local literary events; and from Amazon. Holland Park Press was the joint winner of the Oxford-Weidenfeld Translation Prize in 2016 and was shortlisted for the Etisalat Prize for Literature in 2013.
SUBMISSIONS: Open to all. Submit by email to publishing@ hollandparkpress.co.uk. Guidelines at www.hollandparkpress.co.uk/ submissions.php. Usually responds within one to three months. No feedback offered with rejections. Authors are paid royalties only and receive free copies of the book.
For further information, including what We Say, see also: prose publisher p121

HONEST PUBLISHING
COLLECTIONS, MIXED-FORM ANTHOLOGIES AND E-BOOKS
Unit 1B, Clapham North Arts Centre, 26-32 Voltaire Road, London SW4 6DH
info@honestpublishing.com
www.honestpublishing.com
Editors: Chris Greenhough, Daniel Marsh
Established 2010. Mixed output – also publishes prose and graphic novels (see p122). Publications available direct from publisher website; from major chain and independent bookshops; and from Amazon and other bookshop websites.
SUBMISSIONS: Open to all, but only during submission windows. Submit by post (Unit 1B, Clapham North Arts Centre, 26-32 Voltaire Road, London SW4 6DH) or by email (info@honestpublishing. com). Guidelines at www. honestpublishing.com/submissions. Usually responds within one to three months. No feedback offered with rejection. Authors are paid royalties and receive free copies of the book.
See also: prose publisher p122

HURST STREET PRESS
COLLECTIONS, ANTHOLOGIES
AND CHAPBOOKS/PAMPHLETS
OVADA, 14a Osney Lane, Oxford
OX1 1NJ
general@hurststreetpress.co.uk
www.hurststreetpress.co.uk
Editors: Beth Sparks,
Shoshana Kessler
Established 2015. Mixed form.
As well as poetry, Hurst Street
Press also publishes short story
collections and anthologies,
non-fiction books and mixed-
form anthologies (see p124).
Publications available direct from
publisher website; from selected/
local chain bookshops and from
independent bookshops.
SUBMISSIONS: Open to all. Submit
by post (Studio 1, OVADA, 14a
Osney Lane, Oxford OX1 1NJ) or
by email (general@hurststreetpress.
co.uk). Usually responds within one
to three months. Rejections may
occasionally include unsolicited
feedback. Authors are paid
royalties only.
**See also: prose publisher p124 and
mixed-form magazine *IRIS* p202**

IF A LEAF FALLS PRESS
CHAPBOOKS/PAMPHLETS
www.samriviere.com/index.php?/
together/if-a-leaf-falls-press
Editor: Sam Riviere
Established 2015. 23 works
released in 2016. Publications
available direct from the publisher
website. Subscription information
available on request.
GENRES: Procedural writing;
conceptual writing; appropriation.
SUBMISSIONS: Submission
guidelines are available at
www.samriviere.com/index.php?/
together/if-a-leaf-falls-press.

IF P THEN Q
COLLECTIONS
41 Fulford Street, Old Trafford,
Manchester M16 9PX
mail@ifpthenq.co.uk
www.ifpthenq.co.uk
Editor: James Davies
Innovative poetry press (publisher
of 'Poetry Wholes' as well as
collections). The publisher website
shares performance videos as well
as details of launches. Check site
for details of open submission
times.

INK SWEAT & TEARS PRESS ☆
ANTHOLOGIES
www.inksweatandtears.co.uk
Editor: Helen Ivory
Established 2007. Publications
available from Amazon.
SUBMISSIONS: Open to
all. Guidelines at www.
inksweatandtears.co.uk/
pages/?page_id=23. Usually
responds within one to three
months. No feedback offered with
rejections. Writers are unpaid.
**For a fuller description of this press,
see *Ink Sweat and Tears*
(mixed-form e-zine) p200**

IRON PRESS
COLLECTIONS, ANTHOLOGIES,
CHAPBOOKS/PAMPHLETS AND
E-BOOKS
5 Marden Terrace, Cullercoats,
North Shields NE30 4PD
0191 2531901
ironpress@blueyonder.co.uk
www.ironpress.co.uk
Editor: Peter Mortimer
Established 1973. Primarily
publishes poetry, but also releases
some prose (fiction, drama etc) –
see p126. Publications available
direct from publisher website;
by post and email order; from

INDIGO DREAMS ☆

COLLECTIONS, ANTHOLOGIES AND
CHAPBOOKS/PAMPHLETS
24 Forest Houses, Halwill, Beaworthy,
Devon EX21 5UU
publishing@indigodreams.com
www.indigodreams.co.uk
Editors: Ronnie Goodyer,
Dawn Bauling

Established 2005 (Ltd company 2010). Publications available direct from publisher website; by post and email order; from chain bookshops and independent bookshops nationwide; and from Amazon. Indigo Dreams won the Most Innovative Publisher 2017 category at the annual Saboteur Awards for publishing and literature. The Indigo Dreams editors won the Ted Slade Award for Services to Poetry (2015), organised by Poetry Kit. They were the first joint winners.
SUBMISSIONS: Open to all, but a publication history is required. Complete the appropriate publication enquiry form at www.indigodreams.co.uk/submissions/4591467549 (guidelines at the same address). Submit the form by email to publishing@indigodreams.co.uk. Usually responds within four weeks. Rejections may occasionally include unsolicited feedback. Authors are paid royalties and receive free copies of the book.
WE SAY: We looked at *Take Your Experience and Peel It* by Mab Jones, a 48-page paperback with a glossy finish. With poems such as 'Aquaeous', where a swimmer peels away her layers of clothing to dive into dark water, the collection focuses on the theme of metanoia –

They say

We consider work from new and established poets, publishing around 40 poetry collections/pamphlets annually, plus *Reach Poetry, Sarasvati* and *The Dawntreader* magazines. Further publishing opportunities are available through two competitions. We won the Most Innovative Publisher 2017 award in the Saboteur Awards and The Ted Slade Award for Services to Poetry (Yay!) with a respected newspaper calling us 'shining examples' of presses who 'keep the doors open for different kinds of voices and experiences.' We have a reputation for high production qualities and enjoy excellent working relationships with our poets. 'Pleasure, not pressure' all the way!

profound change and growth. Jones' work was the 2015 winner of IDP's Geoff Stevens Memorial Poetry Prize. **See also: *Reach Poetry* p251; and *Sarasvati* p220 and *The Dawntreader* p192**

selected/local chain bookshops; from independent bookshops; and via Inpress Ltd.

Iron Press's 2014 Iron Age Literary Festival won Best Event: Tyneside in The Journal Culture Awards.

GENRES: All poetry including haiku.

SUBMISSIONS: Contact the press before submitting work: see the website for guidelines. Submit by post (5 Marden Terrace, Cullercoats, North Shields NE30 4PD) or by email (ironpress@blueyonder.co.uk). Usually responds within one to three months. Rejections may occasionally include unsolicited feedback. Authors are paid a flat fee.

WE SAY: We saw *Connectomics* by Alison Calder, a 54-page perfect bound A5 collection of poetry inspired by science and the brain. Though the poems could stand alone, the notes included at the bottom of each enhance the reading; for example, one piece references research into Alzheimer's conducted by splicing firefly genes into mice and utilising the resultant florescences of the brain to conduct neural mapping.

See also: prose publisher p126

KATABASIS

COLLECTIONS, ANTHOLOGIES, CHAPBOOKS/PAMPHLETS

10 St Martin's Close, London NW1 0HR

020 7485 3830

katabasis@katabasis.co.uk

www.katabasis.co.uk

Publishes both poetry and prose. The poetry focus is on English and bilingual editions of Latin American poetry.

See also: prose publisher p128

KETTILLONIA

COLLECTIONS AND CHAPBOOKS/PAMPHLETS

Sidlaw House, South Street, Newtyle, Angus PH12 8UQ

01828 650615

www.kettillonia.co.uk

Editor: James Robertson

Established 1999, this press looks for new Scottish writing. The press aims 'to put "original, adventurous, neglected and rare writing" into print'.

KNIVES FORKS AND SPOONS

COLLECTIONS, ANTHOLOGIES, CHAPBOOKS/PAMPHLETS AND E-BOOKS

theknivesforksandspoonspress@
hotmail.com

www.knivesforksandspoonspress.co.uk

Editor: Alec Newman

Established 2010. Publications available direct from publisher website; by post and email order; from chain bookshops and independent bookshops nationwide; at national and local literary events; and from Amazon and other bookshop websites. Some online content (videos and audio) is also freely available to all. Knives Forks and Spoons was shortlisted for the Michael Marks Publisher of the Year Award (2010).

SUBMISSIONS: During submissions windows, submit by email to theknivesforksandspoonspress@ hotmail.com. Usually responds in over six months. No feedback offered with rejections. Authors receive free copies of the book.

WE SAY: We saw *Oh-Zones* by Elizabeth-Jane Burnett, a 20-page pamphlet. The cover design, which prominently features tree bark, appears ambiguous until you've read the pamphlet, at which point it's revealed as simple yet effective. Contemporary environmental poetry with an urban edge.

LAGAN PRESS
COLLECTIONS
Verbal Arts Centre, Stable Lane & Mall Wall, Bishop Street Within, Derry-Londonderry BT48 6PU
028 7126 6946

info@laganpress.co
www.laganpress.co
Mixed form: also publishes non-fiction and novels. Looks for work of 'literary, artistic, social and cultural importance to the north of Ireland'. Irish and Ulster-Scots language work also welcomed.
See also: prose publisher p128

LAUDANUM
ANTHOLOGIES AND CHAPBOOKS/PAMPHLETS
37 Hartham Road, London N7 9JQ
editor@laudanumpublishing.co.uk
www.laudanumpublishing.co.uk
Editor: Tiffany Anne Tondut

Established 2016. Publications available direct from publisher website; from independent bookshops; and at local and national literary events.
SUBMISSIONS: Submissions for anthologies open to all, during submission windows; submissions for chapbooks are currently by invitation only. Submit by email to anthology@laudanumpublishing.co.uk. Guidelines at www.laudanumpublishing.co.uk/about. Usually responds within four weeks. Rejections may occasionally include unsolicited feedback. Authors receive free copies of the book.
WE SAY: The perfect-bound paperback anthologies are slightly thinner than A5 size, with matt covers adorned with eye-catching art. The inner pages use standard paper, but we especially

liked the 50-page *Chapbook Anthology: Volume One*, which continued the theme of the cover art's colourful vegetation by including a pattern of apples and flowers at the beginning of each new section. Laudanum has taken the chapbook, often a brief and economically produced piece, and increased its design quality by presenting anthologies of three per volume. We also saw *Asterism*, a 64-page anthology of poems inspired by punctuation.

LAPWING PUBLICATIONS
COLLECTIONS AND
CHAPBOOKS/PAMPHLETS,
E-BOOKS
1 Ballysillan Drive, Belfast BT14 8HQ
lapwing.poetry@ntlworld.com
www.lapwingpoetry.com
Editor: Dennis Greig
Established 1988. Primarily
a poetry publisher, but
does occasionally produce
autobiographical memoirs and
novellas. Publications available
direct from publisher website;
by post and email order and at
author events, self-organised
or in partnership. Any five PDF
books available for requested £5
donation.
SUBMISSIONS: Open to all within
Western Europe (due to logistical
costs). Submit by email to lapwing.
poetry@ntlworld.com, ideally
using Word doc or docx format.
Guidelines at www.lapwingpoetry.
com/submissiondetails.htm.
Usually responds within four
weeks. Rejections may occasionally
include unsolicited feedback.
Authors receive ten free copies of
their book.
WE SAY: We looked at several
collections, all in digital format.
These A5 publications maintained
a cohesive design, with covers
featuring a photo or piece of
artwork framed by the title and
author's name, though sometimes
only text, on a white background.
Digital versions are available as
PDFs, rather than HTML-based
e-books, to maintain the house
style. Hard copies also sold.

LEAFE PRESS
COLLECTIONS AND
CHAPBOOKS/PAMPHLETS
leafepress@hotmail.com
www.leafepress.com
Editor: Alan Baker
Established 2000. Publications
available direct from publisher
website; by post and email order;
from chain bookshops nationwide;
from independent bookshops; at
national and local literary events;
and from Amazon and other
bookshop websites.
SUBMISSIONS: Submissions
currently by invitation only.
**For a fuller description of this
press, see *Litter Magazine* (poetry
magazine) p243**

LIBERTIES PRESS
COLLECTIONS AND ANTHOLOGIES
140 Terenure Road North, Dublin 6W,
Ireland
info@libertiespress.com
www.libertiespress.com
Founded in 2003. Mostly publishes
non-fiction and fiction (see p129)
but also some poetry. Open to
unsolicited submissions, but it does
charge a hefty reading fee. See the
website for full details.
See also: prose publisher p129

LISTEN SOFTLY LONDON
COLLECTIONS AND ANTHOLOGIES
07814 695751
listen_softly_london@hotmail.com
www.listensoftlylondon.com
Editor: Dominic Stevenson
Established 2015. Primarily
publishes poetry, but also some
prose (see p131) and mixed-form
anthologies. Publications available
direct from publisher website; and
from Amazon and other websites.
Listen Softly London was
nominated for the 2016 Saboteur
Awards.
SUBMISSIONS: Open to all.
Submit via www.listensoftlylondon.
com/submissions (guidelines are

available on the same page).
Usually responds within four weeks.
Rejections will get a full response:
'You have taken the time to write
to us, so we'll take time to write to
you.' Authors are paid royalties
and receive free copies of the
book.
WE SAY: The A5 collection that
we saw, *Your Attempt To Enjoy
These Poems is Considered
Unsatisfactory* by Gary from Leeds,
used space very frugally; while
never placing more than one poem
to a page, no facing pages were
left blank. Vibrant digital artwork
on the cover shows a bottle of
mouthwash against a mottled, teal
background. Although we saw
a digital version, books are only
available as hard copies.
See also: prose publisher p131

LITERARY POCKET BOOK, THE
CHAPBOOKS/PAMPHLETS
hitchinssteven@gmail.com
literarypocketblog.wordpress.com
Editor: Steven Hitchins
Established 2007. Publications
available by direct mail and e-mail
orders.
GENRES: Experimental; innovative;
performative; conceptual.
SUBMISSIONS: Open to all, but
please look at the sorts of books
published by the press before
submitting your work. Submit
via email (hitchinssteven@gmail.
com). Usually responds within one
to three months, with a personal
email, to each submission.
Accepted poets receive free copies
of their publication, and any further
copies at half price.

LITTLE ISLAND PRESS
COLLECTIONS, ANTHOLOGIES AND
CHAPBOOKS/PAMPHLETS

Lodgemore Lane, Stroud GL5 3EQ
07980 647187
info@littleislandpress.com
www.littleislandpress.com
Editor: Andrew Latimer
Established 2016. Mixed form:
publishes both poetry and prose
(see p131). Offers a subscription
of ten books for £50. Publications
available direct from publisher
website; from chain bookshops
nationwide; from independent
bookshops; and from Amazon and
other websites.
GENRES: Experimental; formal.
SUBMISSIONS: Submit during
submissions windows only, either
by post (to Little Island Press,
Lodgemore Lane, Stroud GL5 3EQ)
or by email (info@littleislandpress.
co.uk). Guidelines are available
at www.littleislandpress.co.uk/
about-the-press. Usually responds
in four to six months. Rejections
only include feedback on request.
Authors are paid royalties only.
**For a slightly fuller description of
this press, see also: prose publisher
p131**

MAGIC OXYGEN ☆
POETRY ANTHOLOGIES /
MIXED-FORM ANTHOLOGIES
The Flat, 53 Broad Street, Lyme Regis
DT7 3QF
01297 442824
simon@magicoxygen.co.uk
www.magicoxygen.co.uk
Editor: Simon West
Established 2012. Mainly publishes
fiction (see p132). Publications
available direct from publisher
website; from major chain and
independent bookshops; at local
literary events; and from Amazon
and other bookshop websites.
SUBMISSIONS: Submissions
are usually by invitation only.

Work should be sent to editor@
magicoxygen.co.uk. Usually
responds within one to three
months. Rejections may include
occasional unsolicited feedback.
Authors receive royalties.
**For further information, see also:
prose publisher p132**

MARISCAT PRESS
COLLECTIONS, ANTHOLOGIES AND
CHAPBOOKS/PAMPHLETS
10 Bell Place, Edinburgh EH3 5HT
0131 332 3451
hamish.whyte@btinternet.com
www.mariscatpress.com
Editors: Hamish Whyte, Diana Hendry
Established 1982. Publications
available direct from publisher
website; by post and email
order; from selected/local chain
bookshops; from independent
bookshops; and at local literary
events.
Mariscat Press won the 2015
Callum Macdonald Memorial
Award for poetry pamphlet
publishing, as well as the 2015
Michael Marks Award for poetry
pamphlet publishing.
SUBMISSIONS: Open to all.
Submit by post (10 Bell Place,
Edinburgh EH3 5HT) or by email
(hamish.whyte@btinternet.com).
Usually responds within one to
three months. Rejections may
occasionally include unsolicited
feedback. Authors are paid
royalties only, or an advance/fee
plus royalties.
WE SAY: The A5 saddle-stitched
pamphlets feature a sparse cover
design focused on the text of the
title and author's name, though
occasionally adding a simple
graphic or image. Though the
cover of *Toots* by Alyson Hallett
is printed on plain purple paper,

its heavy weight and added grey
endpapers enhance it slightly.
Additionally, the 32 inner pages
are printed on quality paper with
a simple design typical of other
collections.

MELOS PRESS
COLLECTIONS AND
CHAPBOOKS/PAMPHLETS
melos.press@btinternet.com
www.melospress.blogspot.co.uk
Editor: William Palmer
Established 2007. Publications
available direct from publisher
website; by post and email order;
in chain bookshops nationwide;
in independent bookshops; and
on Amazon and other bookshop
websites. Strictly poetry only.
SUBMISSIONS: Publication history
required. Submit by email to
melos.press@btinternet.com.
Usually responds within one to
three months. Rejections may
occasionally include unsolicited
feedback. Authors receive free
copies of their book.
WE SAY: Saddle-stitched
pamphlets with plain card covers
and white printer paper inside. We
flicked through *Black and Blue*,
a sequence of sonnets by Cathy
Galvin, which was clean and clear –
focusing on the words themselves
as opposed to the aesthetic.

MICA PRESS
COLLECTIONS, PAMPHLETS,
ANTHOLOGIES, E-BOOKS
47 Belle Vue Rd, Wivenhoe,
Colchester, Essex CO7 9LD
07894 210147
info@micapress.co.uk
www.micapress.co.uk
Editor: Les Bell
Established 2012. Publications
available by post and email order;

from chain and independent bookshops; and from Amazon, in the UK and other countries.
SUBMISSIONS: Open to all. Submit by post (47 Belle Vue Rd, Wivenhoe, Colchester, Essex CO7 9LD) or by email (info@ micapress.co.uk). Usually responds within one to three months. Rejections may occasionally include unsolicited feedback. Authors receive royalties on sales; free copies of the book; and additional copies at a discount rate.
WE SAY: We looked at a digital copy of *Certain Roses* by Angela Livingstone. The collection features a purple cover, with a photograph of a bay window overlooking a brick wall. The prose-poetry inside is given a good amount of space on the page to breathe, which suits the contemplative writing style. The back cover features a very sweet blurb, where the author and publisher discuss the themes of the collection, as well as the author's bio and previous publications.

MONSTROUS REGIMENT PUBLISHING
MIXED-FORM COLLECTIONS/ ANTHOLOGIES
editor@monstrous-regiment.com
www.monstrous-regiment.com
Editors: Lauren Nickodemus, Ellen Desmond
Established 2017. Also publishes prose (see p134). Publications available direct from publisher website; by direct mail and email orders; and at local literary events.
SUBMISSIONS: Open to all, during submission windows. Submit by email (editor@monstrous-regiment. com) or online (www.monstrous-regiment.com/contact). Guidelines

at www.monstrous-regiment.com/ submissions. Usually responds within four weeks, with feedback only if requested. Authors are paid a flat fee.
For further information, including what They Say, see also prose publisher p134 and *Monstrous Regiment* (mixed-form magazine) p209

MOORMAID PRESS
CHAPBOOKS/PAMPHLETS
397 Park Lane, Macclesfield SK11 8JR
hello@moormaidpress.co.uk
www.moormaidpress.co.uk
Editor: Ailsa Holland
Established 2013. Publications available direct from publisher website; by direct mail and email orders; and at local literary events.
SUBMISSIONS: By invitation only. Submit by email to hello@ moormaidpress.co.uk. Usually responds within four weeks. Feedback provided with all solicited submissions.
WE SAY: The digital version of the prose-poetry collection *Mermaids and Other Devices* by Nell Farrell features a black cover with a photo manipulated image of winged girls, flying away from a figure in the foreground. The work is divided into two halves; the first having poetry that flows together to form a loose narrative, the other being a more traditional anthology of poetry. The back cover has three quotes in praise of the book, and the author's bio and photo.

MOTHER'S MILK BOOKS ☆
COLLECTIONS, ANTHOLOGIES AND CHAPBOOKS/PAMPHLETS
teika@mothersmilkbooks.com
www.mothersmilkbooks.com
Editor: Dr Teika Bellamy

Established 2011. Mixed form: also publishes prose (see p136). Publications available direct from publisher website; from independent bookshops; at national and local literary events; and from Amazon.

Mother's Milk Books has won numerous awards. Founder Teika Bellamy received the Women in Publishing's New Venture Award for pioneering work on behalf of under-represented groups in society. Mother's Milk Books title *Baby X* won the Commercial Fiction category of the Eric Hoffer Award in 2017.

SUBMISSIONS: During submission windows only. Submit by email to submissions@mothersmilkbooks.com. Guidelines at www.mothersmilkbooks.com/index.php/submissions. Submitters are required to buy a book from the press. Usually responds within one to three months. Rejections may occasionally include unsolicited feedback. Authors are paid an advance/fee plus royalties and receive free copies of the book.
For further information, see prose publisher p136

MUDFOG PRESS
COLLECTIONS AND ANTHOLOGIES
c/o Beacon Guest, Chop Gate, Stokesley TS9 7JS
contact@mudfog.co.uk
www.mudfog.co.uk
Editors: Pauline Plummer, Jo Heather, Liz Geraghty, David Lynch
Established 1993. Mixed form: also publishes prose (see p135). Publications available direct from the publisher website.
GENRES: All considered.
SUBMISSIONS: Favours writers in the Tees Valley, stretching from Whitby to Sunderland, and west to Darlington. However also occasionally publishes writers outside this area. Submit by post (Beacon Guest, Chop Gate, Stokesley TS9 7JS) or by email (contact@mudfog.co.uk). Guidelines at www.mudfog.co.uk/submissions. Usually responds within one to three months. Rejections may occasionally include unsolicited feedback. Authors are able to buy a number of their books at cost-price and sell them at sales price.
WE SAY: We looked at PDF proof of the collection *Will and Breath* by George Hodgeon. What first strikes the reader is that the first poem, pre-contents, 'Exit' is not by George Hodgeon at all, but is a tribute to the poet and this collection, which is his last. With this, the poems in this collection are all the more affecting: 'After the shock of sleep where I can talk and walk / I wake to feel the long withdrawing of the tide'. The cover shows a black fingerprint on a white background, below an abstract image of scratched space – the making of a mark. This is a quietly beautiful and highly personal work, executed with style by Mudfog.
See also: prose publisher p135

MULFRAN PRESS
COLLECTIONS AND CHAPBOOKS/PAMPHLETS
2 Aber Street, Cardiff CF11 7AG
queries@mulfran.co.uk
www.mulfran.co.uk
As well as poetry, Mulfran also publishes essay pamphlets on topics in poetics. The editors read widely and like contemporary poetry from the 20th and 21st

centuries, as well as poetry from earlier periods and translated poetry. See the website for examples.

NEON BOOKS
COLLECTIONS, ANTHOLOGIES AND CHAPBOOKS/PAMPHLETS
info@neonbooks.org.uk
www.neonbooks.org.uk
Editor: Krishan Coupland
Established 2006. Also publishes prose (see p138). Publications available direct from publisher website; by direct mail and email orders; from independent bookshops; at national literary events; and from Amazon and other bookshop websites. Neon Books title *The Mesmerist's Daughter* won the 2015 Best Novellas Saboteur Award.
SUBMISSIONS: Open to all, during submission windows. Submit by email to info@neonbooks.org.uk. Guidelines at www.neonbooks.org. uk/guidelines. Usually responds within one to three months. Rejections may occasionally include unsolicited feedback for a fee. Submissions hold a tip-jar option, but this does not affect publisher's decision. Authors are paid royalties only and receive free copies of the book.
See also: prose publisher p138. For further information, including what We Say, see *Neon Literary Magazine* (mixed-form magazine) p212

NEWCON PRESS
COLLECTIONS
41 Wheatsheaf Road, Alconbury Weston, Cambridgeshire PE28 4LF
finiang@aol.com
www.newconpress.co.uk
Editor: Ian Whates

Established 2006. Mainly publishes fiction (see p138). Publications available direct from publisher website; from chain bookshops nationwide; from Amazon; and at genre themed literary events. Jaine Fenn's short story 'Liberty Bird' from NewCon Press anthology *Now We Are Ten* won the BSFA Award for best short fiction in 2017.
SUBMISSIONS: Submissions by invitation only. Author payment varies depending on the published work.
See also: prose publisher p138

NEW ISLAND
COLLECTIONS
16 Priory Office Park, Stillorgan, County Dublin
+353 1 278 42 25
info@newisland.ie
www.newisland.ie
New Island started out as Raven Arts Press in the 1980s and continues to commit to publishing 'exceptional literature'. Mixed form, it also publishes drama, fiction and Irish-focussed non-fiction.
See also: prose publisher p139

NEW WALK EDITIONS
PAMPHLETS
c/o Dr Rory Waterman, Department of English, Mary Ann Evans Building, Nottingham Trent University, Clifton Campus, Clifton Lane, Nottingham NG11 8NS
newwalkmagazine@gmail.com
newwalkmagazine.wordpress.com
Editors: Rory Waterman, Nick Everett, Libby Peake
Established 2010 as *New Walk Magazine*; turned to pamphlet publication Autumn 2017. 18-month subscription (four

pamphlets per year) £19.95.
Available direct from publisher
website; from independent
bookshops; and at national and
local literary events.
SUBMISSIONS: Open to all.
Submit 1-20 pages of poems
by email to newwalkmagazine@
gmail.com. Guidelines at www.
newwalkmagazine.com/purchase-
submit. Usually responds within
two months. Only successful
submissions receive a response.

NINE ARCHES PRESS ☆
COLLECTIONS, ANTHOLOGIES AND
E-BOOKS
mail@ninearchespress.com
www.ninearchespress.com
Editors: Matt Merritt, Jane Commane
Established 2008. Publications
available direct from publisher
website; by post and email
order; from chain bookshops
and independent bookshops
nationwide; at national and local
literary events; and from Amazon
and other bookshop websites.
Nine Arches Press won the
2014 Saboteur Award for Most
Innovative Publisher.
SUBMISSIONS: Open to all,
during submissions windows.
Submit through Submittable at
ninearchespress.submittable.
com/submit. Guidelines at www.
ninearchespress.com/submissions.
html. Usually responds within one
to three months. No feedback
offered with rejections. Contracts
vary.
WE SAY: Nine Arches produce
excellent books. *Kith* by Jo Bell
is a perfect-bound, 74-page
publication complete with a
high-quality dust-cover. It has
an abstract artistic cover design
that lends itself well to the title:

the more you read, the more you
understand. Made from quality
materials and containing engaging
poetry inspired by Bell's community
and friends. Ideal for readers who
wish to be immersed in various
poetry techniques.
See also: *Under the Radar* **(poetry
magazine) p229**

OFFA'S PRESS
COLLECTIONS AND ANTHOLOGIES
info@offaspress.co.uk
www.offaspress.co.uk
Publishes and promotes
contemporary poetry by West
Midland poets. 'Eclectic' in range,
it focuses on both the performance
and publication merit of the work
it publishes. Its watchword is 'good
on the page and good on the
stage'.

OFFORD ROAD BOOKS
COLLECTIONS, ANTHOLOGIES AND
CHAPBOOKS/PAMPHLETS
offordroadbooks@gmail.com
www.twitter.com/offordroadbooks
Editors: Martha Sprackland, Patrick
Davidson Roberts
Established 2017. Also publishes
prose (see p141). Publications
available by direct mail and email
orders; from selected/local chain
bookshops; from independent
bookshops; at local literary events;
and from Amazon.
SUBMISSIONS: Open to all. Submit
by post (29a Womersley Road,
Crouch End, London N8 9AP) or
by email (offordroadbooks@gmail.
com). Usually responds within four
weeks. Rejections may occasionally
include unsolicited feedback.
Authors receive a small fee.
WE SAY: Offord Road are so new
that we could see only the PDF
proof of Melissa Houghton's

Cumshot in D Minor, and the not-yet-typeset MS of James Brookes' *Spoils*. This press does not print poetry to comfort the reader. With no opening poem title and no warning, *Cumshot in D Minor* plunges the reader into prose poetry like an angry stream of consciousness, leaping from moment to explicit moment. This writing challenges and jolts the reader right out of their comfort zone from the first. *Spoils*, while less caustic, is just as merciless in its own way. No chicken soup for the soul here, but unrelenting realism.

See also: prose publisher p141

ORIGINAL PLUS

COLLECTIONS AND CHAPBOOKS/ PAMPHLETS
38 Pwllcarn Terrace, Blaengarw, Bridgend, South Wales CF32 8AS
smithsssj@aol.com
thesamsmith.webs.com
Editor: Sam Smith
Established 1996. Publications available direct from publisher website; and by post and email order.
SUBMISSIONS: Poets should preferably have some history of publication in *The Journal*. Submit by post (38 Pwllcarn Terrace, Blaengarw, Bridgend, South Wales CF32 8AS) or by email (smithsssj@ aol.com). Usually responds within four weeks. Rejections may occasionally include unsolicited feedback. Writers can buy copies of their publication for resale at 33% discount.
WE SAY: We looked at a digital version of *Catch Ourselves in Glass* by Samantha Roden and *West Abutment Mirror Image* by Geoffrey Winch, which are also

available in print. Although both poetry collections are subjectively different, both are well crafted, with great variety of poems and poetic voices that are raw and refreshing. The covers of both are stylistically eye-catching and their websites is clear and easy to navigate.
For a fuller description of the press, see *The Journal* (poetry magazine) p243

OUTSPOKEN PRESS

COLLECTIONS AND CHAPBOOKS/ PAMPHLETS
www.outspokenldn.com/
outspokenpress
Aims to give a literary platform to poets and writers whose work is innovative, sensual and plural. Also known for running superb live poetry and music events.

OVERSTEPS BOOKS LTD

COLLECTIONS
6 Halwell House, South Pool, nr Kingsbridge, Devon TQ7 2RX
01548 531969
alwynmarriage@overstepsbooks.com
www.overstepsbooks.com
Editor: Alwyn Marriage
Established 1992. Publications available direct from publisher website; by post and email order; independent bookshops; at national and local literary events; and from bookshop websites.
SUBMISSIONS: Publication history required. Guidelines at www. overstepsbooks.com/submissions. Usually responds within one to three months. Authors receive free copies of the book.
WE SAY: We looked at digital proofs of *Another Life* by Fokkina McDonnell. This 58-page collection is split into three parts, showing

a clear journey: 'Still casting a shadow', 'Trying' and 'Another life'. There is a lengthy page of acknowledgements, noting where the poems have previously been published and won prizes – testament to the quality of poetry Oversteps prints. The layout is clean – one poem per page, in a reasonable sized font. The cover of the book is eye catching – bright blue, with an abstract picture of sailboats against a sunset on the front, a small picture of the poet on the back, and praise for the collection.

OYSTERCATCHER PRESS

CHAPBOOKS/PAMPHLETS
4 Eden Street, Cambridge CB1 1EL
oystercatcherpress@gmail.com
www.oystercatcherpress.com
Editor: Peter Hughes
Established 2007. Publications available direct from publisher website, and by post and email order. All online content is available to all. Offers an annual subscription of £25 for six pamphlets.
Oystercatcher Press won the 2008 Michael Marks Award for Outstanding UK Publisher of Poetry in Pamphlet Form.
SUBMISSIONS: Submissions by invitation only. Usually responds within one to three months. Rejections may occasionally include unsolicited feedback. Authors receive initial free copies of the book, plus a discount on all further copies.

PAEKAKARIKI PRESS

COLLECTIONS, ANTHOLOGIES AND CHAPBOOKS/PAMPHLETS
4 Mitre Ave, Walthamstow, London E17 6QG

07836 785505
matt@paekakarikipress.com
www.paekakarikipress.com
Established 2010. Printed by traditional letterpress techniques. Publications available direct from publisher website; by post and email order; and from Amazon.
SUBMISSIONS: Open to all, but for a single author collection poems must be mostly unpublished. Submit by email to poetry@ paekakarikipress.com. Guidelines at www.paekakarikipress. com/?content=poetrysubmissions. html. Usually responds within four weeks. No feedback offered with rejections. Authors receive a small number of copies free of charge and others at trade price. If sales enter profit, then a 10% royalty pool is shared between creators, e.g. author, illustrator etc.

PALEWELL PRESS LTD

COLLECTIONS, ANTHOLOGIES AND CHAPBOOKS/PAMPHLETS
enquiries@palewellpress.co.uk
www.palewellpress.co.uk
Editor: Camilla Reeve
Established 2016. Mixed form: also publishes prose (see p142). Publications available direct from publisher website; at local literary events; and from Amazon and other bookshop websites.
SUBMISSIONS: Open to all, but must relate to subject areas of human rights, history, environment, or wellbeing methodology. Submit by email (enquiries@palewellpress. co.uk) or by post (384 Upper Richmond Road West, London SW14 7JU). Usually responds within four weeks. Rejections may occasionally include unsolicited feedback. Authors are paid royalties only and receive free

PAPER SWANS PRESS ☆

COLLECTIONS, ANTHOLOGIES AND
CHAPBOOKS/PAMPHLETS
37 Stone Street, Tunbridge Wells,
Kent TN1 2QU
sarah@paperswans.co.uk
www.paperswans.co.uk
Editor: Sarah Miles

Established 2014. Publications
available direct from publisher
website and at national and local
literary events.
Paper Swans Press was shortlisted
for the award for Best Anthology
in the Saboteur Awards 2016 and
2017 and their pamphlet, *Glass* by
Elisabeth Sennitt Clough, won Best
Pamphlet in the 2017 awards.
SUBMISSIONS: Open to all, during
submission windows. Submit via
submissions page on website.
Guidelines at www.paperswans.
co.uk/submissions. Reading
fee applies only for single-
author pamphlet submissions.
Usually responds within one to
three months. Rejections may
occasionally include unsolicited
feedback. Authors receive free
copies of the book.
WE SAY: We looked at *Best
of British*, a poetry anthology.
Conceived pre-Brexit vote, this
is an A5 book, 84 pages long,
perfect bound. The cover features
the British flag, semi-opaque,
overlaying an image of sheep in a
field. It looks smart and appealing.
Inside, blue endpapers lead to
well-laid out text – poem titles
and poets are in a bold font, with
emphasising lines; poems are laid

They say

Paper Swans Press is a small,
independent publisher of
poetry and flash fiction.
We publish high quality
anthologies and pamphlets
and run an annual single-
author pamphlet prize. We
also host online competitions
and events and co-founded
'The Poetry Shelf' which aims
to bring poetry into the local
community/festivals. Paper
Swans is run by Sarah Miles,
supported by a team of talented
editors. Our aim is to support
emerging poets/writers as
well as showcase those who
are more established in their
field. We are also very keen to
give a platform to young poets/
writers and recently published
our first teen anthology.

out clearly with plenty of white
space. At the end of the book,
the complete poet biographies
are collected in a smaller font.
The poems cover every topic
from motorways, to Songs of
Praise, to the citizen test.

copies of the book. For authors in mainland UK, publisher shares cost of launch.

For further information see also prose publisher p142

PARALLEL UNIVERSE PUBLICATIONS

COLLECTIONS

130 Union Road, Oswaldtwistle, Lancashire BB5 3DR

paralleluniversepublications@gmx.co.uk

parallelpublications.blogspot.co.uk

Editors: David A. Riley, Linden Riley

Established 2012. Mainly publishes prose (see p143). Publications available direct from publisher website; by direct mail and email orders; from chain bookshops nationwide; from independent bookshops; and from Amazon and other bookshop websites.

SUBMISSIONS: Open to all. Submit by post (Parallel Universe Publications, 130 Union Road, Oswaldtwistle, Lancashire BB5 3DR) or by email (paralleluniversepublications@ gmx.co.uk). Guidelines at parallelpublications.blogspot. co.uk/p/submissions.html. Usually responds within one to three months. Rejections may occasionally include unsolicited feedback. Authors are paid royalties only.

For what We Say, see also prose publisher p143

PARTHIAN BOOKS

COLLECTIONS AND ANTHOLOGIES

022 Keir Hardie, Swansea University SA2 8PP

01792 606605

maria@parthianbooks.com

www.parthianbooks.com

Editor: Susie Wild

Established 1993. Also publishes prose (see p143). Publications available direct from publisher website; from chain bookshops nationwide; from independent bookshops; at national and local literary events; and from Amazon and other bookshop websites. Parthian Books title *Pigeon* by Alys Conran was shortlisted for the International Dylan Thomas Prize 2017.

SUBMISSIONS: Open to all. Submit by post to 022 Keir Hardie, Swansea University SA2 8PP. Guidelines at www.parthianbooks.com/pages/ contact-us. Usually responds within one to three months. No feedback offered with rejections. Author payment is dependent on deal but mostly fee/royalties.

WE SAY: We saw the less-than-A5 perfect bound collection *More than you were* by Christina Thatcher and A5 hardcover copy of *Rebel Sun* by Sophie McKeand. McKeand's collection, which explores land and myth, Socialism and starlings, features an eye-catching graphic sun radiating red stripes; while the matt paperback cover of Thatcher's features the title superimposed over an image of birds in flight. In 84 cream-coloured pages, Thatcher presents a raw exploration of the loss of her father to a drug overdose in America. These sharp, moving poems weave together unpleasant memories as well as moments of tenderness and love.

See also: prose publisher p143

PATRICIAN PRESS

COLLECTIONS AND CHAPBOOKS/PAMPHLETS

51 Free Rodwell House, School Lane, Mistley, Manningtree CO11 1HW

07968 288651

patricia@patricianpress.com

www.patricianpress.com
Editor: Patricia Borlenghi
Established 2012. Mainly publishes
fiction (see p144), but also some
poetry books and poetry-and-
prose anthologies. Publications
available direct from publisher
website; from selected/local chain
bookshops; from independent
bookshops; at local literary events;
and from Amazon and other
bookshop websites, including The
Great British Bookshop website.
SUBMISSIONS: Open to new
and unpublished writers without
agents. Submit during submissions
windows, by email (patricia@
patricianpress.com) or via
the form at www.patricianpress.
com/submissions (guidelines at
the same address). Usually
responds within one to three
months. Rejections may
occasionally include unsolicited
feedback. Authors are paid
royalties only.
**For a fuller description of this press,
including a cover image and what
we say, see prose publisher p144**

PB PRESS
COLLECTIONS AND CHAPBOOKS/
PAMPHLETS
Co. Wicklow, Éire
+353 4022 3556
buspoems@gmail.com
www.thepoetrybusmag.wixsite.com/
change
Editors: Peadar and Collette
O'Donoghue
Established 2013. Publications
available direct from publisher
website; by post and email order;
and at independent bookshops.
SUBMISSIONS: Open to all. During
submissions windows, submit by
email to buspoems@gmail.com.
Usually responds within one to

three months. Rejections may
occasionally include unsolicited
feedback. Authors receive free
copies of their book.
**For further information, including
what We Say, see also: *PB Mag*
(poetry magazine) p246**

PEEPAL TREE PRESS
COLLECTIONS, ANTHOLOGIES AND
CHAPBOOKS/PAMPHLETS
contact@peepaltreepress.com
www.peepaltreepress.com
Editors: Jeremy Poynting, Kwame
Dawes, Jacob Ross, Kadija Sesay
Established 1986. Mixed form:
also publishes short stories and
novels (see p145). Specialises
in Caribbean and Black British
writing.
Publications available direct from
publisher website; by post and
email order; from chain bookshops
and independent bookshops
nationwide; at national and local
literary events; and from Amazon
and other bookshop websites.
Peepal Tree title *Sounding Ground*
by Vladimir Lucien was overall
winner for The OCM Bocas Prize
for Caribbean Literature 2015.
SUBMISSIONS: Open to all,
specialising in Caribbean and Black
British writing. Submit through
Submittable at peepaltreepress.
submittable.com (guidelines at
same address). Usually responds
within four to six months.
Rejections may occasionally include
unsolicited feedback, and some
manuscripts by UK-based authors
are offered a (free) in-depth reader
report through the press's Inscribe
Writer Development Programme
Authors are paid royalties only.
WE SAY: A prolific publisher of
exclusively Caribbean and Black
British writing with over 300

titles to its name, from memoir and fiction to historical studies and literary criticism. We looked at *Wife*, a poetry collection by Tiphanie Yanique, which was formatted beautifully inside but admittedly had a few cover issues, in the form of low resolution stock photography and poorly aligned blurb text.
See also: prose publisher p145

PENNED IN THE MARGINS
COLLECTIONS AND ANTHOLOGIES
Toynbee Studios, 28 Commercial Street, London E1 6AB
020 7375 0121
info@pennedinthemargins.co.uk
www.pennedinthemargins.co.uk
Editor: Tom Chivers
Established 2006. Mixed form: also publishes prose (see p146). Publications available direct from publisher website; by post and email order; from selected/local chain bookshops; from independent bookshops; at local literary events; and from Amazon. In 2017 Penned in the Margins titles were shortlisted for the Costa Poetry Award, Ted Hughes Award & Dylan Thomas Prize.
SUBMISSIONS: Submit by email to submissions@pennedinthemargins.co.uk. Guidelines on website. Usually responds within one to three months. Rejections may occasionally include unsolicited feedback. Authors are paid royalties only.
WE SAY: We saw a copy of Melissa Lee-Houghton's 88-page collection *Sunshine*, which features a bubblegum pink cover, with a dropped ice cream cone in the centre. This cover was simple, but the use of both imagery and colour were very effective. The work

inside is mostly prose poetry, with acknowledgements, notes on the text, and quotes after the contents page. The tone is sensual, with a focus on both emotion and the female body – a really fascinating read.
See also: prose publisher p146

PICAROON POETRY
COLLECTIONS, ANTHOLOGIES, CHAPBOOKS/PAMPHLETS AND E-BOOKS
picaroonpoetry.wordpress.com
Editor: Kate Garrett
Established 2016. Publications available by direct mail and email orders; from independent bookshops; at local literary events; and from Amazon and Lulu.
GENRE: Literary; gritty realism; magical realism; absurdism.
SUBMISSIONS: Anthology submissions are open to all, during submission windows. Chapbook/collection submissions are by invitation only. Submit by email to picaroonpoetry@gmail.com. Usually responds within one to three months, with feedback only if requested. Anthology authors are paid royalties only. Authors of chapbooks/collections get five free copies and a royalty share, and pay a discounted price if they wish to sell copies at readings, etc.
For further information, including what We Say, see poetry magazine p245

PLATYPUS PRESS
COLLECTIONS, ANTHOLOGIES AND CHAPBOOKS/PAMPHLETS
enquiries@platypuspress.co.uk
www.platypuspress.co.uk
Editors: Michelle Tudor, Peter Barnfather
Established 2015. Also publishes

prose (see p148). Publications available direct from publisher website; at local literary events; and from Amazon and other bookshop websites.
GENRES: Literary.

PINDROP PRESS
COLLECTIONS
Gardoussel, 30940 St Andre
de Valborgne, France
editor@pindroppress.com
www.pindroppress.com
Editor: Sharon Black

Established 2010. Publications available direct from publisher website; from independent bookshops; at national and local literary events; and from Amazon. Though a UK press, Pindrop Press founding editor Jo Hemmant passed the reins to France-based Sharon Black in early 2016.
SUBMISSIONS: Publication history required. Submit by email to editor@pindroppress.com. Usually responds within one month. No feedback offered with rejections. Authors receive free copies of the book.
WE SAY: We looked at digital editions of *Sightings* by Elisabeth Sennitt Clough and *Oysterlight* by Cheryl Pearson. The covers of both feature striking artwork, with *Sightings* using stylised artwork of two peacocks, while *Oysterlight* shows sheer material lit with very soft, pale light. Each collection features a blurb at the top, and quotes about the work from prize-winning poets such as Helen Mort and Mona Arshi. The layout of the poetry is clean and uncrowded; however, there are a lot of blank pages at the beginning of each

They say

Our mission is to publish poetry that is exciting, juicy and innovative. We select books we feel passionate about, and create collections that are not only beautiful to read but also to handle. Authors include Alicia Stubbersfield, Abegail Morley, Graham Burchell, Kiran Millwood Hargrave and Jeremy Page. We operate no submissions window at present so authors are invited to send a sample of 10 poems from a full collection of at least 60 poems via the website at any time. We publish four collections a year and welcome work from début as well as established poets.

book – between the copyright information and the dedication, for example – which feels like a slight waste. The work itself is mostly prose poetry, with a dreamy, mythological feel.

SUBMISSIONS: Open to all. Submit by email to submissions@ platypuspress.co.uk. Guidelines at www.platypuspress.co.uk/ submit. Usually responds within four weeks. No feedback offered with rejections. Authors are paid royalties only and receive free copies of the book.

See also: prose publisher p148 and *Wildness* (mixed-form magazine) p231

POEM FLYER
POETRY FLYERS
Bobz Cardz, PO Box 8031, Melton Mowbray LE13 9AE
robertrichardson@poemflyer.com
www.facebook.com/poemflyer
Editor: Robert Richardson
Established 2015. Publications available at local and national literary events.

GENRES: Contemporary; lyrics and epigrams; translations.

SUBMISSIONS: By invitation only. Authors receive 100 free flyers.

WE SAY: We looked at the first ten Poem Flyers: perfect short poems, printed on one side of glossy coated A6 paper. The Poem Flyer logo catches the eye at the top left, and bottom right is the price (20p), the poem's series number and slogan: 'collect them all'. The paper feels tough enough that you could carry your favourites with you without worry, and the poetry is relatable, capturing moments and emotions, but is in no way corny. We particularly loved the deep yearning in Number 7: 'Escaping the Singer' by Maria Taylor.

POETRY IRELAND ☆
MIXED-FORM AND POETRY ANTHOLOGIES / E-BOOKS
11 Parnell Square, Dublin 1, Ireland
+353 1 6789815
publications@poetryireland.ie
www.poetryireland.ie
Editors: various
Established 1999. Mainly publishes poetry, though some mixed-form anthologies. Publications available direct from publisher website; by post and email order; at chain and independent bookshops nationwide; at literary events; and from Amazon and other bookshop websites.

Poetry Ireland was shortlisted for two categories at the 2016 Irish Book Awards: The Ryan Tubridy Listeners' Choice Award, and Best Irish Published Book of the Year.

GENRE: Literary.

SUBMISSIONS: Open to all. Submit by post to Poetry Ireland, 11 Parnell Square, Dublin 1, Ireland. Usually responds within four to six months. Rejection may occasionally include unsolicited feedback. Authors receive a flat fee and free copies of the book.

For further information, including what We Say, see also: *Poetry Ireland Review* (poetry magazine) p248

POETRY LONDON ☆
ANTHOLOGIES
The Albany, Deptford, London SE8 4AG
admin@poetrylondon.co.uk
www.poetrylondon.co.uk
Editors: Jess Chandler, Ahren Warner, Sam Buchan-Watts, Martha Kapos
Established 1988. Publications available direct from publisher website and from chain bookshops nationwide.

For a fuller description of this press, see *Poetry London* (poetry magazine) p248

61

POETRY SPACE ☆
COLLECTIONS, ANTHOLOGIES AND
CHAPBOOKS/PAMPHLETS
www.poetryspace.co.uk
Editor: Susan Sims
Publications available direct
from publisher website and from
Amazon.
SUBMISSIONS: Open to all.
Submit by email to susan@
poetryspace.co.uk. Guidelines at
www.poetryspace.co.uk/about.
Usually responds within one to
three months. Rejections may
occasionally include unsolicited
feedback. Authors receive free
copies of the book.
**For a fuller description of this press
see *Poetry Space Showcase* (poetry
e-zine) p249**

PROLEBOOKS ☆
COLLECTIONS, ANTHOLOGIES AND
CHAPBOOKS/PAMPHLETS
01204 497726
admin@prolebooks.co.uk
www.prolebooks.co.uk
Editors: Brett Evans, Phil Robertson
Established 2010. Primarily a
poetry press, but does also publish
prose in mixed-form collections
and anthologies (see p149).
Publications available direct from
publisher website and by direct
mail and email orders.
SUBMISSIONS: Work for anthology
and collection publication is usually
selected from competition entries.
Authors are paid royalties only.
**See also prose publisher p149 and
Prole (mixed-form magazine) p218**

PS PUBLISHING
COLLECTIONS, ANTHOLOGIES AND
CHAPBOOKS/PAMPHLETS
Grosvenor House, 1 New Road,
Hornsea, East Yorkshire HU18 1PG
01964 537575

nickycrowther@pspublishing.co.uk
www.pspublishing.co.uk
Editor: Nicky Crowther
Established 1991. Mainly publishes
fiction (see p150), but also some
poetry. Publications available
direct from publisher website;
from Amazon and other bookshop
websites; and at the British Science
Fiction Convention and British
Fantasy Convention.
PS Publishing won The Karl
Wagner Award at the British
Fantasy Awards 2012.
SUBMISSIONS: Submissions
welcome by invitation only or
from agents, during submissions
windows. Submit by email to
nickycrowther@pspublishing.
co.uk. Usually responds within one
to three months. Rejections may
occasionally include unsolicited
feedback. Authors may receive a
flat fee; royalties only; an advance/
fee plus royalties; and/or free
copies of the book (depending on
agreement).
See also: prose publisher p150

PYRAMID EDITIONS
ART BOOKS
owen@pyramideditions.co.uk
www.pyramideditions.co.uk
Editor: Owen Vince
Established 2015. Publications
available direct from publisher
website; from chain bookshops
nationwide and from independent
bookshops.
SUBMISSIONS: Submit during
submission windows only (closed
submissions throughout 2018).
Usually responds within one to
three months. Rejections may
occasionally include unsolicited
feedback. Authors are paid a flat
fee and receive free copies of the
book.

RACK PRESS

CHAPBOOKS/PAMPHLETS
The Rack, Kinnerton, Presteigne,
Powys, Wales LD8 2PF
07817 424560
rackpress@nicholasmurray.co.uk
www.rackpress.blogspot.com
Editor: Nicholas Murray

Established 2005. Primarily
publishes poetry, but also
publishes some criticism (see
p150). Publications available
direct from publisher website; by
post and email order; from chain
bookshops and independent
bookshops nationwide; at national
and local literary events; and from
bookshop websites.

Rack Press won the 2014 Michael
Marks Award for Publisher of the
Year.

SUBMISSIONS: Open to all. Submit
by post (The Rack, Kinnerton,
Presteigne, Powys, Wales LD8
2PF) or by email (rackpress@
nicholasmurray.co.uk). Guidelines
at www.nicholasmurray.co.uk/
About_Rack_Press.html. Please
check the publisher's website to
confirm whether submissions are
currently being accepted. Usually
responds within four weeks.
Rejections may occasionally
include unsolicited feedback.
Authors receive free copies of the
book, plus other copies at discount
price for sale at readings etc.
WE SAY: Rack Press pamphlets
are part of the Rack Press Editions
imprint 'Little Green Books'. They
are simple affairs, with clean, cream
covers; and a bold font for the
title and poet name. The name
of the press takes a backseat in
the branding, as they focus on
the poetry. However, the press
does also sell limited sets of the
pamphlets, signed by the poets
and numbered accordingly, which
we think adds a 'must read now'
edge.
See also: prose publisher p150

RED CEILINGS PRESS, THE

CHAPBOOKS/PAMPHLETS AND
E-BOOKS
53 High Street, New Mills, High Peak,
Derbyshire SK22 4BR
theredceilings@gmail.com
www.theredceilingspress.co.uk
Editor: Mark Cobley

Publications available direct from
publisher website and from the
poets themselves.
SUBMISSIONS: Chapbooks from
UK poets only; e-books open to
all. Publication history required.
Submit by email to theredceilings@
gmail.com. Guidelines on the
website. Author contributions
needed. Usually responds within
one to three months. No feedback
offered with rejections. Authors
receive at least ten copies of the
book.
WE SAY: We looked at a digital
version of *anyone for anymore* by
Rufo Quintavalle. A simple design
with an abstract photograph on
the cover, reflecting its content.
The publication is modern and
experimental, the poem building
up by one word, and one line
per page to begin with. An
experimental piece that challenges
conventional poetry and is smartly
presented. A press that's ideal for
poets whose work doesn't fit the
traditional mould.

RED SQUIRREL PRESS

COLLECTIONS, ANTHOLOGIES AND
CHAPBOOKS/PAMPHLETS
Briery Hill Cottage, Stannington,
Morpeth NE61 6ES
info@redsquirrelpress.com

www.redsquirrelpress.com
Editor: Sheila Wakefield

Established 2006. Mainly publishes poetry, but also some prose (see p151). Publications available direct from publisher website; by post and email order; from chain bookshops nationwide; from independent bookshops; at national and local literary events; from Amazon and other bookshop websites; and from Inpress.
Red Squirrel was shortlisted for the Callum Macdonald Memorial Award 2015.
SUBMISSIONS: Open to all. Submit by post to Briery Hill Cottage, Stannington, Morpeth NE61 6ES. Guidelines at www.redsquirrelpress.com/submissions. Usually responds in over six months. No feedback offered with rejections. Authors receive free copies of the book.
WE SAY: Red Squirrel press has a reputation for promoting its poets well, and working with local groups to create events. Its print output doesn't have a strong branded feel – title design varies from book to book – but the formatting is well done and the materials good quality.
See also: prose publisher p151

RIALTO, THE/BRIDGE PAMPHLETS ☆

PAMPHLETS/CHAPBOOKS
PO Box 309 Aylsham, Norwich NR11 6LN
info@therialto.co.uk
www.therialto.co.uk
Editor: Michael Mackmin.
Assistant Editor: Fiona Moore

Established 1984. Publications available direct from publisher website; from selected/local chain bookshops; and from independent bookshops.
Rialto title *What I Saw* by Laura Scott won the 2014 Michael Marks Pamphlet Award.
SUBMISSIONS: Currently by invitation only, but with plans to open a submission programme for pamphlets. Please keep checking the website, www.therialto.co.uk. Chapbook authors receive all profits.
WE SAY: We looked at *What I Saw* by Laura Scott. Printed on quality cream paper, with a line sketch of the Thames and London skyline on the cover. A light, but compelling look that matches a light but compelling selection of poems. Stapled spine and lovely texture to the paper.
See also: *The Rialto* (poetry magazine) p251

ROCKINGHAM PRESS

COLLECTIONS
11 Musley Lane, Ware, Herts SG12 7EN
01920 467 868
rockpress@ntlworld.com
www.rockinghampress.co.uk
Editor: David Perman

Established 1991. Primarily publishes poetry, but also some non-fiction on Hertfordshire local history. Publications available by post and email order; at local literary events; from Amazon; and from Inpress.
SUBMISSIONS: Submissions by invitation only, to rockpress@ntlworld.com. Usually responds within one to three months. Rejections may occasionally include unsolicited feedback. Authors are paid royalties only.
WE SAY: *More New and Collected Poems* by Lotte Kramer is a perfect-bound 411-page poetry

64

publication with a simple design.
Plain cover, with a photo of the
poet, and plenty of blurb on the
back. This collection is a nostalgic
tour of Germany and England, with
poems focussing on family and
nature within both countries. The
book includes a good introduction,
some marketing of other titles and
well-formatted poems.

ROUTE PUBLISHING LTD
COLLECTIONS
01977 793442
info@route-online.com
www.route-online.com
Editor: Ian Daley
Established 2000. Primarily
publishes non-fiction above other
prose (see p151) and poetry.
Publications available direct from
publisher website; by post and
email order; from chain bookshops
nationwide; from independent
bookshops; at national and local
literary events; and from Amazon
and other bookshop websites.
Route has been shortlisted for
the Pen/Ackerley Prize (2008); the
James Tait Black Memorial Prize
for Fiction (2011); NME Book of
the Year (2015); and the Penderyn
Prize (Music Book of the Year)
(2015).
GENRES: Literary fiction; biography
and true stories; music, stage and
screen; and sports and leisure.
SUBMISSIONS: Guidelines at www.
route-online.com/submissions.
Usually responds within four to
six months, with feedback only if
an SAE is provided. No feedback
offered with rejections. Authors
receive a flat fee, or royalties only,
or an advance/fee plus royalties.
**For a fuller description of this press,
see prose publisher p151**

SACRISTY PRESS
COLLECTIONS AND ANTHOLOGIES
PO Box 612, Durham DH1 9HT
01913 038313
enquiries@sacristy.co.uk
www.sacristy.co.uk
Editor: Thomas Ball
Established 2011. Primarily
publishes non-fiction (see p152).
Publications available direct
from publisher website; from
independent bookshops; and
from Amazon and other bookshop
websites.
GENRES: History; theology;
religious poetry.
SUBMISSIONS: Open to all.
Guidelines at www.sacristy.co.uk/
info/authors. Usually responds
within one to three months.
Rejections may occasionally
include unsolicited feedback.
Authors contribute to editorial/
publication/marketing costs and
are paid royalties only.
WE SAY: We looked at a digital
edition *Hope in Dark Places* by
David Grieve: a collection of
'poems about depression and
the Christian'. It contains a well-
considered introduction by Chris
Cook looking at the difficulties of
maintaining faith while struggling
with depression. The poems
themselves are simply arranged
in alphabetical order and offered
as a 'resource' for people needing
the companionship of Christ while
depressed. The poems are laid
out with an eye to use of space,
and we found the writing quietly
buoying, even for those readers
who aren't religious.

SAD PRESS
COLLECTIONS, ANTHOLOGIES AND
CHAPBOOKS/PAMPHLETS
c/o Samantha Walton,

Bath Spa University, Newton Park,
Bath BA2 9BN
franciscrot@gmail.com
sadpresspoetry.wordpress.com
Editors: Joseph Walton,
Samantha Walton

Established 2009. Look for experimental and linguistically innovative poetry as well as eco-poetry. £30 for bundle of six books. Publications available direct from publisher website; from independent bookshops; and at local literary events.

SUBMISSIONS: Open to all during occasional submission windows. Submit by email to franciscrot@gmail.com. Usually responds within one to three months. Rejections may include reasons for decision and suggestions of alternative publishers. Authors receive free copies of the book.

WE SAY: Although some collections, such as *Landscaping Change*, edited by Samantha Walton, conform to a standard e-book style, Sad Press does focus on experimental writing. Chapbooks such as Nick-E Melville's eclectic *Alert Stage is Heightened* clearly reflect this, with mixed styles of blocks of text and sparse collections of lines; a brightly coloured background featuring only the words 'Spend Happy'; a scan of a letter from Jobseeker's or Barclays; et al. The style of the chapbook is made to reflect the writing, and back catalogue titles which have sold out are available as e-books.

SALMON POETRY
COLLECTIONS, ANTHOLOGIES AND LITERARY CRITICISM
Knockeven, Cliffs of Moher,
County Clare, Ireland
jessie@salmonpoetry.com
www.salmonpoetry.com
Editor: Jessie Lendennie

Established 1981. Publications available direct from publisher website; by post and email order; from chain bookshops and independent bookshops nationwide; at national and local literary events; and from Amazon and other bookshop websites. Salmon Poetry was one of five finalists for the 2015 Association of Writers and Writing Programs (AWP) Small Press Publisher Award.

SUBMISSIONS: Publication history required. Submit by email to jessie@salmonpoetry.com. Usually responds within two to six months. Authors are paid royalties only and receive a certain number of free copies of the book.

WE SAY: The 80-page A5 collection by Millicent Borges Accardi we saw, *Only More So*, had a vibrant purple matt cover featuring a mandala design. Accardi's poetry varies from the atrocities of war to tender moments between brothers, such as in 'Buying Sleep' when the elder brother offers to sell the other 'a cocoon of sleep', which he tucks in around the boy.

SALÒ PRESS
COLLECTIONS, ANTHOLOGIES AND CHAPBOOKS/PAMPHLETS
85 Gertrude Road, Norwich NR3 4SG
editorsalopress@gmail.com
www.salopress.weebly.com
Editor: Sophie Essex

Established 2015. Also publishes prose (see p152). Publications available direct from publisher website.

SUBMISSIONS: Open to all. Submit by email to editorsalopress@gmail.com. Guidelines at www.

66

salopress.weebly.com. Usually
responds within one to three
months. Feedback not offered
with rejections. Authors are paid
royalties only.
WE SAY: We looked at PDFs of
the anthology *A Galaxy of Starfish*
and Bradley J Fest's collection
The Shape of Things. The cover
of *Shape* features abstract shapes
and *Starfish* shows a rather
charming illustration of a star
woman hugging a moon. Both use
sans serif fonts for inner pages.
Fest's poetry style is long lines and
prose poetry, with plenty of focus
on the future and the present,
science and technology. *Starfish*
is far more surreal, as promised
by the subtitle. The contents list
notes 'two poems by X' rather
than titles, so it's a lucky dip for the
reader. Both are clearly laid out,
and *Starfish* includes writer biogs in
paler text after each set of poems.
See also: prose publisher p152

SAQI BOOKS
MIXED-FORM COLLECTIONS AND
ANTHOLOGIES
26 Westbourne Grove, London
W2 5RH
020 7221 9347
elizabeth@saqibooks.com
www.saqibooks.com
Publisher and Managing Director:
Lynn Gaspard
Editor and Marketing Manager:
Elizabeth Briggs
Established 1983. Primarily
publishes prose (see p153), and
widely publishes work from and
about the Middle East and North
Africa. Publications available from
chain bookshops nationwide;
from independent bookshops; at
national and local literary events;
and from Amazon and other

bookshop websites.
Saqi Books won the IPG Diversity
Award in 2013, the Arab British
Culture and Society Award in 2008
and the British Book Industry Award
for Diversity in Literature in 2009.
SUBMISSIONS: Open to all.
Guidelines at www.saqibooks.
com/contact/submissions.
Usually responds within one to
three months. Rejections may
occasionally include unsolicited
feedback. Authors are paid an
advance/fee plus royalties.
See also: prose publisher p153

SEREN BOOKS
COLLECTIONS, ANTHOLOGIES
AND CHAPBOOKS/PAMPHLETS
57 Nolton Street, Bridgend, Wales
CF31 3AE
01656 663018
seren@serenbooks.com
www.serenbooks.com
Editor: Amy Wack
Established 1963. Mixed form: also
publishes fiction and
non-fiction (see p155). Publications
available direct from publisher
website; by post and email order;
from chain bookshops nationwide;
from independent bookshops; at
national and local literary events;
and from Amazon.
Winner of the Costa Poetry Award
2014.
SUBMISSIONS: Open to all.
Submit by post to 57 Nolton
Street, Bridgend CF31 3AE.
Guidelines at www.serenbooks.
com/seren/submissions-policy.
Usually responds within one to
three months. Rejections may
occasionally include unsolicited
feedback. Authors are paid an
advance/fee plus royalties and
receive free copies of the book,
as well as other copies at a

discount price.

WE SAY: Seren is one of the most established and respected poetry publishing houses, and certainly one for poets to aspire to. *My Family and Other Superheroes* by Jonathan Edwards is a 72-page award-winning publication with an artistic design, available in both print and digital format. Provides nostalgia and naivety through the poet's voice. Various poetic forms are used throughout, including free-verse; ideal for readers who wish to escape into a good book.

See also: prose publisher p155 and *Poetry Wales* (poetry magazine) p250

SHEARSMAN BOOKS LTD

COLLECTIONS, ANTHOLOGIES AND CHAPBOOKS/PAMPHLETS
50 Westons Hill Drive,
Emersons Green BS16 7DF
editor@shearsman.com
www.shearsman.com
Editor: Tony Frazer
Established 1982. Publications available direct from publisher website; by post and email order; from selected/local chain bookshops; from independent bookshops; and from Amazon and other bookshop websites. Shearman Books is a multi-award-nominated press, and has been nominated for the Forward Prize for Best First Collection (2011, 2012); the Forward Prize for Best Collection (2012, 2015); Jerwood Aldeburgh First Collection Prize (2007); the Popescu Translation Prize (2009, 2001, 2013); the Michael Murphy Award for First Collections (2015) and the Michael Marks Awards for Pamphlets (Publisher Award) (2013, 2014).

SUBMISSIONS: Publication history required. Submit during submissions windows, by post (Shearsman Books Ltd, 50 Westons Hill Drive, Emersons Green, Bristol BS16 7DF) or via the online PDF submissions portal (www.shearsman.com/how-to-contact-shearsman-books). Please read the guidelines at www.shearsman.com/shearsman-book-submissions. Usually responds within four to six months. No feedback offered with rejections. Authors are paid royalties only and receive free copies of the book.

For a fuller description of this press, see *Shearsman Magazine* (poetry magazine) p252

SHIT VALLEY

PAMPHLETS
shitvalleyverlag@gmail.com
shitvalley.tumblr.com
Cambridge-based publisher, producing 'laboriously cheap pamphlets by morally expensive poets'.

SHOESTRING PRESS

COLLECTIONS, ANTHOLOGIES AND CHAPBOOKS/PAMPHLETS
19 Devonshire Avenue, Beeston, Nottingham NG9 1BS
info@shoestring-press.com
www.shoestring-press.com
Editor: John Lucas
Mainly publishes poetry, but also some prose (see p155). Publications available direct from publisher website; by post and email order; from independent bookshops; at national and local literary events; and from Amazon. Shoestring titles have been shortlisted for Vondel Prize for Translation and for the Cricket Club Writers Book of the Year.

SUBMISSIONS: Submit by invitation only.
WE SAY: A stalwart of poetry publishing, Shoestring have moved with the times in terms of production. Its designs are modern and clean, with clear formatting that looks stylish on the page (we looked at *A Night of Islands* by Angus Martin). This is a press widely acknowledged to be publishing important work, and doing it well.
See also: prose publisher p155

SIDEKICK BOOKS
ANTHOLOGIES, CHAPBOOKS/ PAMPHLETS, POETRY-BASED MIXED CONTENT
hello@sidekickbooks.com
www.sidekickbooks.com
Editors: Kirsten Irving, Jon Stone
Established 2009. Primarily publishes poetry, with mixed content including poems with essays, poets teamed with illustrators, poetry comics etc. Publications available direct from publisher website; from independent bookshops; and at local literary events. All online content is available to all.
Sidekick title *Riotous* won Best Collaboration at the Saboteur Awards 2014, and *Finders Keepers* (poems by Harry Man, illustrations by Sophie Gainsley) was shortlisted for the Ted Hughes Award.
SUBMISSIONS: Open during submissions windows (check the website). Usually responds within four to six months. Rejections may occasionally include unsolicited feedback. Writers receive a flat fee and free copies of the book.
WE SAY: We looked at *Birdbook: Farmland, Heathland, Mountain, Moorland*, in which poets 'poemify'

birds of Britain. The book is printed on high quality materials with a striking silhouette image cover, and filled with glorious illustrations and poems in a range of styles. Sidekick is a particularly creative press, and this really shines through here.

SILHOUETTE PRESS
COLLECTIONS, ANTHOLOGIES AND CHAPBOOKS/PAMPHLETS
adam.steiner@silhouettepress.co.uk
www.silhouettepress.co.uk
Editor: Adam Steiner
Established 2012. Also publishes prose (see p155). Publications available direct from publisher website; by direct mail and email orders; from independent bookshops; and at national literary events.
SUBMISSIONS: Open to all, although publication history, covering letter, and/or completed manuscript will be advantageous. Submit online at silhouettepress. submittable.com/submit. Usually responds in over six months. Some but limited feedback offered with rejections. Authors receive free copies of the book.
WE SAY: Each of the covers for the digital books we saw from Silhouette Press were very striking – Andrea Mbarushimana's *The Africa in My House* features a red-orange background with black masks running down the left-hand side, while Jamie Thrasivoulou's *The Best of a Bad Situation* is black 'crumpled' paper with the title in a simple white print. The cover of Jonathan Pinnock's *Love and Loss and Other Important Stuff* is slightly less impactful, as some of the text is difficult to read at a glance because of colour choice, but

the purple background and white skull still catch the eye. All three collections mostly feature prose-poetry, though Thrasivoulou's work is the most experimental with form. Mbarushimana's collection also contains illustrations that relate to the work, as does Pinnock's.

See also: prose publisher p155

SINE WAVE PEAK

COLLECTIONS, ANTHOLOGIES AND CHAPBOOKS/PAMPHLETS

114 Sandy Lane, Cholton, Manchester M21 8TZ

www.sinewavepeak.com

Managing Editor: Valgerður Þóroddsdóttir

Established 2011. Poetry and philosophy/criticism. Available direct from publisher website and at independent bookshops. Winner of the Creative Futures Award, NALD, 2012.

GENRES: Emphasis on philosophy and typography.

SUBMISSIONS: Open to all. Submit by email (luke@sinewavepeak. com). Usually responds within four weeks. A rejection may occasionally include unsolicited feedback. Authors receive copies of the book.

WE SAY: Extremely high quality publications. Both hardcover and paperback have very simple, white designs on the cover, with folded flaps. The paper is thick and textured, and the formatting clean and sophisticated, with light illustration on occasion.

See also: *Quait* (poetry magazine) p250

SINGING APPLE PRESS

COLLECTIONS AND CHAPBOOKS/ PAMPHLETS

info@singingapplepress.com

www.singingapplepress.com

Editor: Camilla A. Nelson

Established 2014. Also publish book art, hand-made books, bookworks and text art. Publications available direct from publisher website; by direct mail and email orders; and at local and national literary events.

SUBMISSIONS: By invitation only. Usually responds within one to three months. Rejections may occasionally include unsolicited feedback. Authors receive free copies of the book.

WE SAY: As Singing Apple Press's products are all handcrafted and limited edition, we settled for looking at the catalogue available on the website. The publications appear to be carefully constructed out of textured (homemade?) paper, with leaf prints, text embossed into leaves, hand-stamped logos and stickered titles. The effect is earthy and natural, and we imagine anyone would prize such a publication in their collection.

SMITH|DOORSTOP BOOKS ☆

COLLECTIONS, ANTHOLOGIES, CHAPBOOKS/PAMPHLETS AND E-BOOKS

The Poetry Business, Bank Street Arts, 32-40 Bank Street, Sheffield S1 2DS

0114 346 3037

office@poetrybusiness.co.uk

www.poetrybusiness.co.uk

Editors: Ann Sansom, Peter Sansom

Established 1986. Publications available direct from publisher website; by post and email order; online at Newsstand; at Salts Mill (Shipley), Heffer's Bookshop (Cambridge), Five Leaves Bookshop (Nottingham), Magazine (Brighton), and Blackwell's Bookshop.

smithldoorstop won the 2012 Michael Marks publisher award.

SUBMISSIONS: Open to all, during submissions windows.

Submit by post to The Poetry Business, Bank Street Arts, 32-40 Bank Street, Sheffield, S1 2DS. Online submissions accepted only from overseas writers (see www.poetrybusiness.co.uk/north-menu/international-submissions). Full guidelines at www.poetrybusiness.co.uk/north-menu/submissions. Usually responds within one to three months. No feedback offered with rejection. Authors receive free copies of their books. Only book authors (not pamphlet) receive royalties.

WE SAY: We looked at a digital version of a 35-page poetry bundle, which contains a range of poems from Geraldine Clarkson. Although complementing illustrations would have worked well here, the plain design also holds up as simple and fitting. The left aligned text in the middle of the page and the variations of poems make for a pleasant whole.

See also: *The North Magazine* **(poetry magazine) p244**

SMOKESTACK BOOKS

POETRY COLLECTIONS AND ANTHOLOGIES
1 Lake Terrace, Grewelthorpe, Ripon, North Yorkshire HG4 3BU
01765 658917
info@smokestack-books.co.uk
www.smokestack-books.co.uk
Editor: Andy Croft
Established 2003. Publications available direct from publisher website; by post and email order; at chain bookshops and independent bookshops nationwide; at national and local literary events; and from Amazon and other bookshop websites. Smokestack poet Steve Ely's collection, *Oswald's Book of Hours*, was shortlisted for the 2013 Forward Best First Collection and shortlisted for the 2014 Ted Hughes Award.

SUBMISSIONS: Publication history required. Submit by post (1 Lake Terrace, Grewelthorpe, Ripon, North Yorkshire HG4 3BU) or by email (info@smokestack-books.co.uk). Guidelines at www.smokestack-books.co.uk/publish.php. Usually responds within four weeks. Rejections may occasionally include unsolicited feedback. Author payment in the form of free copies of the book.

WE SAY: The A5 paperback titles we saw (*Little Blue Hut* by Nancy Charley, *Articles of War* by Marilyn Longstaff and *Liberties* by Victoria Bean) featured a cohesive matt cover design of an image bordered by two light grey bands, and a bright red spine. Victoria Bean's collection, *Liberties*, is about trouble – those who cause it, are looking for it, or have found it; poems such as 'Joy' leave you wondering about the outcome of that trouble, giving you only the image of a car at the end of a pair of skid marks, doors open like 'a game show prize'.

SOUNDSWRITE PRESS

COLLECTIONS, ANTHOLOGIES AND CHAPBOOKS/PAMPHLETS
52 Holmfield Road, Leicester LE2 1SA
01162 702661
soundswritepoetry@gmail.com
www.soundswritepress.co.uk
Editors: Karin Koller, D.A. Prince
Established 2005. Publications available direct from publisher

website and from Amazon.
SUBMISSIONS: By invitation
only. Publication history
required. Guidelines at
www.soundswritepress.co.uk/
submissions.html. Rejections may
occasionally include unsolicited
feedback. No fee or royalties at
this time.
WE SAY: We looked at *Beyond the
Tune* by Jayne Stanton, a 31-page
A5 chapbook with a simple design.
The poems are printed on high-
quality cream paper; the cover is
glossy and attractive. The poems
are subtly nostalgic, referring to
past experiences and stories, and
the writing is contemporary and
descriptive.

SOUTHWORD EDITIONS ☆
CHAPBOOKS/PAMPHLETS
Munster Literature Centre, Frank
O'Connor House, 84 Douglas Street,
Cork, Ireland
+353 21 431 2955
munsterlit@eircom.net
www.munsterlit.ie
Editors: Patrick Cotter, Danielle
McLaughlin, Matthew Sweeney,
Colm Breathnach
Established 2001. Publications
available direct from publisher
website; by post and email order;
at national and local literary events;
and from Amazon.
SUBMISSIONS: Open to all, during
submissions windows – chapbook
publication comes as part of
the Fool for Poetry competition.
Guidelines at www.munsterlit.ie/
Fool%20for%20Poetry.html. Usually
responds within one to three
months. No feedback offered with
rejections. Authors are paid a flat
fee and receive free copies of the
book.
For a fuller description of this press,

**see *Southword Journal* (mixed-
output literary e-zine) p223**

SPIRIT DUPLICATOR
CHAPBOOKS/PAMPHLETS AND
ANTHOLOGIES
touch@spiritduplicator.org.uk
www.spiritduplicator.org
Pamphlets and books are printed
using digital or risograph.
Publishes *The British Esperantist*
alongside other titles and is
interested in the interface between
design and writing. Always looking
for collaborations, commissions
and submissions.
See also: prose publisher p157

STONEWOOD PRESS
COLLECTIONS, ANTHOLOGIES AND
CHAPBOOKS/PAMPHLETS
Diversity House, 72 Nottingham Road,
Arnold Nottingham NG5 6LF
0845 456 4838
stonewoodpress@gmail.com
www.stonewoodpress.co.uk
Editor: Martin Parker
Established 2011. Publications
available direct from publisher
website; from chain bookshops
and independent bookshops
nationwide; and from Amazon and
other bookshop websites.
SUBMISSIONS: See guidelines at
www.stonewoodpress.co.uk/about/
submissions. Usually responds
within four months. Rejections may
occasionally include unsolicited
feedback. Authors are paid
royalties only and receive free
copies of the book.
WE SAY: A boutique publisher
with a petite catalogue of a dozen
titles. *Small Grass*, the special
edition poetry collection we pored
over, was a perfect-bound, A6
hardcover in a striking slipcase. The
vivid orange cover with silver title

and grass graphic was incredibly eye-catching, and the short poetry inside, paired with black and white illustrations, was dainty and satisfying. Exceptionally well presented.

See also: prose publisher p157

STRANGER PRESS

COLLECTIONS, CHAPBOOKS/ PAMPHLETS AND BROADSIDES
strangerpress@gmail.com
www.strangerpress.com
'Modern innovative poetry'. Interested in publishing new and innovative, experimental poetry and writing. Check the website to find out whether submissions are being accepted.

STRUCTO PRESS

CHAPBOOKS/PAMPHLETS
editor@structomagazine.co.uk
www.structomagazine.co.uk
Editor: Euan Monaghan
Established 2015. Mixed form: also publishes fiction (see p159). Publications available direct from publisher website.
GENRES: All considered.
SUBMISSIONS: Open only to poets previously published in *Structo*.
WE SAY: We looked at a digital version of David Russomano's chapbook *(Reasons for) Moving*. The cover features a blue and white geometric illustration by the poet, which wraps around the book. Russomano's biography and praise for the work are on the back cover. Acknowledgements, rights and thanks are within the first few pages, after which the 19 poems, set in a serif font, are left to sing out without interruption. The poems themselves move from location to location around the world, a sense of unrest throughout.

We were struck by the vivid but simple phrasing: for example, 'our doughnut town' perfectly conjuring up an area in three words.
For furthes descriptions of this press, see *Structo* (mixed-output magazine) p225 and prose publisher p159

SYNCHRONISE WITCHES PRESS

ANTHOLOGIES AND CHAPBOOKS/ PAMPHLETS
cherrystyles@hotmail.co.uk
www.cherrystyles.co.uk
Editor: Cherry Styles
Established 2012. Mixed form: also publishes fiction (see p159). Publications available direct from publisher website; by post and email order; from independent bookshops; at national and local literary events; at zine fairs; and in art bookshops.
The press was shortlisted for the Turn The Page artists' book award, 2015.
GENRES: Poetry; art, fashion and photography; biography and true stories; music, stage and screen; society, education and politics.
SUBMISSIONS: Open to women writers only. Submit by email (thechapess@gmail. com) or via online form (www. cherrystyles.co.uk/the-chapess). Usually responds within one to three months. Rejections may occasionally include unsolicited feedback.
For a fuller description of this press, see *The Chapess* (mixed-form magazine) p189. See also prose publisher p159

TALL-LIGHTHOUSE PRESS

COLLECTIONS AND CHAPBOOKS/ PAMPHLETS

22 Twigden Court, Luton LU3 2RL
info@tall-lighthouse.co.uk
www.tall-lighthouse.co.uk
Editor: Gareth Lewis
Established 1999. Primarily
publishes pamphlets. Publications
available direct from publisher
website. Titles from tall-lighthouse
have been on various Michael
Marks shortlists for Best Pamphlet
of the Year over the course of the
award, including in 2012 for Ben
Parker's *The Escape Artists*. *Harry
Man's Lift* (2013) has also won or
been nominated for various poetry
awards.
SUBMISSIONS: Open to all, during
submissions windows. Submit by
post (22 Twigden Court, Luton LU3
2RL) or by email (tall.lighthouse@
btinternet.com). Guidelines
at www.tall-lighthouse.co.uk/
submissions.html. Authors are
paid royalties only and receive
free copies of the book. Usually
responds within one to three
months, and tries to offer feedback
with all rejections, especially to
work of exceptional quality.
WE SAY: tall-lighthouse's
pamphlets are neat affairs, and
somewhat surprising. We looked
at Josephine Corcoran's *The
Misplaced House*, 36 pages long
with a glossy cover and perfect
bound. The materials are high
quality – higher than you'll often
see for pamphlets – and the
formatting is clean and accessible.
The cover design includes
professional blurb and a photo
image that gives the impression
of a more domestic collection of
poems than this is (a couple of
reviews note that they were wrong-
footed by this, and were pleased
to discover politically charged,
darker poems than expected).

TANGERINE PRESS
COLLECTIONS AND CHAPBOOKS/
PAMPHLETS
18 Riverside Rd, Garratt Business Park,
London SW17 0BA
michael@eatmytangerine.com
www.eatmytangerine.com
Editor: Michael Curran
Established 2006. Mainly publishes
fiction (see p160). Publications
available direct from publisher
website; by post and email order;
from major chain and independent
bookshops; and at local literary
events.
SUBMISSIONS: No feedback
offered with rejections.
See also: prose publisher p160

TAPSALTEERIE
COLLECTIONS, ANTHOLOGIES AND
CHAPBOOKS/PAMPHLETS
9 Anderson Terrace, Tarland,
Aberdeenshire AB34 4YH
info@tapsalteerie.co.uk
www.tapsalteerie.co.uk
Editors: Duncan Lockerbie, Eddie
Gibbons, Christie Williamson,
Rebecca Parker
Established 2013. Publications
available direct from publisher
website; by direct mail and email
orders; and from the Scottish
Poetry Library shop and Scottish
Design Exchange in Ocean
Terminal, Leith.
Tapsalteerie pamphlet *Nae Flooers*
by Ann Mackinnon was shortlisted
for the 2016 Callum Macdonald
Memorial Award for Best Scottish
Poetry Pamphlet, and pamphlet
Tilt-Shift by Kate Tough was runner
up in the 2017 Callum Macdonald
Memorial Award for Best Scottish
Poetry Pamphlet.
SUBMISSIONS: Open to all.
Submit by email to submissions@
tapsalteerie.co.uk. Guidelines

74

at www.tapsalteerie.co.uk/
submissions. Usually responds
within one to three months.
Rejections include explanation of
reason for decision. Authors are
paid a flat fee and receive free
copies of the book.
WE SAY: Tapsalteerie emphasise
that design is important to them
– something we can see in the
PDF samples sent to us. Careful
consideration has been given to
how individual poems look on
the page, and though serif fonts
are favoured, we can see from
the change to sans-serif in Kate
Tough's more experimental *Tilt
Shift*, that this is not standard.
Samples included a collection of
haiku, poetry in Scottish Gaelic,
and poetry in Scots dialect. The
cover designs are all very different,
but all eye-catching and utterly
appropriate to the content within
– from Stuart A. Paterson's swirling
blue abstract *Aye,* to the soft
watercolours of Iain Maloney's
Fractures, to the calligraphy of
Owersettin by AC Clarke, Maggie
Rabatski and Sheila Templeton.

TEMPLAR POETRY
COLLECTIONS, ANTHOLOGIES AND
CHAPBOOKS/PAMPHLETS
58 Dale Road, Matlock, Derbyshire
DE4 3NB
01629 582500
info@templarpoetry.com
www.templarpoetry.com
Originally founded in Scotland in
2005. A modern poetry list, with
the press's poets having received
recognition in major book awards
and in national and international
competitions. Regular pamphlet
publication as part of their Templar
Quarterly Portfolio awards, with
launches at Keats House.

See also: *Iota Poetry* (poetry
magazine) p243

TEST CENTRE
COLLECTIONS AND ANTHOLOGIES
71 Oriel Road, London E9 5SG
admin@testcentre.org.uk
www.testcentre.org.uk
Editors: Jess Chandler, Will Shutes
Established 2011. Also publishes
prose (see p162). Publications
available direct from publisher
website; from selected/local chain
bookshops; from independent
bookshops; and at local literary
events.
Test Centre was nominated for
Most Innovative Publisher at the
Saboteur Awards 2015.
SUBMISSIONS: During submission
windows only. Submit by post (71
Oriel Road, London E9 5SG) or
by email (admin@testcentre.org.
uk). Guidelines at www.testcentre.
org.uk/about/submissions. Usually
responds within one to three
months. Rejections may occasionally
include unsolicited feedback.
Authors are paid a flat fee and
receive free copies of the book.
WE SAY: A boutique publisher,
producing high quality publications
in limited editions. While
pamphlets are basic prints, of
folded paper and stapled spines,
the paperback perfect-bound
books are increasingly attractive:
litho-printed, with French flaps
and beautifully formatted. We
particularly loved the dark and
minimalist design of Jen Calleja's
collection *Serious Justice*.
**See also: prose publisher p162 and
mixed-form magazine p227**

THREE DROPS PRESS
COLLECTIONS AND ANTHOLOGIES
www.threedropspress.co.uk

Editor: Kate Garrett
Established 2015. Also publishes prose (see p163). Publications available by direct mail and email orders; from independent bookshops; from Amazon and other bookshop websites; and from www.lulu.com.
GENRES: Mythology; folklore; fairytales; literary.
SUBMISSIONS: During submission windows only. Submit by email to threedropspoetry@gmail.com. Usually responds within one to three months. Rejections may occasionally include unsolicited feedback. Anthology authors are paid royalties only. Authors of collections get five free copies and a royalty share, and pay a discounted price if they wish to sell copies at readings, etc.
See also: prose publisher p163. For what We Say, see *Three Drops from a Cauldron* (mixed-form magazine) p228

TOLLINGTON PRESS

COLLECTIONS
helensandler@gmail.com
www.tollingtonpress.co.uk
Editor: Helen Sandler
Established 2008. Mixed form: also publishes prose (see p164). Publications available from chain bookshops nationwide; from independent bookshops; at local literary events; and on Amazon. Tollington Press titles have been longlisted (2015) and shortlisted (2011) for the Polari Prize.
SUBMISSIONS: Open to all. Submit by query only to helensandler@gmail.com. Guidelines at www.tollingtonpress.co.uk/about.html. Usually responds within four weeks. Rejections may occasionally include unsolicited feedback.

Authors contribute to editorial/publication/marketing costs.
WE SAY: We saw PDF proofs of *Grit* by Carey Wood-Duffy, a 77-page collection of very short poems – often no more than three or four lines long – each capturing a moment or sensation. The font used is courier-style – in keeping with the font used by Tollington on their website. The poems are spaced one per page, with no titles, so as a reader it is easy to scroll through and read them almost as flash fiction. Even the acknowledgements and the closest thing to the author bio (The Author's Style as a Drinks Recipe) are in poetry form.
See also: prose publisher p164

TUBA PRESS

COLLECTIONS AND CHAPBOOKS/PAMPHLETS
Tunley Cottage, Tunley, Near Cirencester, Gloucestershire GL7 6LW
tubapoetry@icloud.com
www.tubapress.eu
Long-established press with over 30 authors on its backlist. Submissions are open, but send only three A4 pages maximum for first approach.

UNBOUND

COLLECTIONS, ANTHOLOGIES AND E-BOOKS
Unit 18, Waterside, 44-48 Wharf Road, London N1 7UX
020 7253 4230
www.unbound.co.uk
Established 2011. Mixed form: also publishes prose (see p166). Publications available direct from publisher website; by post and email order; at chain and independent bookshops nationwide; at national and local

literary events; and through Amazon and other bookshop websites. Publications are subsidised by crowdfunding. Multi-award-winning: Unbound title *The Wake* won Book of the Year at the 2015 Bookseller Industry Awards and the 2014 Gordon Burn Prize; was shortlisted for the 2014 Goldsmiths Prize; and longlisted for the Man Booker Prize 2014, the Desmond Elliott Prize 2014, and The Folio Prize 2014. Unbound won Best Publisher Website 2014 at the FutureBook Innovation Awards and British Book Design and Production Awards, and Best Start-Up at the 2011 FutureBook Innovation Awards. The press also won the Literature Award 2013, for *26 Treasures*, at the British Book Design and Production Awards.
SUBMISSIONS: Open to all. Submit via the online form at www. unbound.co.uk/authors/work-with-us. Guidelines at the same address. Usually responds within one to three months. Rejections may occasionally include unsolicited feedback. Authors are paid royalties: a 50/50 profit share from crowdfunding.
For a fuller description of this press see prose publisher p166

UNIFORMBOOKS

COLLECTIONS
info@uniformbooks.co.uk
www.uniformbooks.co.uk
Editor: Colin Sackett
Established 2011. Primarily publishes non-fiction (see p166). Publications available direct from publisher website; by direct mail and email orders; from chain bookshops nationwide; from independent bookshops; and from Amazon.

SUBMISSIONS: Open to all. Submit by email to info@uniformbooks. co.uk. Usually responds within four weeks. Rejections may occasionally include unsolicited feedback. Authors are paid royalties only and receive free copies of the book.
See also prose publisher p166 and *Uniformagazine* (prose magazine) p271

UNTITLED FALKIRK ☆

CHAPBOOKS/PAMPHLETS
untitledfalkirk@gmail.com
www.untitledfalkirk.co.uk
Editor: Craig Allan
Established 2012. Publications available direct from publisher website; by post and email order; from selected/local chain bookshops; from independent bookshops; and at local literary events.

SUBMISSIONS: During submissions windows, submit by email to untitledfalkirksubmissions@gmail. com. Submissions are now open nationally and internationally. Guidelines at www.untitledfalkirk. blogspot.co.uk/2015/07/ untitledsix.html. Usually responds within four weeks. Rejections may occasionally include unsolicited feedback. Authors receive no fee or royalties at this time.
For a fuller description of this press see *[Untitled]* (mixed-form magazine) p229

V. PRESS

COLLECTIONS, ANTHOLOGIES AND CHAPBOOKS/PAMPHLETS
vpresspoetry@hotmail.com
vpresspoetry.blogspot.co.uk
Editor: Sarah Leavesley
Established 2013. Publishes poetry and flash fiction. Publications available direct from publisher

website; at national and local literary events; and from Amazon.
SUBMISSIONS: Submit by email to vpresspoetry@hotmail.com, but only when the submissions window is open. Guidelines at vpresspoetry.blogspot.co.uk/p/submissions.html. Usually responds within three months. Rejections may occasionally include feedback. Authors receive initial free copies of the book, followed by copies at a discount rate.
WE SAY: As with their prose entry (p168) V. Press shared a favourite poem with us, but were careful to remind us that their tastes are eclectic. 'Chromosomes' comes from Romelyn Ante's first collection, *Rice and Rain*, which has a plain pale green cover featuring a line-drawing of rice 'dripping' from a drooping plant. It's a rich poem, painting the collapse of a marriage through a series of snapshot imagery.
See also: prose publisher p168

VALLEY PRESS

COLLECTIONS, ANTHOLOGIES AND CHAPBOOKS/PAMPHLETS
Woodend, The Crescent, Scarborough YO11 2PW
01723 332077
office@valleypressuk.com
www.valleypressuk.com
Editor: Jamie McGarry
Established 2008. Also publishes prose (see p169). Publications available direct from publisher website; from chain bookshops nationwide; from independent bookshops; at national and local literary events; and from Amazon and other bookshop websites.
In 2017, Valley Press title *Remembering Oluwale* won the Saboteur Award for Best Anthology.

SUBMISSIONS: Open to all. Submit online at www.valleypressuk.com/submissions. Usually responds within one to three months. Rejections may occasionally include unsolicited feedback. Submitters are required to buy a magazine/book from the press. Authors are paid a flat fee and royalties only and receive free copies of the book.
WE SAY: We saw Cath Nichols' *This is Not a Stunt*, a moving collection in which living with a disability or being trans are not tragedies to overcome but ways of being, considering their own instances of humour, romance, stories and mundanity. In the second section, 'Bo(d)y-in-Waiting', the poems loop back on themselves, repeating certain lines and images to reinforce their kaleidoscoping meaning. The perfect-bound A5 book is wrapped by an attractive, green matt paperback cover, featuring a photograph of two children at play.
See also: prose publisher p169

VANE WOMEN PRESS

COLLECTIONS, ANTHOLOGIES AND PAMPHLETS
low.down@vanewomen.co.uk
www.vanewomen.co.uk
Editors: SJ Litherland, Marilyn Longstaff (assistant editor), Pat Maycroft (art editor)
Established 1993. Mainly publishes poetry, but also short stories (see p169). Publications available direct from publisher website; by post and email order; at local literary events; and at Vane Women events and workshops.
Vane Women title *The Spar Box* by Pippa Little was the 2006 Poetry Book Society Pamphlet choice.

SUBMISSIONS: Open to previously unpublished women in North East England. Contact by email (submissions@vanewomen.co.uk) in the first instance, and a postal address to send poems and short stories to will be provided if appropriate. Full submission guidelines at www.vanewomen. co.uk/submissions.html. Usually responds in up to six months. Rejections may occasionally include unsolicited feedback. Authors receive free copies of their book.

WE SAY: We looked at Lisa Matthews' *The Eternally Packed Suitcase*. Matt laminate cover, with a bright, modern, elegant design and a clear, fresh typeface. With the professional blurb on the back and clean, spacious formatting inside, all on quality paper, this had the appearance of something from a much larger press. The Vane Women collective are a supportive group who do much to market their poets.

See also: prose publisher p169

VOIDERY APERTURE, THE
COLLECTIONS
information@thevoideryaperture.com
www.thevoideryaperture.com
Editor: Christopher Pickard
Established 2016. Mixed form: also publishes prose (see p169). Publications available from chain bookshops nationwide; from independent bookshops; on Amazon; and at other bookshop websites.

SUBMISSIONS: Submissions by invitation only. Rejections may occasionally include unsolicited feedback. Authors are paid royalties only.

For further information, including what We Say, see also: prose publisher p169

WARD WOOD PUBLISHING
COLLECTIONS / MIXED-FORM ANTHOLOGIES / E-BOOKS
6 The Drive, Golders Green, London NW11 9SR
07504 863024
adele@wardwoodpublishing.co.uk
www.wardwoodpublishing.co.uk
Editor: Adele Ward
Established 2010. Mixed output – also publishes prose (see p170), as well as the *Bedford Square MA Anthology* from from Royal Holloway, University of London, with work by graduates of the poetry and fiction courses. Publications available direct from publisher website; from major chain and independent bookshops; at literary events; and from Amazon and other bookshop websites.

SUBMISSIONS: By invitation only, to adele@wardwoodpublishing. co.uk. Please check www. wardwoodpublishing.co.uk/ manuscripts.htm for submissions information. Usually responds within one to three months. Rejections may occasionally include unsolicited feedback. Authors are paid royalties.

WE SAY: Three weathered dolls stare out from the matt cover of Ann Alexander's A5 sized book, *Old Things*. The off white, perfect bound pages have a pleasing, slight texture. Poems included in the collection vary from witnessing the age of an elderly parent; the shift from treating a pet as familiar to an object after death; to the comparison of a midwife to a gardener, the child like a nut, its grown self folded within.

See also: prose publisher p170

WAYWISER PRESS, THE ☆
COLLECTIONS AND ANTHOLOGIES
Christmas Cottage, Church Enstone,
Oxfordshire OX7 4NN
www.waywiser-press.com
Editors: Philip Hoy, Joseph Harrison,
Dora Malech, V Penelope Pelizzon,
Eric McHenry, Greg Williamson,
Clive Watkins, Matthew Yorke
Established 2001. Also publishes
some prose (see p170).
Publications available direct from
publisher website; by post and
email order; at chain bookshops
and independent bookshops
nationwide; and from Amazon
and other bookshop websites,
including Inpress Books.
SUBMISSIONS: Poetry can be
submitted only during submission
windows, and should be from
authors who have had two or more
collections published. Authors who
have had one collection published
should look at competition entry
(see p296). Submit by post to
Christmas Cottage, Church
Enstone Chipping Norton OX7
4NN. Guidelines at www.waywiser-
press.com/authors.html. Usually
responds within one to three
months. No feedback offered if
rejected. Authors receive royalties
and free copies of their book.
WE SAY: We looked at a PDF of
How to Avoid Speaking by Jaimee
Hills, a 96-page publication with
a simple cover design (slightly
unpolished – the title runs close to
the edge) and clean layout. The
collection won the Anthony Hecht
award, and includes a foreword
from prize judge Anthony Thwaite.
Includes both contemporary
free poetry and more traditional
forms, all experimenting with and
confronting language.
See also: prose publisher p170

WINTER GOOSE PUBLISHING
COLLECTIONS
www.wintergoosepublishing.com
Editors: James Logan Koukis,
Sherry Foley
Accepts poetry and prose
poetry, but publishes a limited
amount of poetry each year (see
prose publisher p171). Strongly
suggest writers read work by the
press's authors to get a feel for
preference.
See also: prose publisher p171

WORPLE PRESS
COLLECTIONS
Achill Sound, 2b Dry Hill Road,
Tonbridge, Kent TN9 1LX
theworpleco@aol.com
www.worplepress.com
Co-directors: Peter Carpenter,
Amanda Carpenter
Mainly publishes poetry, but also
translations, anthologies, arts
essays and writing other than
poetry. Looks for excellence and
diversity of format and approach.
International submissions
welcomed – but not before the
end of January 2019. Check the
site to find out when submissions
re-open.

WRECKING BALL PRESS ☆
COLLECTIONS, ANTHOLOGIES
AND CHAPBOOKS/PAMPHLETS
5 Theatre Mews, Egginton Street,
Hull HU2 8DL
01482 211499
editor@wreckingballpress.com
www.wreckingballpress.com
Editors: Shane Rhodes, Russ Litten
Established 1997. Also publishes
prose (see p171). Publications
available direct from publisher
website; by post and email
order; at chain and independent
bookshops nationwide; at literary

events; and from Amazon. Some online content available to all. Wrecking Ball Press title *The Scene of My Former Triumph* by Matthew Caley was nominated for Best First Collection, The Forward Prize 2005.

SUBMISSIONS: Open to all. Submit by post (Wrecking Ball Press, 5 Theatre Mews, Egginton Street, Hull HU2 8DL) or by email (editor@wreckingballpress.com). Guidelines on the website. Usually responds within one to three months. Rejection may occasionally include unsolicited feedback. Authors receive royalties and free copies of the book.
See also: prose publisher p171

YEW TREE PRESS
COLLECTIONS, ANTHOLOGIES AND CHAPBOOKS/PAMPHLETS
Yew Tree Cottages, The Lagger, Randwick, Stroud GL6 6HP
yewtreepress@gmail.com
www.yewtreepress.co.uk
Editor: Philip Rush
Established 2012. Publications available direct from publisher website and from Amazon.
SUBMISSIONS: By invitation only, although local poets are welcome to contact. Submit by email to yewtreepress@gmail.com. Usually responds within four weeks. Rejections may occasionally include unsolicited feedback. Authors receive free copies of the book.
WE SAY: We looked at four pamphlets from Yew Tree Press: three from their Stroud Poets series (which each contain work by three local poets), and the fourth *Skinny White Kids* by Mark Husband. A little smaller than A5, the pamphlets all have staple spines and cardboard covers (in bright colours for the Stroud Poets and cream for Husband), and all are neatly printed, with no feeling of cramped text. The poets each have their own title pages with biographies, and the poetry is a pleasure to read. The Stroud pamphlets also have a growing list of other pamphlets in the Stroud series on their back covers. It's a small touch, but a really nice one.

ZIMZALLA
COLLECTIONS AND CHAPBOOKS/PAMPHLETS
mail@zimzalla.co.uk
www.zimzalla.co.uk
Editor: Tom Jenks
Established 2009. Publications available direct from publisher website.
SUBMISSIONS: Open to all. Submit by email to mail@zimzalla.co.uk. Guidelines at www.zimzalla.co.uk/about. Usually responds within four weeks. Rejections may occasionally include unsolicited feedback. Authors receive free copies of the book.
WE SAY: This is a publisher looking at the world askew, and we love it. Emma Hammond's *Waves on a Beach* is the most 'traditional' of the samples we looked at. It's slim, perfect-bound poetry; gloss cover featuring a photo image – but no title. That's on the first page with the author name and publisher details, but there are no page numbers and barely any poem titles. *Chaingrass* by Catherine Vidler is all concrete poetry, all constructed by repetitions of the word 'chaingrass'. It is spiro-bound, and both the back and front have poems on. Our favourite was Piotr Kalisz' *Flags of the Countries from*

Space, filled with line-drawing designs for the flags of the 270 planets with symptoms of life. If you think your work is too out there to be published, try here.

Listed in this section are publishers of every kind of prose, including full-length fiction, short stories, non-fiction, essays, memoir and other types of creative non-fiction, as well as a few graphic novel publishers. There are more fiction than non-fiction publishers, but many of the presses cover a range of prose publishing. Remember that, particularly with indie presses, and particularly with regards to short story collections, it helps to have a publication history in journals and magazines, so don't forget to check out the prose (p257) and mixed-form magazines (p179).

Also listed in this section are a number of presses that publish both prose and poetry. In these cases we have indicated, where appropriate, what their dominant area of publishing is.

nh Notting Hill Editions

Notting Hill Editions is an independent British Publisher devoted to reviving the art of the essay. The company was founded by Tom Kremer, champion of innovation and the man responsible for popularising the Rubik's Cube.

After a successful business career in toy invention Tom decided, at the age of eighty, to engage his life-long passion for the essay. In a digital world, where time is short and books are cheap, he judged the moment was right to launch a counter-culture. He founded Notting Hill Editions with a mission: to restore this largely neglected art as a cornerstone of literary culture, and to produce beautiful hardback books that would not be thrown away.

The unique purpose of the essay is to try out ideas and see where they lead. Hailed as 'the shape of things to come' we aim to publish books that shift perspectives, prompt argument, make imaginative leaps and reveal truth. In short, books that grow their readers.

ESSAY: A loose sally of the mind; an irregular, indigested piece – Samuel Johnson

www.nottinghilleditions.com

ABADDON BOOKS

NOVELS
www.abaddonbooks.com
Part of the Rebellion stable
of publishers (which includes
Ravenstone and Solaris).
Dedicated to high-quality science-
fiction, fantasy and horror, their
books are mostly violent and 'all
pretty dark'.

ACCENT PRESS

NOVELS / NON-FICTION
Octavo House, West Bute Street,
Cardiff Bay CF10 5LJ
029 2000 2880
info@accentpress.co.uk
www.accentpress.co.uk
Managing director: Hazel Cushion
Editors: Rebecca Lloyd, Greg Rees,
Alex Davies
Established 2003. Award-winning
independent publisher, now a
major name in trade publishing.
Includes imprints Xcite, Cariad and
YA Café.
Named Specialist Publisher
of the Year and shortlisted for
Independent Publisher of the Year
at the IPG Awards.
GENRES: Commercial fiction; non-
fiction; YA. Strictly no short stories
or poetry.
SUBMISSIONS: Open to all, during
submissions windows. Guidelines
at www.accentpress.co.uk/
submission-guidelines.

AESTHETICA MAGAZINE ☆

ANTHOLOGIES
PO Box 371, York YO23 1WL
01904 629 137
info@aestheticamagazine.com
www.aestheticamagazine.com
Editor: Cherie Federico
Established 2003. Stunning
anthology resulting from the
Aesthetica Creative Writing Award.
Publications available direct from
publisher website and at chain
bookshops nationwide.

ALANNA BOOKS

CHILDRENS BOOKS /
PICTURE BOOKS
info@alannabooks.com
www.alannabooks.com
Editor: Maria Pembroke
Established 2006. Publications
available from chain bookshops
nationwide; from independent
bookshops; at national literary
events; from Amazon and other
bookshop websites; and from
inclusive book clubs like Letterbox
Library. Alanna Books was
shortlisted by the Independent
Publishers Guild for Diversity
Publisher of the Year 2016.
GENRES: Picture books; board
books and card for babies and
toddlers.
SUBMISSIONS: Open to all. Submit
online at alannabooks.weebly.com/
submissions.html. Usually responds
in over six months. No feedback
offered with rejections. Authors are
paid an advance plus royalties.
WE SAY: We looked at an online
preview of *Zeki Can Swim*, by
Anna McQuinn, illustrated by
Ruth Hearson. We can't comment
on the quality of materials (though
the book is described as having
24 'sturdy' pages with baby-
friendly rounded corners), but

the illustrations are bright, charming and pleasingly diverse with their characters. The story is a sweet, straightforward narration of a baby swim class relayed in large rounded letters, one sentence per page – ideal for fun and education. This book is part of the Lulu series, which is equally bright and beautiful.

404 INK

NOVELS / SHORT STORY COLLECTIONS AND ANTHOLOGIES / NON-FICTION / E-BOOKS
hello@404ink.com
www.404ink.com
Editors: Heather McDaid, Laura Jones

Established 2016. Mixed form: alongside short stories, novels and non-fiction, it also publishes some poetry, including mixed prose/poetry anthologies (see p181). Publications available direct from publisher website; by post and email order; from chain bookshops nationwide; from independent bookshops; at national and local literary events; and from Amazon.
GENRES: Contemporary fiction; literary fiction; experimental fiction; social and political commentary (non-fiction); humour.
SUBMISSIONS: Open to all. Submit by email to hello@404ink. com. Guidelines are available www.404ink.com/submissions. Usually responds in one to three months. Rejections may occasionally include unsolicited feedback. Authors are paid an advance and royalties, and receive free copies of the book.

WE SAY: We looked a digital version of *Nasty Women*, the first book published by 404 Ink. This 242-page collection of essays and non-fiction places the emphasis on the work included by leaving the editors' note until the end, in which editors Laura Jones and Heather McDaid voice their objective to continue to give a platform to new voices, especially those shouting back at political corruption and the hateful divides they exacerbate. Also available in print, this crowdfunded collection was fully funded within three days on Kickstarter, and ended at 369%.
See also: *404 Ink* (mixed-form magazine) p181

ALBA PUBLISHING
SHORT STORY COLLECTIONS AND
ANTHOLOGIES / NON-FICTION
PO Box 266, Uxbridge UB9 5NX
01895 832444

info@albapublishing.com
www.albapublishing.com
Editor: Kim Richardson
Established 1990. Mainly publishes
poetry (see p15). Publications

AD HOC FICTION ☆
E-BOOKS / SHORT STORY
COLLECTIONS AND ANTHOLOGIES
/ NOVELLAS-IN-FLASH
helpdesk@adhocfiction.com
www.adhocfiction.com
Editor: John O'Shea

Established 2015. Publications
available direct from publisher
website; by direct mail and
email orders; from independent
bookshops; and at national and
local literary events. Ad Hoc Fiction
was longlisted for the Saboteur
Awards in 2016 and 2017 in the
Wild Card Category.
GENRES: Flash/micro fiction; hybrid
form (prose poetry/flash fiction/art);
creative non-fiction.
SUBMISSIONS: By invitation only.
Usually responds within four weeks.
Authors are paid a flat fee and
receive free copies of the book.
WE SAY: We looked at two Ad
Hoc anthologies: *How to Make
a Window Snake* (three novellas-
in-flash), and *To Carry Her Home*
(vol. 1 of the Bath Flash Fiction
anthologies). Both books are
brightly bound, using a frame
effect around the title text, against
a backdrop of bold colour. Quality
paper and a tidy layout all reinforce
the professionalism. Both books
are pleasure to dip into, assigning
one flash to a page.
See also: prose magazine p259

They say

At Ad Hoc Fiction, we aim to
produce high quality books of
short-short fiction to spread
knowledge and interest
in this developing genre.
The full collections and
chapbooks give opportunities
for publication to emerging
and established authors
of single flash fictions and
novellas-in-flash. Our yearly
anthologies contain stories
longlisted in the Bath Flash
Fiction Awards and from
writers who attend our Flash
Fiction Festivals. The Ad Hoc
Fiction weekly micro e-book
aims to encourage writers to
experiment with the form.

88

available by post and email order; and from Amazon.
A title from Alba Publishing was shortlisted for the Haiku Foundation Touchstone Distinguished Book Award 2013.
GENRES: Spirituality and beliefs.
SUBMISSIONS: Publication history required. Submit by post (PO Box 266, Uxbridge UB9 5NX) or by email (info@albapublishing.com). Usually responds within four weeks, with submission feedback only if requested. Authors contribute to editorial/publication/marketing costs.
For a fuller description of this press, see also poetry publisher p15

ALCHEMY PRESS

SHORT STORY COLLECTIONS AND ANTHOLOGIES / NON-FICTION / E-BOOKS
alchemypress@gmail.com
www.alchemypress.co.uk
Editors: Peter Coleborn, Jan Edwards
Established 1998. Publications available direct from publisher website; by direct mail and email orders; at national literary events; and from Amazon and other bookshop websites.
Alchemy Press has won Best Collection in 2015 and Best Small Press in 2014 at the British Fantasy Society Awards.
GENRES: Horror; weird fiction; dark fantasy; supernatural; science fantasy.
SUBMISSIONS: Anthology submissions open to all during submission windows; other submissions by invitation only. Submit online at www.alchemypress.wordpress.com/submissions. Guidelines at alchemypress.wordpress.com/submissions/formatting and

specific details are posted for individual anthologies when submissions are open. Usually responds within one to three months. Rejections may occasionally include unsolicited feedback; for a fee a further feedback is available. Authors are currently paid an advance/fee plus royalties and receive free copies of the book, although payment structure is subject to change.

ALLARDYCE, BARNETT, PUBLISHERS

MIXED-FORM COLLECTIONS AND ANTHOLOGIES
14 Mount Street, Lewes, East Sussex BN7 1HL
www.abar.net
Editor: Anthony Barnett
Mainly publishes poetry (see p16). Publications available direct from publisher website; by direct mail and email orders; from independent bookshops; from Amazon; and from SPD in the US.
GENRES: Literary; music.
SUBMISSIONS: By invitation only.
See also poetry publisher p16 and *Snow Lit Rev* (mixed-form magazine) p222

ALMOND PRESS ☆

SHORT STORY COLLECTIONS AND ANTHOLOGIES / E-BOOKS
office@almondpress.co.uk
www.almondpress.co.uk
Editor: Marek Lewandowski
Established 2012. Primarily publishes fiction. Publications available from Amazon and other bookshop websites.
GENRES: Fantasy/sci-fi; horror; dystopian. No non-fiction.
SUBMISSIONS: Submissions take place during competition time, with competitions being the

submissions windows (see p287). Usually responds within one to three months. No feedback offered. Authors receive an advance/fee plus royalties and free copies of the book.

AND OTHER STORIES
NOVELS / SHORT STORY COLLECTIONS AND ANTHOLOGIES / NON-FICTION / E-BOOKS
Central Library, Surrey Street, Sheffield S1 1XZ
nichola@andotherstories.org
www.andotherstories.org
Editors: Tara Tobler, Stefan Tobler
Established 2010. Mainly publishes fiction. Publications available in chain bookshops nationwide; from independent bookshops; at local literary events; and from Amazon and other bookshop websites. Plans are in place for purchase direct from the publisher. Also offers a subscription: £20, £35 or £50 per year for two, four or six books per year.
And Other Stories was shortlisted for the 2013 IPG Newcomer Award. Its authors have also been shortlisted for and won awards.
GENRES: Literary fiction and literary non-fiction (subjects have included death, migration and family).
SUBMISSIONS: Open to all, but submitters are required to show proof of purchase from the press. Submit by post to Central Library, Surrey Street, Sheffield S1 1XZ. Guidelines at www.andotherstories.org/about/contact-us. Usually responds within one to three months. A standard rejection may occasionally include unsolicited feedback. Author payment is an advance/fee plus royalties.
WE SAY: The 144-page collection of short stories we saw by Fleur Jaeggy, *I Am the Brother of XX*, featured a very thick, matt cover, with a rather rigid perfect binding. On off-white pages, the stylish design allowed for wide margins and a somewhat larger font size. Jaeggy, a widely translated Swiss author, has been noted for her terse style; this collection maintains her unwavering, brutal calm.
See also: poetry publisher p16

ANGRY ROBOT
NOVELS / E-BOOKS
20 Fletcher Gate, Nottingham NG1 2FZ
incoming@angryrobotbooks.com
www.angryrobotbooks.com
Established 2008. Fiction publisher. Publications available direct from publisher website; in chain and independent bookshops; and from Amazon and other bookshop websites.
Angry Robot publication *Apex*, by Ramez Naam, won the 2016 Philip K Dick Award.
GENRES: Sci-fi; fantasy.
SUBMISSIONS: Usually agent-only, but there is a short window for open submissions every 18-24 months. Submit by email to www.angryrobotbooks.com/submissions. Usually responds within one to three months. Rejections may occasionally include unsolicited feedback. Authors receive an advance and royalties.
WE SAY: Based on the e-book excerpt we saw, 396-page long *The Stars are Legion*, by Hugo Award winning and widely translated author Kameron Hurley, Angry Robot's books are on trend with fellow contemporary SF titles – and leading the pack in terms of quality of writing. Angry Robot have chosen a

ARACHNE PRESS ☆

NOVELS / SHORT STORY
COLLECTIONS AND
ANTHOLOGIES / NON-FICTION/
AUDIO BOOKS / E-BOOKS
100 Grierson Road, London
SE23 1NX
020 8699 0206
www.arachnepress.com
Editor: Cherry Potts

Established 2012. Mainly
publishes fiction (particularly
short stories), but also publishes
some poetry (see p17).
Publications available direct
from publisher website; by
post and email order; at chain
bookshops and independent
bookshops nationwide; at local
literary events; and from
Amazon and other bookshop
websites, including distributor
www.inpressbooks.co.uk.
Arachne Press title *Devilskein
& Dearlove* by Alex Smith was
nominated for the Carnegie
Medal 2015, and title *Weird Lies*,
edited by Cherry Potts and Katy
Darby, won Best Anthology in
the 2014 Saboteur Awards.
GENRES: literary fiction; poetry;
Children's fiction; fantasy/sci-fi;
photography.
SUBMISSIONS: Particularly
welcome from all women, and
D/deaf writers. During
submissions windows, submit
through Submittable at
arachnepress.submittable.com/
submit. Guidelines at www.
arachnepress.com/submissions.
Usually responds within one
to three months, and provides

They say

Arachne Press is a micro-
publisher just celebrating our
5th anniversary. We use our live
events to promote our books
and find new writers – your best
route to publication with us is
to do a floor spot at an event
or submit to a call out for an
anthology. If we love your work
and you are prepared to back
your writing by doing readings
or bragging on social media,
then we might invite you to put
forward a collection or novel. If
we don't choose to publish we
will give feedback. If we say it
shows promise we mean it!

feedback on submissions where the
editor thinks it would be useful to
the author, unless explicitly asked
not to. Authors receive royalties and
free copies of the book.
**For more information, including
what We Say, see also poetry
publisher p17**

cover and format that allows fans of the genre to easily identify the title as something they might enjoy. The book itself has an immediate hook, being dedicated to 'all the brutal women' and has the sort of abrupt opening that snares the reader.

ARLEN HOUSE
NOVELS / SHORT STORY COLLECTIONS
arlenhouse@gmail.com
arlenhouse.blogspot.co.uk
One of Ireland's leading presses, a literary publisher with a focus on 'works of cultural importance'.

ASLS
PRINT
ASLS, 7 University Gardens, Glasgow G12 8QH
0141 330 5309
office@asls.org.uk
www.asls.org.uk
Established 1970. Publications available direct from publisher website; by post and email order; from chain bookshops nationwide; from independent bookshops; at national and local literary events; and from Amazon and other bookshop websites.
ASLS titles have won Saltire Society Research Book of the Year awards,

AS YET UNTITLED
ARTISTS' BOOKS
5 Veales Rd, Kingsbridge, Devon TQ7 1EX
admin@asyetuntitled.org
www.asyetuntitled.org
Editor: Rosie Sherwood

Established 2012. Mixed form: artists' books. Publications available direct from publisher website; from selected/local chain bookshops; from independent bookshops; at local literary events; and at Artists' Book Fairs (National) and the Small Publishers Fair.
GENRES: Fantasy/sci-fi; graphic/comics; literary fiction; poetry; visual arts. Strictly no non-fiction.
SUBMISSIONS: As Yet Untitled does not take submissions. Artists and writers are invited to collaborate with the press.
WE SAY: As Yet Untitled's books are works of art, exploring the concept of space within pages – we looked at digital images of the publications as the physical books are of limited availability. Publications include a photobook containing tissue-thin, loose-leaf pages that can be reordered; and a short comic/photography/poetry book. All materials appear to be of high quality.
See also: poetry publisher p18 and *Elbow Room* (mixed-form literary magazine) p193

and an ASLS title was shortlisted for the Saltire Society Scottish Book of the Year award in 2011.
GENRES: Short fiction and poetry (in New Writing Scotland); reprints of classic Scottish texts; collections of scholarly papers; study guides.
SUBMISSIONS: Submit by proposal form at www.asls.arts.gla.ac.uk/contact.html#A1. Usually responds within four to six months. No feedback offered with rejections. Successful contributors to New Writing Scotland are paid a fee and receive print copy/ies of the book.
WE SAY: We looked at *A Portable Shelter* by Kirsty Logan: a beautiful, limited edition hardback, clothbound with silver embossed text on the cover, and thick inner paper for the 13 short stories in the collection. A high-art production, worthy of the Folio Society.
See also: poetry publisher p18 and *New Writing Scotland* (mixed-form literary magazine) p213

ASTON BAY PRESS
NOVELS
c/o Daniel Goldsmith Associates, Dallam Court, Dallam Lane WA2 7LT
www.astonbay.co.uk
Publishes crime and historical fiction; detective stories with female leads. Welcomes submissions from agents and authors.

ATLANTIC PRESS
GRAPHIC LITERATURE
info@atlanticpressbooks.com
www.atlanticpressbooks.com
Publishes limited edition first books by authorial illustrators. Looks for intriguing stories illustrated for an adult audience, or for an audience of all ages. Works in association with the MA in Authorial Illustration at Falmouth University,

AUGUR PRESS
NOVELS / NON-FICTION
info@augurpress.com
www.augurpress.com
Non-fiction and fiction. Books with an emphasis on enabling the reader 'to reflect, and to look beyond ... that which is immediately apparent'.
See also: poetry publisher p18

AURORA METRO ☆
NOVELS / NON-FICTION / E-BOOKS
67 Grove Avenue, Twickenham TW1 4HX
020 3261 0000
submissions@aurorametro.com
www.aurorametro.com
Editor: Cheryl Robson
Established 1989. Also publishes scripts (see p277). Publications available direct from publisher website; by direct mail and email orders; from chain bookshops nationwide; from independent bookshops; at national and local literary events, and from Amazon and other bookshop websites. Aurora Metro title *The Leipzig Affair* by Fiona Rintoul was shortlisted for the Scottish First Book of the Year Award 2015 by the Saltire Society.
GENRES: Fiction by women; historical fiction; arts & culture non-fiction.
SUBMISSIONS: Open to all. Submit by post (67 Grove Avenue, Twickenham TW1 4HX) or email (submissions@aurorametro.com). Guidelines at www.aurorametro.com/newsite/contact-us/submit-your-work/#gsc.tab=0. Usually responds within one to three months. Rejections may

occasionally include unsolicited feedback. Authors are paid an advance/fee plus royalties and receive free copies of the book.
WE SAY: We looked at PDF proofs of three samples. A glance at the covers shows that Aurora Metro understands its bookshelf front-views: Ewa Dodd's *The Walls Came Down* is clearly adult political historical fiction; the cover of Lars-Henrik Olsen's translated YA book *Erik and the Gods* features illustrated figures with a quirky font, and non-fiction *Silent Women: Pioneers of Cinema* features a black background with gold text, and a 1920's photo of a camera woman – serious but accessible. The inner page layouts also reflect this: professional and clear, but Erik uses that quirky font for chapter titles. The marketing on the website is also in-depth and effective.
See also: script publisher p277

AVERY HILL PUBLISHING
GRAPHIC NOVELS
19 Aspinall Road, Brockley, London SE4 2EH
07725 595307
ricky@averyhillublishing.com
www.averyhillpublishing.com
Editors: Ricky Miller, David White
Established 2012. Primarily publishes graphic fiction. Publications available direct from publisher website; by post and email order; at major chain and independent bookshops; at literary events; and from amazon.com and other bookshops websites.
Avery Hill Publishing author Tillie Walden won the awards for Best Newcomer and Best Artist at the 2016 Ignatz Awards.

GENRES: Science fiction; LGBTW; comedy; literary; romance
SUBMISSIONS: Submissions by invitation only. Usually responds to solicited submissions within four weeks. Rejections may occasionally include unsolicited feedback. Authors are paid royalties.
WE SAY: We looked at a digital version of *I Love This Part* by Tillie Walden. This graphic novel documenting the day-to-day conversations of two teenage girls slowly falling in love has an almost zine-like style – coloured entirely with black and white, with purple watercolours. The writing style is subtle and delicate, the images conveying mood as much as the words do. There is a small author's bio at the end of the novel, as well as a dedication on the last.

AWEN PUBLICATIONS
NOVELS / NON-FICTION
www.awenpublications.co.uk
Awen looks for 'writing that is imaginative, boundary-pushing, eco-conscious, enchanting, and challenging of received wisdoms'. The majority of Awen's authors are skilled performers, whether as poets or storytellers.
See also: poetry publisher p18

BACKLASH PRESS
FICTION
www.backlashpress.com
Publisher: Gretchen Heffernan
Dedicated to releasing work that 'narrates a contemplated resistance to obedience and trend'. Looks for experimental, yet enduring fiction.
See also: poetry publisher p19 and *Backlash Journal* (poetry magazine) p239

BARBICAN PRESS

FICTION / SHORT STORY
COLLECTIONS AND ANTHOLOGIES
/ NON-FICTION / E-BOOKS
www.barbicanpress.com
Looks for 'distinct voices' and
books that dare to be different,
across a range of disciplines.

Current catalogue includes works
from translated fiction to true-life
short stories.

BIRLINN PRESS

E-BOOKS / NOVELS / NON-FICTION
West Newington House,
10 Newington Road, Edinburgh

BIRD'S NEST BOOKS ☆

NOVELS / NON-FICTION /
E-BOOKS
March Town Hall, Market Place,
March, Cambridgeshire PE15 9JF
info@birdsnestbooks.co.uk
www.birdsnestbooks.co.uk
Editor: Jane Levicki

Established 2014. Publications
available direct from publisher
website; from selected/local
chain bookshops; and from
Amazon.
GENRES: Children's/YA books;
realistic fiction; fantasy;
education fiction; picture book;
non-fiction support books.
SUBMISSIONS: Open to all,
during submission windows.
Submit by email to jane@
birdsnestbooks.co.uk. Guidelines
at www.birdsnestbooks.co.uk/
submissions. Usually responds
within one to three months.
Rejections may occasionally
include unsolicited feedback.
Authors are paid royalties only
and receive free copies of the
book.
WE SAY: We looked at a digital
version of *A Home Education
Notebook*, a 212-page book
published in 2016. It shares the
experiences of Ross Mountney

They say

Bird's Nest Books publishes
fiction featuring home educated
characters and non-fiction
aimed at supporting the home
educating community. We also
feature other communities
traditionally under-represented
in fiction and support authors
and illustrators local to us in
Cambridgeshire.

in home-educating her children,
with the goal of providing a guide
that will help and inspire other
home educators. An interesting,
easy-read story, even for non-home
educators, with a full-colour cover,
a spacious layout and incidental
black-white illustrations.

EH9 1QS
info@birlinn.co.uk
www.birlinn.co.uk
Managing director: Hugh Andrews
One of the larger independent
presses, with a wide range of
publications. Mixed form, fiction
and non-fiction. Imprints include
John Donald, Arena Sport and BC
Books.
See also: poetry publisher p19

BITTER LEMON PRESS

NOVELS / E-BOOKS
47 Wilmington Square, London
WC1 X0ET
fvh@bitterlemonpress.com
www.bitterlemonpress.com
Editor: François von Hurter
Established 2003. Fiction
publisher. Available from chain and
independent bookshops; and from
amazon.com and other bookshop
websites.
GENRES: Crime.
SUBMISSIONS: Submissions from
agents only. Usually responds
within three months. Rejections
may occasionally include
unsolicited feedback. Authors are
paid an advance fee plus royalties.
WE SAY: We looked at two
digital books of Bitter Lemon
Press. The first, *Three Drops of
Blood and a Cloud of Cocaine*
by Quentin Mouron, is a from-
French translated 206-page crime
novel. The second, *A Quiet Place*
by Seichō Matsumoto, is a 235-
page criminal story, translated
from Japanese. The layout of
both books is nice, with justified
text and not-too-full pages, and
attractive, high-quality covers.
Bitter Lemon Press focuses on
translating and publishing thrillers,
plus a non-fiction list that publishes
writing about culture and society.

BLACK & WHITE PUBLISHING

NOVELS / NON-FICTION / E-BOOKS
Nautical House, 104 Commercial
Street, Edinburgh, EH6 6NF
0131 625 4500
mail@blackandwhitepublishing.com
www.blackandwhitepublishing.com
Editor: Karyn Millar
Established 1992. Mainly publishes
fiction. Publications available from
chain bookshops nationwide; from
independent bookshops; at local
literary events; and from Amazon
and all other UK bookshop
websites.
GENRES: Crime/thriller/mystery;
historical fiction; literary fiction;
romance; YA; biography and true
stories; humour; sports and leisure.
SUBMISSIONS: Open to all.
Submit by email to submissions@
blackandwhitepublishing.
com. Guidelines at www.
blackandwhitepublishing.com/
index.php/infopages/submissions.
Usually responds within one to
three months. If no response after
three months, assume rejection.
Individual contracts for each writer.

BLACKHEATH BOOKS

NOVELS
grunt.blackheath@virgin.net
www.blackheathbooks.org.uk
'A home for literary outsiders.' A
very small press which hand-prints
books using vintage equipment.
Publications are limited print
runs, with signed and numbered
editions. Looking for 'future cult
classic novels'.
See also: poetry publisher p19

BLACK DOG

NON-FICTION
10A Acton Street, London WC1X 9NG
info@blackdogonline.com
www.blackdogonline.com

Publishing art, fashion and photography; and music, stage and screen, illustrated books, Black Dog aims for a 'fresh, eclectic take on contemporary culture'.

BLACK PEAR PRESS ☆

NOVELS / SHORT STORY COLLECTIONS AND ANTHOLOGIES / E-BOOKS
office@blackpear.net
www.blackpear.net
Editors: Rod Griffiths, Polly Robinson, Tony Judge
Established 2013. Mixed form. Publications available direct from publisher website, by post and email order, at local literary events, on Amazon and other bookshop websites.
GENRES: Crime/thriller/mystery; literary fiction; poetry; YA. No non-fiction.
SUBMISSIONS: Welcome during submissions windows, otherwise submissions are by invitation only. Guidelines at www.blackpear.net/submissions. Usually responds within one to three months. Rejections may occasionally include unsolicited feedback. Authors receive royalties and a discount on the price of the book.
WE SAY: We looked at a PDF of *Seeds of Destruction* by Frances Bennett: a perfect-bound, 216-page publication. A black cover with a coloured pencil sketch of a dandelion clock against stormy cliffs, and a rounded font. The layout is tidy and professional. The writing is tight and well-presented.
See also: poetry publisher p20

BLACK SHUCK BOOKS

NOVELS / SHORT STORY COLLECTIONS AND ANTHOLOGIES / E-BOOKS
blackshuck@greatbritishhorror.com
www.blackshuckbooks.co.uk
Editor: Steve J Shaw
Established 2015. Publications available direct from publisher website; by direct mail and email orders; at national and local literary events; and from Amazon.
GENRES: Horror.
SUBMISSIONS: By invitation only. Usually responds within one to three months, with feedback only if requested. Authors are paid an advance/fee plus royalties and receives free copies of the book.
WE SAY: We looked at a digital version of *Green and Pleasant Land*, a collection of 11 original horror stories by various authors. The print version comes with a green-black spooky coloured cover, with the authors' names printed in a large font. Although this contains all the need-to-know facts, a more creative cover would also have worked well here. The stories are presented in different fonts, all starting with a black-white sketched illustration depicting the location of the story.

BLUEMOOSE BOOKS

NOVELS / NON-FICTION / E-BOOKS
25 Sackville Street, Hebden Bridge, Yorkshire HX7 7DJ
01422 842731
kevin@bluemoosebooks.com
www.bluemoosebooks.com
Editors: Lin Webb, Leonora Rustamova, Hetha Duffy
Established 2006. Mainly publishes fiction. Publications available direct from publisher website; by post and email order; at chain bookshops nationwide; at independent bookshops; at national and local literary events;

and from Amazon and other bookshop websites.

Authors at Bluemoose books have won The Portico Literature Prize 2015. The Gordon Burn Prize 2013 (Faber & New Writing North) and Northern Writers' Award 2014 (New Writing North) and been shortlisted for The Jerwood Fiction Uncovered Award 2015.

GENRES: Literary fiction.

SUBMISSIONS: Open to all. Submit by email to kevin@bluemoosebooks.com. Guidelines at www.bluemoosebooks.com/about. Usually responds within four to six months. Rejections may occasionally include unsolicited feedback. Authors receive royalties only, or advance/fee plus royalties, and free copies of the book.

WE SAY: The perfect-bound title we saw, *The Gallows Pole* by Benjamin Myers, had an eye-catching cover and an equally vibrant spine – the matt cover featuring the shadowing image of a man with pink coins covering his eyes, and the spine a dizzying pattern of bright pink and black lines. The other covers on their website are similarly imaginative and striking. With 374 off-white pages, Myers' novel about the Cragg Vale Coiners was forensically assembled from historical accounts and legal documents, and is a recipient of the Roger Deakin Award.

BOOKOUTURE

NOVELS / E-BOOKS
7 Pancras Square, London N1C 4AG
pitch@bookouture.com
www.bookouture.com
Established 2012. Fiction publisher. Publications available from amazon.com and from other bookshop websites.

Bookouture author Robert Bryndza won The Paper Cut Award for Best Page Turner, while Bookouture founder Oliver Rhodes won the Romantic Novelists Association's Publisher of the Year Award 2016.

GENRES: Crime; psychological thrillers; romance; women's fiction; saga.

SUBMISSIONS: Open to all. Guidelines at www.bookouture.com/submission-guidelines. Usually responds within four weeks. Does not usually offer feedback with rejections, though may on occasion. Authors are paid a 45% royalty, and receive free copies of the book.

WE SAY: The 647-page e-book we saw, *The Girl in the Ice* by Robert Bryndza, featured a cover on trend with contemporary thriller novels. The simple style and wider font made it easy to read, additionally helped by the standard contents page featuring links to the chapters.

CALISI PRESS

NOVELS / E-BOOKS
1D Grimston Avenue, Folkestone CT20 2QE
info@calisipress.com
www.calisipress.com
Editor: Franca Simpson
Established 2014. Publications available direct from publisher website; from chain bookshops nationwide; from independent bookshops; and from Amazon.

GENRES: Literary; translations.

SUBMISSIONS: By invitation only. Usually responds within four weeks. Rejections may occasionally include unsolicited feedback. Authors are paid an advance/fee plus royalties.

WE SAY: We looked at online samples of two of Calisi Press's translated books: *Bella Mia* and *My Mother Was a River*, both by Donatella Di Pietrantonio and both translated by Franca Scurti Simpson. The cover of *River* features a watercolour painting, while the cover of Bella Mia shows a photograph of the remains of a collapsing clock tower, but both feature bright background colours, and black bands of colour across the lower section displaying the title, author and translator. The branding is impactful. The books themselves both seem to focus on reconstruction – of the self, of families and of relationships after devastating events.

CANDLESTICK PRESS
SHORT STORY COLLECTIONS
Diversity House, 72 Nottingham Road, Arnold, Nottingham NG5 6LF
01159 674455
info@candlestickpress.co.uk
www.candlestickpress.co.uk
Editors: Di Slaney, Katharine Towers
Established 2008. Mainly publishes poetry (see p21). Publications available direct from publisher website; by direct mail and email orders; from chain bookshops nationwide; from independent bookshops; at national and local literary events; and from Amazon and other bookshop websites.
GENRES: None specified.
SUBMISSIONS: By invitation only. Feedback not offered with rejections. Authors are paid a flat fee and receive free copies of the book.
For further information see also poetry publisher p21

CANONGATE
FICTION / NON-FICTION
14 High Street, Edinburgh EH1 1TE
0131 557 5111
support@canongate.co.uk
www.canongate.co.uk
Founded in 1973 this is one of the largest independent presses: twice winner of Publisher of the Year, and behind the publication of Booker Prize winner *Life of Pi* by Yann Martel. Committed to unorthodox and innovative publishing. No submissions by email please.

CARYSFORT PRESS
NON-FICTION
+353 1 493 7383
info@carysfortpress.com
www.carysfortpress.com
Leading Irish publisher of contemporary writing for and about the theatre, and about other performing arts. Publications are academic, but accessible to a general readership.

CATNIP PUBLISHING
NOVELS / PICTURE BOOKS
320 City Road, London EC1V 2NZ
020 7138 3650
liz.bankes@catnippublishing.co.uk
www.catnippublishing.co.uk
Editor: Liz Bankes
Established 2005. Fiction only. Publications available from chain bookshops nationwide; from independent bookshops; at national and local literary events; from Amazon and other bookshop websites; and direct from Bounce Sales and Marketing. Schools and libraries can order through wholesalers.
Catnip title *Girl with a White Dog* was shortlisted for the Waterstones Children's Book Prize 2015.
GENRES: Children's fiction; YA; picture books.
SUBMISSIONS: Agent submissions only. Submit by post (320 City

Road, London EC1V 2NZ) or by email (liz.bankes@catnippublishing.co.uk). Unsolicited submissions are not guaranteed a response. Usually responds within one to three months. Rejections may occasionally include unsolicited feedback, but not guaranteed. Authors are paid an advance/fee plus royalties.

CB EDITIONS
NOVELS / SHORT STORY COLLECTIONS / NON-FICTION / E-BOOKS
146 Percy Road, London W12 9QL
020 8743 2467
info@cbeditions.com
www.cbeditions.com
Editor: Charles Boyle
Established 2007. Publishes poetry (see p22), short fiction and other prose. Publications available direct from publisher website; at chain and independent bookshops nationwide; at national and local literary events; and from Amazon and other bookshop websites.
A multi-award-winning publisher: titles have won the Aldeburgh First Collection Prize (2009, 2011, 2013); the Scott Moncrieff Translation Prize (2014); and the McKitterick Prize (2008), as well as being shortlisted for the Goldsmiths Prize (2014) and the Guardian First Book Award (2014).
GENRES: Literary fiction.
SUBMISSIONS: Currently publishing only a small number of titles; please email (info@cbeditions.com) before submitting. No feedback offered with rejection. Authors are paid an advance/fee plus royalties, and receive free copies of the book.
For a fuller description of this press, see poetry publisher p22

CHICKEN HOUSE BOOKS
CHILDREN'S BOOKS
Chicken House, 2 Palmer Street, Frome, Somerset BA11 1DS
01373 454488
hello@chickenhousebooks.com
www.chickenhousebooks.com
Founded in 2000. Small but with great reach – Chicken House authors are award-winning and best-selling. Submissions 'open' annually during *The Times/Chicken House Children's Fiction Competition*.

CHOC LIT
NOVELS / SHORT STORY COLLECTIONS AND ANTHOLOGIES / E-BOOKS
Penrose House, Crawley Drive, Camberley, Surrey GU15 2AB
01276 274920
info@choc-lit.com
www.choc-lit.com
Established 2009. Fiction. Publications available from chain bookshops nationwide; from independent bookshops; and from Amazon and other bookshop websites.
Winner of 17 awards including, the 2017 Epic Romantic Novel of the Year Award from the Romantic Novelists' Association.
GENRES: Crime/thriller/mystery; fantasy/sci-fi; historical fiction; romance.
SUBMISSIONS: Open to all. Submit through www.submission.choc-lit.com. Usually responds within one to three months. Authors are paid royalties only.
WE SAY: These perfect-bound paperbacks feel like Big Five titles: glossy embossed cover, intriguing blurb (we looked at *How I Wonder What You Are* by Jane Lovering) and nicely formatted, despite

the slightly-too-close page trims. The Surrey-based publisher's key criteria are swoon-worthy heroes ('irresistible like chocolate') and romance-driven plots with or without other genre elements, such as mystery or fantasy. They also require authors to have a stellar web presence, either a popular blog or heaps of followers across the major social media platforms.

CILLIAN PRESS
NOVELS / E-BOOKS
83 Ducie Street, Manchester M1 2JQ
0161 864 2301
info@cillianpress.co.uk
www.cillianpress.co.uk
Established 2012. Fiction publisher. Publications available direct from publisher website; by post and email order; from chain bookshops nationwide; from independent bookshops; and from Amazon and other bookshop websites.
GENRES: Literary fiction; contemporary; YA; adult.

CINNAMON PRESS ☆
NOVELS / SHORT STORY COLLECTIONS AND ANTHOLOGIES
Meirion House, Glan yr afon, Blaenau Ffestiniog, Gwynedd LL41 3SU
01766 832112
jan@cinnamonpress.com
www.cinnamonpress.com
Editors: Jan Fortune and Adam Craig
Established 2005. Mixed form: alongside novels, short stories and creative non-fiction, it also publishes poetry, see p23. Cinnamon Book Club: £40 per annum for six brand-new books. Publications available direct from publisher website; from chain and independent bookshops nationwide; at local literary events; from Amazon; and from Inpress Books.

Titles from Cinnamon have won Scottish Arts Best First Book of the Year; Wales Book of the Year; and Wales Book of the Year Readers' Vote. They've been shortlisted for Wales Book of the Year and the Forward Prize for Best First Collection.
GENRES: Historical fiction; literary fiction; experimental; cross-genre; literary crime/thriller; literary exploratory fiction/sci-fi; landscape; creative biography; creative writing related.
SUBMISSIONS: Submit only during submissions periods. See www.cinnamonpress.com/index.php/about-cinnamon-press/submissions for full submissions details. Usually responds within one to three months. Submissions that came close to publication may receive some feedback with rejection. Authors are paid royalties only.
WE SAY: We saw the A5 perfect-bound *Girl Without Skin* by Connie Ramsay Bott, a matt paperback with cover design fitting for a mystery. This collection of interconnected short stories, set in small town Michigan against the backdrop of 1960s national politics like the Vietnam War, follows a set of characters and the drama and tragedies they experience closer to home.
For a description of this press, including what They Say, see also poetry publisher p23 and *Envoi Poetry Journal* p241

CIRCAIDY GREGORY PRESS
NOVELS / E-BOOKS
Creative Media Centre, 45 Robertson Street, Hastings, Sussex TN34 1HL
sales@circaidygregory.co.uk
www.circaidygregory.co.uk

A mixed form 'independent publisher for independent readers', Circaidy Gregory publishes non-fiction, short stories, childrens' fiction, plays and novels as well as poetry.
See also: poetry publisher p24

CLARET PRESS

NOVELS / SHORT STORY COLLECTIONS AND ANTHOLOGIES / NON-FICTION / E-BOOKS
51 Iveley Road, London SW4 0EN
020 7622 0436
contact@claretpress.com
www.claretpress.com
Editor: Katie Isbester
Established 2015. Publications available from chain bookshops nationwide; from independent bookshops; at local literary events; and from Amazon and other bookshop websites.
Claret Press was shortlisted for the International Book Cover Award: Fiction.
GENRES: YA; paranormal; upmarket literary fiction; fantasy; thrillers.
SUBMISSIONS: Open to all. Submit by email (contact@claretpress. com), by post (51 Iveley Road, London SW4 0EN) or online (www.claretpress.com). Guidelines at www.claretpress.com/about. Usually responds within four weeks. Rejections may occasionally include unsolicited feedback. Authors are paid royalties only.
WE SAY: We looked at a digital version of *Brushstrokes in Time* by Sylvia Vetta, a 187-page diary-style memoir tale about a woman growing up during the Cultural Revolution in Beijing, China, who tells her story to her daughter. The cover, although simple, is stylish and suits the story. The inside shows full pages with calligraphic Chinese characters at the start of every chapter, which suits the story as the main character stresses the importance of the Chinese literary system to her daughter.

COLUMBA PRESS

NOVELS / MIXED-FORM COLLECTIONS AND ANTHOLOGIES / NON-FICTION / E-BOOKS
23 Merrion Square North, Dublin 2, Ireland
garry@columba.ie
www.columba.ie
Editor: Garry O'Sullivan
Established 1985. Also publishes poetry in mixed-form collections and anthologies (see p24). Publications available direct from publisher website; by direct mail and email orders; from chain bookshops nationwide; from independent bookshops; at local literary events; and from Amazon and other bookshop websites.
GENRES: Catholicism; spirituality; history; reflection; prayer.
SUBMISSIONS: Open to all. Submit by email to garry@columba.ie. Usually responds within four weeks. Rejections may occasionally include unsolicited feedback. Authors are paid an advance/ fee plus royalties and receive free copies of the book.
See also: poetry publisher p24

COMMA PRESS ☆

SHORT STORY COLLECTIONS AND ANTHOLOGIES / E-BOOKS
Studio 510a, Fifth Floor, Hope Mill, 113 Pollard Street, Manchester M4 7JA
info@commapress.co.uk
www.commapress.co.uk
Editors: Ra Page, Sarah Cleave, Becky Harrison, Becca Parkinson

Established 2007. Fiction only. Publications available direct from publisher website; from chain bookshops nationwide; from independent bookshops; at national and local literary events; and from Amazon and other bookshop websites.

Comma Press title *Tea at the Midland*, a short story collection by David Constantine, won the 2013 Frank O'Connor International Short Story Prize, and the short story of the same name won the 2010 BBC National Short Story Prize. *The Iraqi Christ* by Hassan Blasim, translated by Jonathan Wright, won the 2014 Independent Foreign Fiction Prize. Comma Press also actively works with writers, running short story courses and hosting the annual National Creative Writing Fair in Manchester.

GENRES: Crime/thriller/mystery; fantasy/sci-fi; literary fiction. No non-fiction.

SUBMISSIONS: Open to all. Submit by email to info@commapress. co.uk. Guidelines at www. commapress.co.uk/resources/ submissions. Usually responds in over six months. Rejections may occasionally include unsolicited feedback. Authors are paid a flat fee or royalties, depending on the type of book/funding.

WE SAY: In print, we saw *The Book of Khartoum*, edited by Raph Cormack and Max Shmookler, and *Iraq + 100*, edited by Hassan Blasim, anthologies that both won the English Pen Award. These collections mix a sans-serif font in the titles with serif in the body text, but otherwise follow a standard design, with matt covers featuring graphic art. *The Book of Khartoum*, the first major anthology of Sudanese stories translated into English, pays homage to the theory that Khartoum takes its name from the Beja word hartooma, or 'meeting place'. We also looked at a digital version of *Protest*, a 459-page anthology of 20 historic stories about resistance. Every story offers an inside perspective on a historic event, which is elaborated on in an Afterword by a historian. Enthralling and informative.

CŌNFINGŌ

SHORT STORY COLLECTIONS
2 Stonecraft, Parkfield Road South, Didsbury, Manchester M20 6DA
www.confingopublishing.uk
Editors: Tim Shearer, Zoe McLean

Established 2014 as *Cōnfingō Magazine* (p189). Branched out into book publication in 2017 with the publication of Nicholas Royle's short story collection *Ornithology*. Check social channels for further information.

See also: *Cōnfingō* (mixed-form magazine) p190

COPY PRESS

NOVELS / SHORT STORY COLLECTIONS / NON-FICTION
51 South Street, Ventnor, Isle of Wight PO38 1NG
info@copypress.co.uk
www.copypress.co.uk

'Dedicated to extending ideas of writing, pictures and readability.' Publishes series including 'Common intellectual' (100-page paperbacks that make propositions for thinking, living and enjoyment) and 'Loop' (short mixed-form anthology volumes).

COTTAGE PUBLICATIONS

NON-FICTION / LOCAL INTEREST
15 Ballyhay Road, Donaghadee,

Co. Down, Northern Ireland
BT21 0NG
info@cottage-publications.com
www.cottage-publications.com
Very small press, interested in many topics, but publishes mainly local interest books and adult non-fiction. Generally does not publish poetry, academic works or children's interest books.

CRESSRELLES PUBLISHING COMPANY LIMITED
NON-FICTION
10 Station Road Industrial Estate, Colwall, Worcestershire WR13 6RN
01684 540154
www.cressrelles.co.uk
simon@cressrelles.co.uk
Editor: Simon Smith
Established 1972. Non-fiction theatre books. Publications available by direct mail and email order; from chain bookshops nationwide; from independent bookshops; Amazon and other online bookshops.
GENRES: Theatre.
SUBMISSIONS: Submissions are open to all. Submit post (10 Station Road Industrial Estate, Colwall, Worcestershire WR13 6RN) or by email (simon@cressrelles.co.uk). Usually responds to submissions within four to six months. Rejections may occasionally include unsolicited feedback. Successful authors receive royalties and free copies of the publication.
See also: script publisher p278

CRINKLE CRANKLE PRESS
NON-FICTION
crinklecranklepress@gmail.com
Editor: Eleanor Margolies
Publications available by direct mail and email orders.
Crinkle Crankle Press won the Nick Reeves Award for Arts and the Environment.
GENRES: Non-fiction.
SUBMISSIONS: Currently closed.
WE SAY: We looked at a PDF of various works, which ranged across articles, interviews and essays that all combine environmentalism and theatre, looking to address issues of e.g. climate change through performance, and examining various approaches, recounting how some projects have come together. The layout was straightforward and rather corporate, but the writing was interesting and accessible.
We enjoyed the interview with Jonathon Porritt, which examined how to strike a balance between sending a message and keeping an audience's attention.

CROOKED CAT PUBLISHING
NOVELS / E-BOOKS
enquiries@crookedcatpublishing.com
www.crookedcatpublishing.com
Publishes fiction including crime/thriller/mystery; historical fiction; literary fiction; romance; YA. Crooked Cat is an international ePublisher, publishing to Kindle in the first instance, then elsewhere. Print books are print-on-demand via Createspace.

CROWN HOUSE PUBLISHING
NON-FICTION / E-BOOKS
Crown Buildings, Bancyfelin, Carmarthenshire SA33 5ND
01267 211345
books@crownhouse.co.uk
www.crownhouse.co.uk
Established 1998. Non-fiction publisher. Publications available direct from publisher website; by post and email order; from chain bookshops nationwide; from

independent bookshops; at local literary events; and from Amazon and other websites.

Winner of the 2013 and 2014 Independent Publishing Guild Education Publisher of the Year Award; two publications from Crown House also won the 2017 ERA Educational Book of the Year Award.

GENRES: Education; health and well-being; neuro-linguistic programming (NLP); counselling, psychotherapy and hypnotherapy; and children's books.

SUBMISSIONS: Open to all. Submit by email to submissions@crownhouse.co.uk. Guidelines are available at www.crownhouse.co.uk/about. Usually responds in up to six months. Rejections may occasionally include unsolicited feedback. Authors are paid royalties and receive free copies of the book.

WE SAY: The digital version of *Rules for Mavericks* by Phil Beadle we saw was entirely black and white, but the simplicity of its design ended there. On less-than-A5 sized pages, playful font choices draw attention to words and phrases, such as a madman posting a letter to the newspaper. Certain paragraphs break down completely and trickle down the page, or feature on bold pages of text twice the normal size, sometimes in all caps and sometimes on a black background. The rest of the book may have calmed down – we only saw the introduction.

CULTURED LLAMA
SHORT STORY COLLECTIONS AND ANTHOLOGIES
Cultured Llama Publishing, INTRA,
337-341 High Street, Rochester
ME1 1DA
07800 522724
info@culturedllama.co.uk
www.culturedllama.co.uk
Editors: Maria C McCarthy, Bob Carling

Established 2011. Mixed form: short fiction and cultural non-fiction, and poetry (see p25). Publications available direct from publisher website; at national and local literary events; and from Amazon and other bookshop websites.

SUBMISSIONS: A publication history is required. Check the guidelines at www.culturedllama.co.uk/publishing/submission to find out when and how to submit your work. Usually responds within one to three months. Rejections may occasionally include unsolicited feedback, but usually not. Authors are paid royalties only, and receive free copies of the book.

WE SAY: Perfect-bound short story anthologies, non-fiction works and poetry collections printed on cream paper. We looked at Emma Timpany's *The Lost of Syros*, a collection with abstract cover art and well-edited prose. The whole product felt simple and polished, from the back cover text (a succinct blurb, author bio and puff quote) to the chic sans serif font used for the headings. Cultured Llama requests more in-depth submissions than other publishers, asking for detailed insights into the author's background and publicity plans, but their stringency yields quality results.

See also: poetry publisher p25

CURRACH PRESS
NOVELS / MIXED-FORM
COLLECTIONS AND ANTHOLOGIES
/ NON-FICTION
23 Merrion Square North, Dublin 2,
Ireland
garry@columba.ie
www.currach.ie
Editor: Garry O'Sullivan
Established 2003. Mixed form:
also publishes poetry (see p25).
Publications available direct from
publisher website; by direct mail
and email orders; from chain
bookshops nationwide; from
independent bookshops; at local
literary events; and from Amazon
and other bookshop websites.
GENRES: Photography; health; Irish
related; history; literary.
SUBMISSIONS: Open to all. Submit
by email to garry@columba.
ie. Usually responds within four
weeks. Rejections may occasionally
include unsolicited feedback.
Authors are paid an advance/
fee plus royalties and receive free
copies of the book.
See also: poetry publisher p25

DAHLIA PUBLISHING ☆
NOVELS / SHORT STORY
COLLECTIONS AND ANTHOLOGIES
shaikhf@hotmail.com
www.dahliapublishing.co.uk
Editor: Farhana Shaikh
Established 2010. Also publishes
poetry anthologies (see p25).
Publications available direct from
publisher website; by direct mail
and email orders; from chain
bookshops nationwide; and from
independent bookshops.
GENRES: Literary.
SUBMISSIONS: Open to all.
Submit by email (submissions@
dahliapublishing.co.uk) or
by post (6 Samphire Close,
Hamilton, Leicester LE5 1RW).
Also accepts a Twitter pitch to @
farhanashaikh. Guidelines at www.
dahliapublishing.co.uk/submission-
guidelines. Usually responds within
four to six months. Rejections may
occasionally include unsolicited
feedback. Authors are paid
royalties only and receive free
copies of the book.
WE SAY: We took a browse
through Dahlia Publishing's
online bookshop, so though we
can't comment on the quality of
materials used, we can say that
this publisher has an eye for cover
design and blurb. With a palette
of bold, dusky colours used across
the various anthologies and novels
published by the press, we feel
we could spot a Dahlia book
anywhere, and the commentary
makes us want to read them. The
covers working in both bookshop
thumbnails, and as a full page:
images are refined, but robust and
modern. The publisher produces a
couple of writing prize anthologies,
and there's particular support for
work by Asian writers.
See also: poetry publisher p25

DARF PUBLISHERS
NON-FICTION / NOVELS /
SHORT STORY COLLECTIONS
submissions@darfpublishers.co.uk
www.darfpublishers.co.uk
Established in 1980, Darf's aim is to
translate world literature for English
audiences, with a focus on new
talents and well-established Arab
writers. Submissions of manuscripts
in any genre are welcome. See
website for guidance.

DAUNT BOOKS PUBLISHING
NOVELS / SHORT STORY
COLLECTIONS / NON-FICTION /

E-BOOKS
158-164 Fulham Road, London
SW10 9PR
020 7373 4997
publishing@dauntbooks.co.uk
www.dauntbookspublishing.co.uk

The publisher behind the popular London bookshops, publishing vibrant books and international authors. Unsolicited manuscripts welcomed, as the press looks for début works by fresh voices.

DEAD INK

NOVELS / SHORT STORY
COLLECTIONS / NON-FICTION /
E-BOOKS
nathan@deadinkbooks.com
www.deadinkbooks.com
Editor: Nathan Connolly

Established 2011. Publications available direct from publisher website; from chain bookshops nationwide; from independent bookshops; at national and local literary events; and from Amazon and other bookshop websites. Dead Ink title *The Night Visitors* by Jenn Ashworth and Richard V Hirst won Best Novella in the 2017 Saboteur Awards.

GENRES: Literary fiction; crossover fiction; non-fiction; horror; speculative realism.

SUBMISSIONS: Open to all. Submit by email to submissions@ deadinkbooks.com. Usually responds within four to six months. Rejections may occasionally include unsolicited feedback. Authors are paid an advance/fee plus royalties and receive crowdfunding and free copies of the book.

WE SAY: We looked at the digital versions of two books; 257-page *Another Justified Sinner* by Sophie Hopesmith and 298-page *Guest* by S J Bradley. Both books have the same layout: simple but smart-looking contents, with spacious pages and long-read friendly fonts. Both books fall under Dead Ink's project 'Publishing the Underground', which develops careers of new and emerging authors through crowdfunding and with support from Arts Council England.

DEDALUS LTD

NOVELS / SHORT STORY
ANTHOLOGIES / NON-FICTION /
E-BOOKS
24-26, St Judith's Lane, Sawtry,
Cambridgeshire PE28 5XE
01487 832382
info@dedalusbooks.com
www.dedalusbooks.com
Editors: Eric Lane, Timothy Lane,
Marie Lane

Established 1983. Mainly publishes fiction. Publications available from chain bookshops nationwide; from independent bookshops; at national literary events; and from Amazon and other bookshop websites. In 2018, Dedalus is doing a special promotion of women's literature to celebrate the centenary of women getting the vote in the UK.

Titles from Dedalus Books have won the Read Russia Prize 2015, the Oxford-Weidenfeld Translation Prize 2012, the Portuguese Translation Prize 2013, and the Polish Translation Prize 2014.

GENRES: Literary fiction, upmarket crime/thriller/mystery, historical fiction. Has a penchant for the bizarre and grotesque. Accepts some literary non-fiction.

SUBMISSIONS: Open to all. Submit by post, sending a covering letter about the author with three sample chapters to Dedalus Limited,

24-26, St Judith's Lane, Sawtry, Cambridgeshire PE28 5XE. Usually responds within one to three months. No feedback usually offered with rejections, unless the writer has come very close to acceptance. Authors are paid an advance/fee plus royalties.

WE SAY: We looked at *Portrait of a Family with a Fat Daughter* by Margherita Giacobino, translated by Judith Langry. The novel cover shows a sepia-toned photograph of a family posing beside a car in semi-formal clothes, with the young girl in the centre wearing a bridal dress and holding a branch of flowers – obviously personal to the author, but presented well within the design. The novel, printed on quality cream paper, is based on the author's own experiences living outside Turin: 'all the names places, dates and facts in this book are true; but the tone… the slants of memory, all these are fiction, reality recreated and invented'.

DIAMOND TWIG

SHORT STORY COLLECTIONS
9 Eversley Place,
Newcastle upon Tyne NE6 5AL
0191 276 3770
diamond.twig@virgin.net
Editor: Ellen Phethean
Established 1992. Predominantly publishes poetry (see p27), but also publishes short story collections. Publications available direct from publisher website; and by post and email order.

Diamond Twig title *The Ropes: poems to hold on to*, an anthology of poems for teenagers, was shortlisted for the 2009 CLPE Poetry Award (Centre for Literacy in Primary Education) (www.clpe.co.uk).

SUBMISSIONS: Submissions for book publication are by invitation only. Usually responds within one to three months. Rejection may include occasional unsolicited feedback. Authors are paid a flat fee and receive free copies of the book.

WE SAY: These perfect bound A6 collections fit a lot into a small, quality book. With thick white covers featuring a black and white image, both *1956* by Margaret Wilkinson and the *Even the Ants Have Names* anthology we saw are printed on white paper. However, the inner margins are a little small, making them a bit harder to read toward the middle, and *Even the Ants Have Names* is done in a smaller font size that may be more difficult for some readers.

See also: poetry publisher p27 and *Diamond Twig* (poetry e-zine) p241

DIRT PIE PRESS

SHORT STORY ANTHOLOGIES
editors@riptidejournal.co.uk
www.riptidejournal.co.uk
Editors: Dr Virginia Baily, Dr Sally Flint
Established 2006. Mainly fiction, but also some poetry (see p27). Publications available direct from publisher website; by post and email order; from independent bookshops; and at local literary events. All stockists are listed on the website.

GENRES: Children's fiction; drama and criticism; erotica; fantasy/sci-fi; graphic/comics; horror; romance.

SUBMISSIONS: Open to all, guidelines on the website. Submit by email to editors@riptidejournal.co.uk. Usually responds within four to six months. No feedback offered with rejections. Authors receive a flat fee.

For a fuller description of this press see *Riptide Journal* (mixed-form literary magazine) p219. See also poetry publisher p27

DODO INK

NOVELS / E-BOOKS
thom@dodoink.com
www.dodoink.com
Editors: Thom Cuell, Sam Mills, Alex Spears

Established 2015. Publications available from chain bookshops nationwide; from independent bookshops; at local literary events; and from Amazon and other bookshop websites.

Dodo Ink was longlisted for the 2016 Republic of Consciousness Prize.

GENRES: Literary; experimental.

SUBMISSIONS: Open to all. Submit by email to thom@dodoink.com. Usually responds within one to three months. Rejections may occasionally include unsolicited feedback. Authors are paid an advance/fee plus royalties and receive free copies of the book.

DOG HORN PUBLISHING ☆

NOVELS / SHORT STORY COLLECTIONS AND ANTHOLOGIES / NON-FICTION / E-BOOKS
45 Monk Ings, Birstall, Batley WF17 9HU
01924 466853
editor@doghornpublishing.com
www.doghornpublishing.com
Editor: Adam Lowe

Established 2005. Also publishes poetry, see p27. Publications available direct from publisher website; by post and email order; from chain bookshops nationwide; from independent bookshops; at

national and local literary events; and from Amazon and other bookshop websites, including www.lulu.com.

Titles from Dog Horn have won the *Guardian* First Book Award (reader nomination); the Noble (not Nobel) Book Prize; and have had multiple honourable mentions in the Year's Best Horror.

GENRES: Drama and criticism; fantasy/sci-fi; horror; literary fiction; YA; food and drink; health and lifestyle; humour; music, stage and screen; society, education and politics; spirituality and beliefs; sports and leisure; travel.

SUBMISSIONS: Submissions by invitation only. On invitation, submit by email to editor@doghornpublishing. com. Guidelines at www. doghornpublishing.com/ wordpress/about. Usually responds in over six months. Rejections may occasionally include unsolicited feedback. Authors are paid royalties only and receive free copies of the book.

For a fuller description of this press see poetry publisher p27

DOIRE PRESS

SHORT STORY COLLECTIONS AND ANTHOLOGIES / E-BOOKS
Aille, Inverin, County Galway, Ireland
+353 091 593290
www.doirepress.com
Editor: John Walsh

Established 2007. Publishes poetry and short stories equally (see p28). Publications available direct from publisher website; from independent bookshops; at national literary events; from Amazon; and from www.kennys.ie. Doire Press title *Waiting for the Bullet* by Madeleine D'Arcy won the 2015 Edge Hill Readers' Prize and Breda Wall Ryan's *In a Hare's Eye* won the 2016 Shine/Strong Prize.

SUBMISSIONS: Only open to writers living in Ireland, and not actively seeking submissions (though open to being approached by writers familiar with Doire's books who are sure their work will be a good fit. Submit by post (Aille, Inverin, County Galway, Ireland) or by email (doirepress@gmail.com). Guidelines at www.doirepress.com/submissions. Usually responds within one to three months. No feedback offered with rejections. Book deals vary: authors may be paid royalties only; may be paid an advance/fee plus royalties; and/or may receive free copies of book – the deal depends on grant funding received.

For a fuller description of this press see poetry publisher p28

DOSTOYEVSKY WANNABE
NOVELS / SHORT STORY COLLECTIONS AND ANTHOLOGIES
dostoyevskywannabe@gmail.com
www.dostoyevskywannabe.com
Editors: Victoria Brown, Richard Brammer
Established 2014. Also publishes poetry and mixed-form anthologies (see p28). Publications available from Amazon.
GENRES: Experimental; literary; do-it-yourself; queer; underground fiction.
SUBMISSIONS: Open to all. Submit by email to dostoyevskywannabe@gmail.com. Guidelines at www.dostoyevsky.com/submit. Usually responds within four weeks. Authors are given two choices regarding royalties which are outlined in the submission guidelines.

WE SAY: We looked at three digital publications from DW, which included a novel (*Gaudy Bauble* by Isabel Waidner), a short story collection (*For We Are Young and Free* by Maddison Stoff) and an anthology of mixed poetry/prose (*Cassette 89*). The covers of each are stylish – they reminded us of the old Penguin book covers, but more contemporary, with 80s edge in the colouring of the images. The contents are professionally laid out, clean and spacious – particularly important in *Gaudy Bauble*, which has long, crowded paragraphs. The writing is unapologetically experimental, sometimes surreal. We particularly loved Kristen Felicetti's 'Reviews' series in *Cassette 89*.

See also: poetry publisher p28 and *The All-New Swimmers Club* (mixed-form magazine) p182

EARLYWORKS PRESS ☆
SHORT STORY COLLECTIONS AND ANTHOLOGIES / MIXED-FORM ANTHOLOGIES
Creative Media Centre,
45 Robertson St, Hastings TN34 1HL
kay@earlyworkspress.co.uk
www.earlyworkspress.co.uk
Editor: Kay Green
Established 2005. Mixed form. Earlyworks publishes short story, flash fiction and local interest (Hastings, Sussex), as well as mixed-form anthologies and poetry (see p29). Most books are anthologies of work by authors from the publisher's competition shortlists. Publications available direct from publisher website; at independent bookshops; at local literary events; and from Amazon. Discounted books are available to club members and competition

shortlisted authors.

GENRES: Literary and all other genres (up to 8,000 words); flash fiction (up to 100 words).

SUBMISSIONS: As Earlyworks Press is a club for authors and illustrators – running writing competitions, producing winners' anthologies and some other books – please submit via competition initially (www.earlyworkspress.co.uk/ Competitions.htm, see p290). The press often invites shortlisted authors to join in other publishing projects.

WE SAY: A5 perfect-bound collections printed on white paper. *Significant Spaces* assembled 15 prize-winning pieces of short fiction in its 154 pages; while *You are here…* featured 98 pages of the best of the press' memoir and journalism competition, including selected photos or artwork with the non-fiction works. This latter anthology focuses on the stories of generations that spanned the millennium, considering what changed or ended, and what was 'eternally human'.

See also: poetry publisher p29

EGG BOX PUBLISHING

ANTHOLOGIES / CHAPBOOKS/ PAMPHLETS

ueapubsoc@gmail.com
www.eggboxpublishing.com
Advisor: Nathan Hamilton

Established 2006, working in partnership with UEA students. Publications available direct from publisher website; by post and email order; from chain bookshops nationwide; from independent bookshops; at national literary events; and from Amazon and other bookshop websites.

See also: poetry publisher p29

ELLIOTT & THOMPSON

NON-FICTION / NOVELS

27 John Street, London WC1N 2BX
020 7831 5013
info@eandtbooks.com
www.eandtbooks.com

Specialises in 'popular and engaging' fiction and non-fiction. Several non-fiction titles from this press have won awards. Not currently open to fiction submissions, but see website for guidance on non-fiction proposals.

ELSEWHEN PRESS

NOVELS

elsewhen.alnpetepress.co.uk

Speculative fiction (in sub-genres including sci-fi, fantasy, alternate history etc) in e-book and print format. Ideally stories must be developed around a strong underlying theme that adds something significant and novel to the genre. Check for open submissions.

EMMA PRESS, THE

SHORT STORY COLLECTIONS / NON-FICTION / E-BOOKS

16-26 Hylton Street, Jewellery Quarter, Birmingham B18 6HQ
queries@theemmapress.com
www.theemmapress.com
Editors: Emma Wright, Rachel Piercey, Richard O'Brien

Established 2012. Mainly publishes poetry (see p30). Publications available direct from publisher website; from chain bookshops nationwide; from independent bookshops; at national and local literary events; and from Amazon and other bookshop websites. In 2016, The Emma Press won the Michael Marks award for Poetry Pamphlet Publishers.

GENRES: Literary.

SUBMISSIONS: Open to all, during submission windows. Submit online at www.theemmapress.com/about/submissions. Usually responds within four to six months. Rejections may occasionally include unsolicited feedback. Submitters are required to buy a book from the press. Authors are paid royalties only and receive free copies of the book.
For a fuller description of this press, including what They Say, see poetry publisher p30

EQUINOX PUBLISHING
NON-FICTION
415 The Workstation,
15 Paternoster Row, Sheffield S1 2BX
info@equinoxpub.com
www.equinoxpub.com
Academic publisher of around 30 books per year, including journals, textbooks, anthologies, monographs and reference books in the areas of archaeology, linguistics, cultural history, the academic study of religion, cookery and popular music.

ESC ZINE
SHORT FICTION AND POETRY ANTHOLOGIES
escpeople@gmail.com
esczine.wordpress.com
Editors: Jessica Maybury, Aine Belton
Established 2011. Mixed form: fiction and poetry (see p194). Publications available direct from publisher website; and at national and local literary events.
GENRES: Literary fiction; slipstream; experimental; art, fashion and photography.
SUBMISSIONS: During submissions windows, submit by email to escpeople@gmail.com. Guidelines at esczine.wordpress.com/submissions. Usually responds within four weeks. Rejections may occasionally include unsolicited feedback. Authors receive free copies of the book.
See also: poetry publisher p31 and *ESC zine* (mixed-form magazine) p194

EYE BOOKS & LIGHTNING BOOKS
NOVELS / SHORT STORY COLLECTIONS AND ANTHOLOGIES / NON-FICTION / E-BOOKS
dan@eye-books.com
www.eye-books.com
Editors: Daniel Hiscocks, Scott Pack
Established 1996. Publications available direct from publisher website; from chain bookshops nationwide; from independent bookshops; at national and local literary events; and from Amazon and other bookshop websites. Eye Books title *Hopkins Conundrum* was nominated for the Not the Booker prize in 2017.
GENRES: Books which don't fit into straight genres.
SUBMISSIONS: Open to all. Submit by email to dan@eye-books.com. Guidelines at www.eye-books.com/submissions. Usually responds within one to three months. No feedback offered with rejections. Authors receive a profit share.
WE SAY: We looked at Eye Books' online catalogue. It's a very professional affair: their non-fiction, adventure-based book-of-the-month has blurb that includes praise from Bear Grylls, and their other titles are equally well turned out and presented. Peppered throughout, looking distinguished with black-band branding and a colourful stripe for the logo, with photographic images, are the 'Eye Classics'.

EYEWEAR PUBLISHING ☆

NOVELS / SHORT STORY
COLLECTIONS / NON-FICTION
Suite 333, 19-21 Crawford Street,
Marylebone, London W1H 1PJ
info@eyewearpublishing.com
www.eyewearpublishing.com
Editors: Todd Swift, Rosanna Hildyard,
Alexandra Payne

Established 2012. Mainly publishes
poetry (see p32). Publications
available direct from publisher
website; from chain bookshops
nationwide; from independent
bookshops; and from Amazon and
other bookshop websites.
Eyewear Publishing title *Psalmody*
by Maria Apichella was shortlisted

FAHRENHEIT PRESS

NOVELS / SHORT STORY
COLLECTIONS AND
ANTHOLOGIES / E-BOOKS
07547 998834
chris@fahrenheit-press.com
www.fahrenheit-press.com
Editor: Chris McVeigh

Established 2015. Mainly
publishes fiction. Subscription
available: £48 for all e-books to
be published in 2017 (approx
70). Publications available
direct from publisher website;
by post and email order; from
selected chain and independent
bookshops; at literary events;
and from Amazon.
Fahrenheit Press publication *A
Place to Bury Strangers* by Grant
Nicol was shortlisted for the
'Ngaio Marsh Award for Crime.
GENRES: Crime and thrillers.
SUBMISSIONS: Open to all.
Submit by email to chris@
fahrenheit-press.com. Guidelines
at www.fahrenheit-press.com/
submissions.html. Usually
responds within one to three
months. Rejections may
occasionally include unsolicited
feedback. Authors are paid
royalties.

They say

Fahrenheit are not your
average publishing house. We
do things our way and we only
dance to our own tune. Our
founders have over 30 years'
experience in the industry and
we're using that experience
to create the fastest growing
crime publisher of the last
decade. In just 18 months
we've published 60+ titles and
we'll double that in the next
12 months. We publish all
our books in both e-book and
paperback editions.

for the Felix Dennis Prize (aka The Forward Prize for Best First Poetry Collection). *Weemoed* by Tim Dooley and Mr Universe by Rich Goodson have also been PBS recommendations.
GENRES: Literary.
SUBMISSIONS: Open to all. Submit by email to info@ eyewearpublishing.com. Usually responds within one to three months. Rejections may occasionally include unsolicited feedback. A reading fee is sometimes required. Authors are paid royalties only.
See also: poetry publisher p32

FAIR ACRE PRESS ☆
NOVELS / NON-FICTION / E-BOOKS
Primrose Cottage, Sweeney Mountain, Oswestry SY10 9EZ
01691 239466
fairacrepress@gmail.com
www.fairacrepress.co.uk
Editor: Nadia Kingsley
Established 2011. Also publishes poetry (see p32). Publications available direct from publisher website; from chain bookshops nationwide; from independent bookshops; at local literary events; and from Amazon.
GENRES: Nature writing; wildlife photography; literary novel.
SUBMISSIONS: By invitation only. Guidelines at www.fairacrepress. co.uk/about. Authors are paid royalties only and receive free copies of the book.
For further information see also poetry publisher p32

FAR HORIZONS PRESS ☆
NOVELS / SHORT STORY COLLECTIONS AND ANTHOLOGIES / E-BOOKS
info.far.horizons@gmail.com

farhorizonsmagazine.wordpress.com
Editors: Peter Sutton, Kimberly Nugent
Established 2014. Primarily publishes prose, but also publishes poetry in mixed-form collections and anthologies (see p33). Publications available at local literary events and from Amazon.
GENRES: Sci-fi; fantasy; horror; erotica.
SUBMISSIONS: Open to all. Submit by email to info.far.horizons@ gmail.com. Guidelines at www. farhorizonmagazine.wordpress. com/about. Usually responds within four weeks. Rejections may occasionally include unsolicited feedback. Authors are paid royalties only and receive free copies of the book.
See also: poetry publisher p33 and *Far Horizons* (mixed-form magazine) p194

FICTION DESK, THE
SHORT STORY ANTHOLOGIES / E-BOOKS
Suite 1, First Floor, 41 Chalton Street, London NW1 1JD
info@thefictiondesk.com
www.thefictiondesk.com
Fiction-specific: short stories anthologies pulled together from open submissions. The resulting book themes depend entirely on what the press has been sent.

FINCHAM PRESS
NON-FICTION / NOVELS / SHORT STORY ANTHOLOGIES
University of Roehampton, Department of English and Creative Writing, Fincham Building, 80 Roehampton Lane, London SW15 5PH
finchampress@roehampton.ac.uk
www.fincham.press

Fincham Press editorial team is based at the University of Roehampton and is run by a team in the Department of English and Creative Writing. Aside from creative writing anthologies, they also wish to publish bespoke educational materials, essays, scholarship and creative work for a general audience.

FISH PUBLISHING ☆

NOVELS / SHORT STORY COLLECTIONS AND ANTHOLOGIES / E-BOOKS
Durrus, Bantry, Co. Cork, Ireland
info@fishpublishing.com
www.fishpublishing.com
Editors: Clem Cairns, Jula Walton, Mary-Jane Holmes

Established 1994. Mixed form: anthologies include short fiction, poetry (see p33) and memoir. Publications available direct from publisher website; by post and email order; from chain bookshops nationwide; from independent bookshops; and from Amazon.
GENRES: Literary fiction; YA; biography and true stories.
SUBMISSIONS: Open to all, during submissions windows. Submit by post to Fish Publishing, Durrus, Bantry, Co Cork, Ireland or by email to info@fishpublishing.com. See guidelines at www.fishpublishing. com. Usually responds within four weeks. Rejections may occasionally include unsolicited feedback. Authors are paid a flat fee or royalties only, depending on the publication, and free copies of the book.
WE SAY: The *Fish Anthology* is a perfect-bound 248-page publication with a gloss laminate cover. We looked at the 2015 edition, which features the prize

winners from its many writing competitions (including memoir, flash, short fiction and poetry) – a must-read for any writer preparing submissions for a Fish Prize.
See also: poetry publisher p33

FITZCARRALDO EDITIONS ☆

NON-FICTION / NOVELS / SHORT STORY COLLECTIONS
243 Knightsbridge, London SW7 1DN
info@fitzcarraldoeditions.com
www.fitzcarraldoeditions.com
Editor: Jacques Testard

Established 2014. Mixed-form publisher: primarily publishes literary fiction and non-fiction/ essays, but also some poetry (see p33). Publications available direct from publisher website; by post and email order; from chain bookshops and independent bookshops nationwide; at national and local literary events; and from Amazon. Offers a books subscription: £70 for eight books, £35 for four.
Fitzcarraldo title *My Documents*, by Alejandro Zambra, was shortlisted for the 2015 Frank O'Connor Short Story Award.
SUBMISSIONS: Open to all. Usually responds within one to three months. Rejections may occasionally include unsolicited feedback. Authors are paid an advance/fee plus royalties.
WE SAY: Fitzcarraldo publications are instantly recognisable and top quality. We looked at *Pond* by Claire Louise-Bennett: an 184-page book of short stories; paperback, with French flaps. The cover is plain: Fitzcarraldo's signature Royal blue, with white text. (The fiction titles invert the colours.) The inner formatting, on high-grade white paper, is clean and

uncluttered, and the press uses its own serif typeface called Fitzcarraldo.

See also: poetry publisher p33

FIVE LEAVES PUBLICATIONS

SHORT STORY COLLECTIONS AND ANTHOLOGIES / NON-FICTION / E-BOOKS
14a Long Row, Nottingham NG1 2DH
0115 837 3097
bookshop@fiveleaves.co.uk
www.fiveleaves.co.uk
Editor: Ross Bradshaw

Established 1995. Also publishes poetry (see p34). Publications available direct from publisher website; by direct mail and email orders; from chain bookshops nationwide; from independent bookshops; at local literary events; and from Amazon and other bookshop websites.

GENRES: Social history; politics; Jewish interest.

SUBMISSIONS: By invitation only. No feedback offered with rejections. Author payment varies between books but a no contribution is required.

For more information, including what We Say, see also poetry publisher p34

FLEDGLING PRESS

NOVELS / NON-FICTION / E-BOOKS
39 Argyle Crescent, Edinburgh EH15 2QE
0131 6572 8188
www.fledglingpress.co.uk
Editor: Clare Cain

Mainly publishes fiction. Publications available direct from publisher website; from chain bookshops nationwide; from independent bookshops; and from Amazon and other bookshop websites.

Fledging Press title *The Incomers* by Moira McPartlin was shortlisted for the 2012 Saltire First Book Prize.

GENRES: Crime/thriller/mystery; historical fiction; YA; biography and true stories with a twist. Strictly no poetry, sci-fi, short stories or writing for children under 12.

SUBMISSIONS: Open to all. Submit by email to submissions@fledglingpress.co.uk. Guidelines at www.fledglingpress.co.uk/submissions. Aims to read submissions within six weeks. Rejections may occasionally include unsolicited feedback; confirmed feedback only if requested. Authors are paid an advance/fee plus royalties.

WE SAY: We looked at the e-book version of *Board* by David C Flanagan. It's hard to convey quality in an e-book, but Fledgling have managed it, with a striking blue-and-green illustrated cover, and a quirky simple line-drawing at the start of every chapter, as well as a differently formatted first paragraph. Looks great as an e-book; presumably even better in print.

FLIPPED EYE PUBLISHING

FICTION
Free Word Centre, 60 Farringdon Road, London EC1R 3GA
books@flippedeye.net
www.flippedeye.net

Established 2001. Predominantly publishes poetry, but also some fiction.

For a fuller description of this press see poetry publisher p35

FOR BOOKS' SAKE

SHORT STORY ANTHOLOGIES
www.forbookssake.net

Mixed-form publisher. Publishes fiction and non-fiction prose, but also some poetry (see p36). Publications available direct from publisher website; from selected/local chain bookshops; from independent bookshops; and at national and local literary events. For Book's Sake title *Furies: A poetry anthology of women warriors* was runner-up for the Best Anthology prize at the 2015 Saboteur Awards.

GENRES: Literary fiction; YA; biography and true stories; music, stage and screen; society, education and politics.

SUBMISSIONS: Open to self-identifying women, and especially encouraged from women of colour, disabled women, queer women, trans women and women from low-income backgrounds. Submit, during submissions windows only, via Submittable (forbookssake.submittable.com/submit – guidelines at same address). Usually responds within four weeks. **For a fuller description of this press see poetry publisher p36. See also: *For Books' Sake* (mixed-form e-zine) p196**

FOX SPIRIT BOOKS

NOVELS / SHORT STORY COLLECTIONS AND ANTHOLOGIES / NON-FICTION / MIXED-FORM ANTHOLOGIES / E-BOOKS
adele@foxspirit.co.uk
www.foxspirit.co.uk
Editor: Adele Wearing
Established 2012. Mainly publishes fiction, but does publish non-fiction, as well as some poetry collections, and prose/poetry anthologies (see p36). Also publishes historical martial arts manuals. Publications available

from Amazon; and at select events. Fox Spirit Books won the 2015 British Fantasy Society award for Best Small Press.

GENRES: Fantasy; sci-fi; horror; crime; mash-ups.

SUBMISSIONS: Submit only during submissions windows. See submissions guidelines at www.foxspirit.co.uk/sample-page/submissions for full instructions and details of author renumeration. Feedback not usually offered with rejections. Will try to provide feedback on request, but this is not always possible.

See also: poetry publisher p36

FREIGHT BOOKS

NOVELS / SHORT STORY COLLECTIONS AND ANTHOLOGIES / NON-FICTION / E-BOOKS
49/53 Virginia Street, Glasgow G1 1TS
info@freightbooks.co.uk
www.freightbooks.co.uk
Editor: Henry Bell
Established 2011. Mainly publishes fiction, but also some non-fiction and poetry (see p37). Publications available direct from publisher website; from chain bookshops nationwide; from independent bookshops; at national and local literary events; and from Amazon and other bookshop websites. Shortlisted for the Saltire Society's Scottish Publisher of the Year Award 2013 and 2014.

GENRES: Crime/thriller/mystery; historical fiction; literary fiction; YA; art and photography; food and drink; humour; sports and leisure; travel. No children's fiction.

SUBMISSIONS: Open to all. Guidelines on the website. Usually responds in over six months, with feedback only if requested. Authors are paid an advance/fee

plus royalties.
See also poetry publisher p37. For a fuller description of this press see *Gutter Magazine* (mixed-form magazine) p198

GALLEY BEGGAR PRESS ☆
NOVELS / SHORT STORY COLLECTIONS / NON-FICTION / E-BOOKS
info@galleybeggar.co.uk
www.galleybeggar.co.uk
Editors: Eloise Millar, Sam Jordison
Established 2012. Mainly publishes fiction, including Galley Beggar singles – long short stories available as downloads. Publications available direct from publisher website; by post and email order; from chain bookshops nationwide; from independent bookshops; at national and local literary events; and from bookshop websites.
Won the Baileys Prize for Fiction 2014 with Eimear McBride's *A Girl is a Half-Formed Thing*.
GENRES: Literary fiction; narrative non-fiction.
SUBMISSIONS: Open to all, within submissions windows. Submit by email to submissions@galleybeggar.co.uk. Guidelines at www.galleybeggar.co.uk/2-submissions. Usually responds within four to six months. Rejections may occasionally include unsolicited feedback. Authors are paid an advance/fee plus royalties.
WE SAY: We looked at one of Galley Beggar's 'singles': the novella *Rabbits* by Ruby Cowling. We were offered three different file formats for this e-book; all equally plain and no-nonsense. E-books of full-length novels are somewhat fancier, but stick with the Galley Beggar aesthetic of plain cover and good formatting. The editors have an eye for experimental fiction, and received an influx of submissions after the success of *A Girl is a Half-formed Thing*. We commend their short story and singles publication options for emerging writers.

GATEHOUSE PRESS
SHORT STORY COLLECTIONS / NOVELLAS
32 Grove Walk, Norwich NR1 2QG
admin@gatehousepress.com
www.gatehousepress.com
Editors: Meirion Jordan, Andrew McDonnell, Julia Webb, Anna de Vaul, Sam Ruddock
Established 2006. Publishes short novellas in their New Fictions series. Publications available direct from publisher website; from selected/local chain bookshops; from independent bookshops; at national and local literary events; and from bookshop websites.
GENRES: Literary fiction.
SUBMISSIONS: Submit during submissions windows. Usually responds within one to three months. No feedback offered with rejections. Writer payment/remuneration varies according to publication.
For a fuller description of this press see *Lighthouse* (mixed-form literary magazine) p204. See also poetry publisher p37

GEMSTONE ROMANCE
NOVELS / NOVELLAS / E-BOOKS
contact@gemstoneromance.com
www.gemstoneromance.com
Editor: Charlotte Courtney
Established 2015. Publications available direct from publisher website; and Amazon.
GENRES: Romance.

SUBMISSIONS: During submissions windows. Submit by email to submissions@gemstoneromance.com. Guidelines at www.gemstoneromance.com/?page_id=4. Usually responds within one to three months. All rejections include some feedback. Authors are paid an advance/fee plus royalties.

WE SAY: Romance publishers, and proud of it. Gemstone design and publish according to what romance fans expect: the painted portrait-type cover images, windswept landscapes, and pink banding are reminiscent of Mills & Boon.

GHASTLING PRESS, THE
SHORT STORY ANTHOLOGIES, ARTWORK AND ILLUSTRATION
editor@theghastling.com
www.theghastling.com
Editor: Rebecca Parfitt
Established 2014. Primarily publishes fiction. Publications available from Amazon.
GENRES: Graphic/comics; horror; literary fiction.
SUBMISSIONS: During submissions windows, by email to editor@theghastling.com. Usually responds within one to three months.
For a fuller description of this press, see *The Ghastling* (prose magazine) p264

GRANTA BOOKS
NOVELS / SHORT STORY COLLECTIONS AND ANTHOLOGIES / NON-FICTION
12 Addison Avenue, London W11 4QR
020 7605 1360
info@grantabooks.com
www.grantabooks.com
Editors: Sigrid Rausing, Laura Barber, Bella Lacey, Max Porter, Anne Meadows, Ka Bradley

Established 1989. Publications available from chain bookshops nationwide; from independent bookshops; at national and local literary events; and from Amazon and other bookshop websites. Shortlisted for the 2014 Independent Publisher of the Year Award.
GENRES: Literary fiction; history; popular science and nature; technology; medicine; society, education and politics; travel.
SUBMISSIONS: Agented submissions only. Usually responds within four weeks. Rejections may occasionally include unsolicited feedback. Writers are paid an advance/fee plus royalties.
WE SAY: One of the most well-heeled presses in this Guide, Granta's titles are of very high quality. *A Ghost's Story* by Lorna Gibb is a literary love story published as a chunky hardback (clothbound, with dust jacket). The cover has a slightly 80s romance aesthetic. Clear formatting and good blurb.
See also: *Granta Magazine* (mixed-form literary magazine) p197 and Portobello Books p149

GRIMBOLD BOOKS
NOVELS / SHORT STORY COLLECTIONS / NOVELLAS /E-BOOKS
admin@grimboldbooks.com
www.grimboldbooks.com
Publishes science fiction, fantasy or dark fiction. Considers both adult and YA works (as it 'tries not to pigeonhole'). Committed to diverse and inclusive representation within texts. Check site for open submission windows.

GRIST

MIXED-FORM ANTHOLOGIES
mhm.hud.ac.uk/grist
Grist is the publishing branch of
the University of Huddersfield, and
produces acclaimed anthology
Grist, which includes poetry
and short prose. Submissions
are through competitions. Also
publishes some single-author
books.
See also: poetry publisher p38

GUG PRESS

NOVELS / SHORT STORY
COLLECTIONS AND ANTHOLOGIES
frogsandjays@gmail.com
www.gugpress.com
Editor: Francis Byrne
Established 2016. Mixed form:
also publishes poetry (see p39).
Publications available direct
from publisher website; by direct
mail and email orders; and from
independent bookshops.
GENRES: Literary; experimental.
SUBMISSIONS: Open to all. Submit
by email to info@gugpress.com.
Usually responds within one to
three months. Rejections may
occasionally include unsolicited
feedback. Authors receive free
copies of the book.
See also: poetry publisher p39

GYLPHI LIMITED

NON-FICTION (ACADEMIC) /
E-BOOKS
PO Box 993, Canterbury CT1 9EP
info@gylphi.co.uk
www.gylphi.co.uk
Established 2007. Academic
non-fiction. Publications available
direct from publisher website; from
chain bookshops nationwide; from
independent bookshops; and from
Amazon.
GENRES: Academic books on
twentieth- and twenty-first-century
arts and humanities subjects for
university-level study and research.
SUBMISSIONS: Usually from writers
holding a university doctorate.
Submit by post (Submissions,
Gylphi Limited, PO Box 993 CT1
9EP) or by email (info@gylphi.
co.uk). Usually responds within one
to three months, with feedback.
Authors receive free copies of the
book.

HAFAN BOOKS (REFUGEES WRITING IN WALES)

SHORT STORY ANTHOLOGIES
c/o Tom Cheesman,
Dept of Languages,
Swansea University
SA2 8PP
t.cheesman@swansea.ac.uk
www.lulu.com/hafan
sbassg.wordpress.com
Editors: Tom Cheesman, Jeni Williams
Established 2003. Mixed form:
publishes poetry (see p39) and
prose, and various refugee-related
books and booklets. Publications
available direct from publisher
website; by post and email order;
at local literary events; and from
Amazon.
SUBMISSIONS: Open to all,
by invitation only. Author
contributions needed. Submit by
email to t.cheesman@swansea.
ac.uk. Usually responds within four
weeks. Rejections may occasionally
include unsolicited feedback.
Authors receive free copies of the
book; no fee or royalties.
WE SAY: Hafan Books is part of
local community efforts to support
asylum seekers and refugees. All
proceeds from sales go to Swansea
Bay Asylum Seekers Support
Group.
See also: poetry publisher p39

HASHTAG PRESS
NOVELS / NON-FICTION
info@hashtagpress.co.uk
www.hashtagpress.co.uk
Editors: Abiola Bello (fiction),
Helen Lewis (non-fiction)
Set up in 2014, the editors have
strong roots in the publishing
community, being the co-founders
of The Author School. For its 2018
list, Hashtag was looking for chick
lit, parenting, YA/children's fiction
with a male lead, horror, and 1920's
mafia themed books. Check the
website for updates.

HEAD OF ZEUS
NOVELS / SHORT STORY
COLLECTIONS AND ANTHOLOGIES
/ NON-FICTION / E-BOOKS
020 7253 5557
hello@headofzeus.com
www.headofzeus.com
Editors: Anthony Cheetham, Amanda
Ridout, Nicolas Cheetham, Laura
Palmer, Rosie de Courcy, Neil Belton,
Richard Milbank, Madeleine O'Shea
Established 2012. Mixed form.
Publications available from chain
bookshops nationwide; from
independent bookshops; at
national and local literary events;
and from Amazon and other
bookshop websites.
Winner: Digital Business of
the Year at The Bookseller Awards
2015.
GENRES: Crime/thriller/mystery;
fantasy/sci-fi; historical fiction;
literary fiction; romance; biography
and true stories; history; popular
science and nature; society,
education and politics.
SUBMISSIONS: Submit through the
online form at www.headofzeus.
com/submissions-login.
WE SAY: One of the largest and
most established indie presses

that are still open to unsolicited
submissions. Titles are available
in print and digital formats.
The paperback we checked
out, *The Washington Stratagem*
by Adam LeBor, is an adult thriller
with a striking cover but slightly
flimsy page quality. A slick website,
elegant catalogue and active social
media presence complete the
polished HoZ package.

HI VIS PRESS
NOVELS / ANTHOLOGIES
contact@hi-vispress.com
www.hi-vispress.com
Editors: Sophie Pitchford, Jim Gibson,
Ben Williams
Established 2016. Also publishes
poetry (see p41). Publications
available direct from publisher
website; from selected/local chain
bookshops; from independent
bookshops; and at national literary
events.
GENRES: Social realism; literary
fiction; working class writing;
experimental form poetry and
prose.
SUBMISSIONS: During submission
windows only. Submit by email
to contact@hi-vispress.com.
Usually responds within one to
three months, with feedback only
if requested. Authors are paid
royalties only and receive free
copies of the book.
**See also: poetry publisher p41
and *Low Light Magazine*
(mixed-form magazine) p206**

HOLLAND HOUSE BOOKS
NOVELS / SHORT STORY
COLLECTIONS / NOVELLAS
Holland House, 47 Greenham Road,
Newbury, Berkshire RG14 7HY
01635 36527
contact@hhousebooks.com

www.hhousebooks.com
Editors: Robert Peett, Bustles Lloyd, Natasha Robson
Established 2012. Fiction.
GENRES: Literary fiction; historical fiction; crime/ mystery. No non-fiction.
SUBMISSIONS: Open to all. Submit via www.hhousebooks.com/submissions (guidelines at the same address). Usually responds within four weeks.

WE SAY: We saw *The Storyteller* by Kate Armstrong and *Presenting the Fabulous O'Learys* by Caron Freeborn, two novels of under 300 pages each, printed on off-white paper. With vibrantly-coloured, matt covers, flexible binding made it easy to peruse the pages. The expressionist painting by Ernst Ludwig Kirchner on Armstrong's

HOLLAND PARK PRESS ☆
NOVELS / NOVELLAS / SHORT STORY COLLECTIONS / E-BOOKS
46 Baskerville, Malmesbury SN16 9BS
publishing@hollandparkpress.co.uk
www.hollandparkpress.co.uk

Holland Park Press

Established 2009. Mixed form: also publishes poetry (see p41). Publications available direct from publisher website; by direct mail and email orders; from chain bookshops nationwide; from independent bookshops; at national and local literary events; and from Amazon.
Holland Park Press was the joint winner of the Oxford-Weidenfeld Translation Prize in 2016 and was shortlisted for the Etisalat Prize for Literature in 2013.
GENRES: Literary.
SUBMISSIONS: Open to all. Submit by email to publishing@ hollandparkpress.co.uk. Guidelines at www.hollandparkpress.co.uk/submissions.php. Usually responds within one to three months. No feedback offered with rejections. Authors are paid royalties only and receive free copies of the book.

WE SAY: We saw Karen Jenning's autobiographical novel *Travels With My Father*. The cover is primarily dark teal with a matt coat, and features a rounded, abstract image of a man writing at a desk. The inner design is clean and professional. The novel is a memoir-travelogue, written in the first person as the narrator faces her emotions in the aftermath of her father's death, and it includes snippets of history about Cape Town (where the father lived) skilfully interwoven with the central story, and sensitive accounts of other family members.
See also: poetry publisher p41

title was especially eye-catching; *The Storyteller* focuses on the relationship between a coalescing young woman who has just regained consciousness, and the declining elderly woman who insists on recording – or creating – her biography.

HONEST PUBLISHING
NOVELS / SHORT STORY COLLECTIONS / GRAPHIC NOVELS / MIXED-FORM ANTHOLOGIES / E-BOOKS
Unit 1B, Clapham North Arts Centre, 26-32 Voltaire Road, London SW4 6DH
info@honestpublishing.com

HONNO WELSH WOMEN'S PRESS
NOVELS / SHORT STORY ANTHOLOGIES / NON-FICTION / E-BOOKS /
14 Creative Units, Aberystwyth Arts Centre, Aberystwyth, Ceredigion SY23 3GL
01970 623150
post@honno.co.uk
www.honno.co.uk
Editor: Caroline Oakley

honno

Gwasg Menywod Cymru
Welsh Women's Press

Established 1986. Mainly fiction, including classics. Publications available direct from publisher website; from chain bookshops nationwide; from independent bookshops; at national and local literary events; and from Amazon and other bookshop websites. Winner of the Bread and Roses Award for Radical Publishing 2015 with *Here We Stand: women changing the world*.
GENRES: Crime/thriller/mystery; historical fiction; literary fiction; biography and true stories.
SUBMISSIONS: Submissions only open to women who are Welsh or living in Wales or have a significant Welsh connection. Submit by post to Commissioning Editor, 14 Creative Units, Aberystwyth Arts Centre, Aberystwyth, Ceredigion SY23 3GL. Guidelines at www.honno.co.uk/infowriters.php. Usually responds within four to six months. Rejections may occasionally include unsolicited feedback. Writers receive a flat fee or an advance/fee plus royalties, as well as free copies of their book.
WE SAY: We looked at *All Shall Be Well*, a perfect-bound 356-page anthology that is professionally designed with a smart matt cover. Printed on quality paper, each item in the anthology is heralded by an image and, interestingly, it includes fiction and non-fiction pieces. This publication is full of wit and demonstrates the talent of Welsh women writers.

www.honestpublishing.com
Editors: Chris Greenhough,
Daniel Marsh
Established 2010. Mixed output
– also publishes poetry (see p41).
Publications available direct from
publisher website; from major
chain and independent bookshops;
and from amazon.com and other
bookshop websites.
Ward Wood author Joe Stein was
on the longlist of 10 for the Crime
Writers' Association Dagger in the
Library award 2016.
GENRES: Literary; satire.
SUBMISSIONS: Open to all, but

HOPEROAD

NOVELS / SHORT STORY
COLLECTIONS AND
ANTHOLOGIES / E-BOOKS
020 7370 5367
info@hoperoadpublishing.com
www.hoperoadpublishing.com
Editor: Rosemarie Hudson

Publications available direct
from publisher website; by direct
mail and email orders; from
chain bookshops nationwide;
from independent bookshops;
at national and local literary
events; and from Amazon and
other bookshop websites.
HopeRoad was longlisted for
the Dublin IMPACT Prize in 2015
and won the Word on Wings
YA Book Award at the Literary
Classics International Book
Awards in 2015.
GENRES: Fiction; YA.
SUBMISSIONS: Submit by email
(info@hoperoadpublishing.
com) or by post (PO Box 55544,
Exhibition Road, London, SW7
2DB). Guidelines at irp-cdn.
multiscreensite.com/3083789e/
files/uploaded/submission_
guidelines.pdf. Usually responds
within two to three months.
Rejections may occasionally
include unsolicited feedback.

HOPEROAD

They say

HopeRoad promotes literature
focussing on Africa, Asia and
the Caribbean. We vigorously
support often neglected voices
and many of our YA titles
focus on issues dealing with
identity, cultural stereotyping
and disability.

WE SAY: We viewed a selection
of publications from the last
few years, and they varied from
glossy to matt paperback, to
hardcover. Though the printing
materials were of a good quality
in each, the image on the
hardcover *Land of my Fathers*
by Vamba Sherif seemed a little
pixelated. We particularly liked
Sugar, Sugar by Lainy Malkani,
which featured black and white
artwork, perhaps a drawing
or watercolour piece, at the
beginning of each chapter.

only during submission windows.
Submit by post (Unit 1B, Clapham
North Arts Centre, 26-32 Voltaire
Road, London SW4 6DH) or by
email (info@honestpublishing.
com). Guidelines at www.
honestpublishing.com/submissions.
Usually responds within one to three
months. No feedback offered with
rejection. Authors are paid royalties
and receive free copies of the book.
See also: poetry publisher p41

HORRIFIC TALES PUBLISHING
NOVELS / E-BOOKS
admin@horrifictales.co.uk
www.horrifictales.co.uk
Editors: Steve Lockley, Lisa Lane,
Dion Winton-Polack, Amanda Rutter,
Kerri Patterson
Established 2011. Fiction.
Publications available from chain
bookshops nationwide; and from
Amazon and other bookshop
websites.
Horrific Tales titles *High Moor*,
High Moor 2: Moonstruck,
Whispers and *Angel Manor* were
all semi-finalists in the Bram Stoker
awards (2011, 2012, 2013, 2014).
GENRES: Horror.
SUBMISSIONS: Open to all, during
submissions windows. Submit by
email to submissions@horrifictales.
co.uk. Guidelines at www.
horrifictales.co.uk/submissions.
Usually responds within one to
three months. Rejections may
occasionally include unsolicited
feedback. Authors are paid an
advance/fee plus royalties and
receive free copies of the book.
WE SAY: We saw PDF copies of
Lucky's Girl by William Holloway
and *Bottled Abyss* by Benjamin
Kane Ethridge – both available
as print and e-books. Horrific
Tales' titles sport classic horror

covers – *Lucky's Girl* is a doozy: a
cross between the old Pan Horror
anthologies and Goosebumps. The
inner pages are well formatted,
with the occasional illustrative
decoration between chapters.

HURST STREET PRESS
SHORT STORY COLLECTIONS AND
ANTHOLOGIES / NON-FICTION
OVADA, 14a Osney Lane, Oxford
OX1 1NJ
general@hurststreetpress.co.uk
www.hurststreetpress.co.uk
Editors: Beth Sparks,
Shoshana Kessler
Established 2015. Mixed form.
Hurst Street Press publishes short
story collections and anthologies
and non-fiction books, as well as
mixed-form anthologies and poetry
(see p42). Publications available
direct from publisher website; from
selected/local chain bookshops
and from independent bookshops.
GENRES: Experimental.
SUBMISSIONS: Open to all. Submit
by post (Studio 1, OVADA,
14a Osney Lane, Oxford, OX1
1NJ) or by email (general@
hurststreetpress.co.uk). Usually
responds within one to three
months. Rejections may
occasionally include unsolicited
feedback. Authors are paid
royalties only.
**See also: poetry publisher p42 and
mixed-form magazine *IRIS* p202**

HYSTERIA PRESS
COLLECTIONS AND ANTHOLOGIES
editorial@hystericalfeminisms.com
www.hystericalfeminisms.com
Editors: Abi Tariq, Caroline Forde,
Jago Rackman, Katarina Strasser,
Madeleine Stack, Malise Rosbech,
Patri Prieto, Rakel Stammer,
Sohini Chatterjee

Established 2013. Publications available direct from publisher website; by direct mail and email orders; from independent bookshops; and at local literary events.

GENRES: Feminist critique.

SUBMISSIONS: Open to all. Submit by email to editorial@hystericalfeminisms.com. Guidelines at www.hystericalfeminisms.com/submit. Usually responds within four weeks. Rejections will usually include feedback. Authors receive no fee or royalties at this time.

WE SAY: Available on Issuu, Hysteria Press's *Hysterical Feminisms* series manages to maintain the look of a traditional, photocopied zine even on the screen. That is not to imply that the publication looks amateurish: this is a carefully designed publication. The publications available on Issuu used a courier-style font throughout and split the text into two columns. The occasional splash of a colour imageis effective, as are the white-letters on black 'highlight' background. We were caught by pieces such as 'Use your privilege' in *Hysteria #4*, a conversation which carefully explores social media, social status and the very concept of hysteria.

IGNITE BOOKS

NOVELS / NON-FICTION
hello@ignitebooks.co.uk
www.ignitebooks.co.uk

Described by one reviewer as 'an act of defiance', Ignite works to prove that 'unmarketable' books can be marketed, taking on entertaining tales and great stories that aren't easily categorised. Bold, genre-defying writing in all forms.

INFINITY PLUS

NOVELS / SHORT STORY COLLECTIONS / NON-FICTION
kbrooke@infinityplus.co.uk
www.infinityplus.co.uk
Editor: Keith Brooke

Established 2010. Publications available in print and as e-books from Amazon and other bookshop websites, and can be ordered by bookshops.

GENRES: Fantasy/sci-fi; horror; biography and true stories.

SUBMISSIONS: Submissions by invitation or query only. Usually responds within four weeks. Rejections may occasionally include unsolicited feedback. Authors are paid royalties and receive free copies of the book.

INFLUX PRESS

NOVELS / SHORT STORY COLLECTIONS AND ANTHOLOGIES / CREATIVE NON-FICTION / E-BOOKS
The Greenhouse, 49 Green Lanes, London NA6 9BU
www.influxpress.com
Editors: Kit Caless, Gary Budden

Established 2012. Mixed form: fiction, creative non-fiction. Publications available direct from publisher website; from chain bookshops nationwide; from independent bookshops; at local literary events; and from Amazon and other bookshop websites. Influx title *Above Sugar Hill* by Linda Mannheim was nominated for the Edge Hill Short Story Prize.

GENRES: Literary fiction; weird fiction; London writing; city literature; biography and true stories; history; society, education and politics; travel.

SUBMISSIONS: During submissions windows only, otherwise agented submissions or submissions by invitation only. Submit by email to submissions@influxpress.com. Guidelines at www.influxpress.com/submissions. Usually responds within four to six months. No feedback offered with rejections. Authors are paid royalties only or an advance/fee plus royalties, and receive free copies of the book.

WE SAY: We looked at *An Unreliable Guide to London*, which features 23 stories by London inhabitants relating tales of their less-known corners of London. The cover design parodies guidebooks: the landscape is there, but not as you know it. This perfectly complements the writing, which features stories that may or may not be rooted in truth, presented cleanly on quality cream paper. The cover warns 'limited scope – bad advice – no practical use' – but we found that this collection reframed a city everyone thinks they know, and commented on the changes taking place there.

INSPIRED QUILL

NOVELS / SHORT STORY COLLECTIONS / NON-FICTION / E-BOOKS
info@inspired-quill.com
www.inspired-quill.com
Established 2011. Publications available direct from mail and e-mail orders; from chain bookshops nationwide; at national and local literary events; and from Amazon and other bookshop websites. In 2016, Inspired Quill was shortlisted by the Polari Literary Salon for the Polari First Book Prize.
GENRES: Literary fiction; fantasy/ sci-fi; steampunk; YA; LGBT.
SUBMISSIONS: Open to all, during submission windows. Submit by email to sjslack@inspired-quill.com. Guidelines at www.inspired-quill.com/submissions. Usually responds in one to three months. Rejections include personalised rejection letter with editorial feedback on the submission and cover letter where appropriate. Depending on workload, occasional on-page edits are also provided (usually up to five pages). Authors are paid royalties only and receive free copies of book.

IRON PRESS

COLLECTIONS AND ANTHOLOGIES
5 Marden Terrace, Cullercoats, North Shields NE30 4PD
0191 253 1901
ironpress@blueyonder.co.uk
www.ironpress.co.uk
Editor: Peter Mortimer
Established 1973. Primarily publishes poetry (see p42), but also releases some prose (fiction, drama, etc). Publications available direct from publisher website; by post and email order; from selected/local chain bookshops; from independent bookshops; and via Inpress Ltd.
Iron Press's 2014 Iron Age Literary Festival won Best Event: Tyneside in The Journal Culture Awards.
GENRES: Literary.
SUBMISSIONS: Contact the press before submitting work: see the website for guidelines. Submit by post (5 Marden Terrace, Cullercoats, North Shields NE30 4PD) or by email (ironpress@blueyonder.co.uk). Usually responds within one to three months. Rejections may occasionally include unsolicited feedback. Authors are paid a flat fee.

WE SAY: The 68-page A5 perfect bound book we considered, *The Water Thief and the Manatee* by Kitty Fitzgerald, used slightly better materials than the poetry collection we saw (see Iron Press, poetry publisher p42). The paperback cover is of a heavier weight, and dark blue endpapers were also included. Designated 'A Modern Fable', beautiful, full colour artwork done by the cover artist is interspersed throughout, but the use of coloured font in each chapter page's title seems a little unnecessary. The font used is larger than normal, though appropriate for the fable styling. **See also: poetry publisher p42**

ISTROS BOOKS
NOVELS / SHORT STORY COLLECTIONS / NON-FICTION / E-BOOKS
Conway Hall, 25 Red Lion Square, London WC1R 4RL
info@istrosbooks.com
www.istrosbooks.com
Editor: Susan Curtis-Kojakovic
Established 2010. Primarily publishes fiction. Publications available direct from publisher website; from chain bookshops nationwide; from independent bookshops; and from Amazon and other bookshop websites.
GENRES: Literary fiction; history; society, education and politics.
SUBMISSIONS: Publication history required, as submissions are by invitation only. Submit by email to contact@istrosbooks.com. Usually responds within four weeks. Rejections may occasionally include unsolicited feedback. Authors are paid royalties and receive free copies of the book.
WE SAY: Specialising in translated work from Eastern Europe, Istros is on a mission to change the image of that region from 'grey tower blocks and cabbage' to the vibrant culture they are familiar with. A glance through their catalogue reveals designs that reflect this ethos: original illustrated covers with grey backgrounds and technicolour images. With their signature bright stripe of colour running down the edge of each cover, Istros books are instantly recognisable.

IVY PRESS
ILLUSTRATED NON-FICTION
210 High Street, Lewes BN7 2NS
www.ivypress.co.uk
Integrated, illustrated non-fiction books for the international market, released under three imprints. Subject areas include popular culture; art and design; crafts; general reference; health and parenting; mind, body, spirit; humour and novelty. Unsolicited proposals welcome (synopses, not manuscripts) by email (ivyauthors@quarto.com) or post.

JACARANDA BOOKS
NOVELS / SHORT STORY COLLECTIONS AND ANTHOLOGIES / NON-FICTION / E-BOOKS
27 Old Gloucester Street, London WC1N 3AX
office@jacarandabooksartmusic.co.uk
www.jacarandabooksartmusic.co.uk
Editor: Valerie Brandes
Established 2013. Also publishes illustrated books. Publications available direct from publisher website; from chain bookshops nationwide; from independent bookshops; at national and local literary events; and from Amazon and other bookshop websites.

128

Jacaranda Books title *The Book of Harlan* by Bernice L. McFadden won the 2017 NAACP Award for Literature.
GENRES: Literary fiction; crime fiction; romance fiction; biography and memoir; travel writing.
SUBMISSIONS: Agented submissions only, during submission windows. Submit by email to office@jacarandabooksartmusic. co.uk. Guidelines at www. jacarandabooksartmusic.co.uk/ contact. Usually responds within one to three months. Rejections may occasionally include unsolicited feedback. Authors are paid an advance/fee plus royalties and receive free copies of the book.

KATABASIS
NON-FICTION
10 St Martin's Close, London
NW1 0HR
0207 485 3830
katabasis@katabasis.co.uk
www.katabasis.co.uk
Publishes both poetry and prose. The prose focus is on essays and personal accounts.
See also: poetry publisher p44

LAGAN PRESS
NOVELS / NON-FICTION
Verbal Arts Centre, Stable Lane & Mall Wall, Bishop Street Within, Derry-Londonderry BT48 6PU
028 7126 6946
info@laganpress.co
www.laganpress.co
Mixed form: also publishes poetry collections. Looks for work of 'literary, artistic, social and cultural importance to the north of Ireland'. Irish and Ulster-Scots language work also welcomed.
See also: poetry publisher p45

LEGEND PRESS
NOVELS
107-111 Fleet Street, London
EC4A 2AB
020 7936 9941
info@legend-paperbooks.co.uk
www.legendtimesgroup.co.uk
Set up in 2005 and shortlisted for numerous awards. Publishes around 30 titles per year focused on literary, women's, historical and crime fiction.

LES FUGITIVES
NOVELS / NON-FICTION / E-BOOKS
91 Cholmley Gardens,
Fortune Green Road, London
NW6 1UN
info@lesfugitives.com
www.lesfugitives.com
Editor: Cécile Menon
Established 2014. A feminist press dedicated to short works of outstanding literary merit by francophone female authors previously unavailable in English. Publications available from chain bookshops nationwide; from independent bookshops; from Amazon and other bookshop websites; and from the CB Editions website (publishing partner). Les Fugitives has won and been nominated for six different awards. This includes being shortlisted for the French-American Foundation Translation Prize and the Best Translated Book Awards, as well as winning an English PEN Award all in 2017, and the 2016 Scott Montcrieff Prize for Translation from the French, which was awarded for the press's first title.
GENRES: Fiction and non-fiction.
SUBMISSIONS: Accepted from translators, agents and French publishing houses. Publication history required. Usually responds

within one to three months.
Authors are paid an advance/fee
plus royalties.
WE SAY: We looked at extracts
on LF's website, with an
admonishment from the editor
that she 'wouldn't know which title
would be most representative of
the press'. The images we looked
at showed flapped paperback
books, with textured, muted
colours (usually blues), and
contrasting title text, with the very
discreet 'double dot' logo in the
bottom right-hand corner. These
are classy affairs, with the extra
appeal that even in thumbnail size,
the name of the translator is clear.
The review blurb with each title is
impressive to say the least.

LEVIATHAN
NOVELS / SHORT STORY
COLLECTIONS AND ANTHOLOGIES
/ E-BOOKS
leviathan@greatbritishhorror.com
www.leviathanbooks.co.uk
Editor: Steve J Shaw
Established 2017. Publications
available direct from publisher
website; by direct mail and email
orders; and from Amazon.
GENRES: Horror.
SUBMISSIONS: Open to all.
Submit by email to leviathan@
greatbritishhorror.com. Usually
responds within one to three
months, with feedback only if
requested. Authors are paid an
advance/fee plus royalties and
receives free copies of the book.
WE SAY: We looked at anthology
Fuck the Rules. This 201-page
short story collection is made up
of eleven stories, for which authors
were encouraged to break a set of
rules. The rules given contained
to-be-broken guidelines for what

the story should be: only literary
fiction, society should only be
shown in a positive light, no
violence, drug use, crimes or any
form of illegal activity, etcetera.
This has resulted in a truly original
and alluring book. Originality is
also found in the design, which
uses multiple typefaces and
printing styles without losing its
cohesion.

LIBERTIES PRESS
NOVELS / NON-FICTION /
COLLECTIONS / ANTHOLOGIES /
E-BOOKS
140 Terenure Road North, Dublin 6W,
Ireland
+353 1905 6072
info@libertiespress.com
www.libertiespress.com
Founded in 2003 and billed as
Ireland's leading independent
publisher. Publishes non-fiction,
fiction and some poetry (see p46).
This press does charge a hefty
reading fee – read the submission
guidelines very carefully.
GENRES: Fiction; non-fiction;
business; memoir; health; history;
sport; short stories; essay.
See also: poetry publisher p46

LILLIPUT PRESS, THE
NOVELS / NON-FICTION
62-63 Sitric Road, Arbour Hill,
Dublin 7, Ireland
editorial@lilliputpress.ie
www.lilliputpress.ie
Small but prestigious, representing
such authors as James Joyce
and John Moriarty. Specialises in
biography, historical non-fiction
and memoir, but also publishes
fiction. All work published is
broadly focused on Irish themes.

LINEN PRESS ☆

NOVELS / SHORT STORY
COLLECTIONS AND
ANTHOLOGIES /
NON-FICTION / E-BOOKS
8 Maltings Lodge, Corney Reach
Way, London W4 2TT
020 8995 4488
lynnmichell0@googlemail.com
www.linen-press.com
Editor: Lynn Michell

Established 2007. Mainly
publishes fiction. Publications
available direct from publisher
website; by post and email
order; at local literary events;
and from amazon.com and other
bookshop websites. Linen Press
was a finalist in the 2015 Women
in Publishing Pandora Award.
GENRES: Literary fiction;
women's writing.
SUBMISSIONS: Open to all.
Submit via www.linen-press.
com/submit, completing
the form which requests
1,000 words. If the sample
is appealing, a further 50
pages may be requested. Full
guidelines are at www.linen-
press.com/submit. Usually
responds within four weeks.
Regretfully, feedback no longer
offered on submissions. Authors
receive an advance fee and
royalties.
WE SAY: The A5-sized, perfect-
bound copy of *The Dancing
Girl & the Turtle* by Karen Kao
we saw had a lovely photo on
the glossy cover of a woman
mid-movement. Printed on white
paper, the novel follows Song

They say

Linen Press is now the
only independent women's
publisher in the UK. Run
by women, for women. Our
policy is to encourage and
promote women writers and
to give voice to a wide range
of perspectives and themes
that are relevant to women.
We display and rejoice in the
differences in female creative
voices, rather than defining
them in terms of a simplistic
and one-dimensional
genre. We work closely and
collaboratively with every
author, chapter by chapter,
making a good book into a
superb one. Many publishers
no longer offer editing but we
believe it's a vital part of the
publishing process.

Anyi's story of survival in her
fight for independence as China
prepares for war with Japan.

LISTEN SOFTLY LONDON
NOVELS / SHORT STORY
COLLECTIONS AND ANTHOLOGIES
07814 695751
listen_softly_london@hotmail.com
www.listensoftlylondon.com
Editor: Dominic Stevenson
Established 2015. Primarily
publishes poetry (see p46), but
also prose, and mixed-form
anthologies. Publications available
direct from publisher website;
and from amazon.com and other
websites.
Listen Softly London was
nominated for the 2016 Saboteur
Awards.
GENRES: Urban; thriller; working
class; literary.
SUBMISSIONS: Open to all.
Submit via www.listensoftlylondon.
com/submissions (guidelines are
available on the same page).
Usually responds within four weeks.
Rejections will get a full response:
'You have taken the time to write
to us, so we'll take time to write to
you.' Authors are paid royalties and
receive free copies of the book.
**For a fuller description of this press
see: poetry publisher p46**

LITRO MAGAZINE LTD
SHORT STORIES COLLECTIONS
020 3371 9971
info@litro.co.uk
www.litro.co.uk
Editors: Eric Akoto, Precious Williams
Established 2005. Fiction. Litro also
runs a literary agency. Publications
available direct from publisher
website; from chain bookshops
nationwide; from independent
bookshops; at national and local
literary events; and at galleries and
public spaces across London.
GENRES: Crime/thriller/mystery;
drama and criticism; literary fiction;

art, fashion and photography; food
and drink; music, stage and screen;
science, technology and medicine;
society, education and politics;
travel.
**For a fuller description of this press,
see Litro Magazine (mixed-form
literary magazine and e-zine) p205**

LITTLE ISLAND
YA AND CHILDREN'S FICTION
7 Kenilworth Park, Dublin 6W, Ireland
www.littleisland.ie
A multi-award-winning publisher.
Most readers are between four
and 16 so works published
include novels for older readers
and illustrated books for younger
readers. Looks for work from
emerging Irish authors, and for
books in translation. No trilogies,
moral tales, fairies or horror,
please.

LITTLE ISLAND PRESS
NOVELS / SHORT STORY
COLLECTIONS AND ANTHOLOGIES
/ NON-FICTION
Lodgemore Lane, Stroud GL5 3EQ
07980 647187
info@littleislandpress.com
www.littleislandpress.com
Editor: Andrew Latimer
Established 2016. Mixed form:
publishes both prose and poetry
(see p47). Offers a subscription
of ten books for £50. Publications
available direct from publisher
website; from chain bookshops
nationwide; from independent
bookshops; and from Amazon and
other websites.
GENRES: Literary modernism.
SUBMISSIONS: Submit during
submissions windows only, either
by post (to Little Island Press,
Lodgemore Lane, Stroud GL5 3EQ)
or by email (info@littleislandpress.

co.uk). Guidelines are available at www.littleislandpress.co.uk/about-the-press. Usually responds in four to six months. Rejections only include feedback on request. Authors are paid royalties only.
WE SAY: These books favour simplicity, with text on covers colour-coded by genre; the dark teal cover of David Hayden's collection of stories, *Darker With The Lights On*, is the exception from the other grey-wrapped fictions. The 208-page digital version we saw included wide margins with the title of each piece and the page numbers resting closely against the body text.
See also: poetry publisher p47

LITTLE TOLLER BOOKS
NON-FICTION
gracie@littletoller.co.uk
www.littletoller.co.uk
Editor: Adrian Cooper
Established 2008. Publications available direct from publisher website; by post and email order; from chain bookshops nationwide; from independent bookshops; at national and local literary events; and from Amazon and other bookshop websites.
Longlisted for the Thwaites Wainwright prize.
GENRES: Travel; natural landscape and place writing. No fiction.
SUBMISSIONS: Agent submissions only, by email to gracie@littletoller.co.uk. Usually responds within four to six months. Rejections may occasionally include unsolicited feedback. Authors are paid an advance/fee plus royalties.
WE SAY: High-quality non-fiction in paperback and hardback, Little Toller books include full-colour illustrations, beautiful layouts and informative reads. We particularly loved *Mermaids* by Sophia Kingshill, which charts the history of mermaid folklore through the ages, complete with images, anecdotes and tales. The limited edition Little Toller hardbacks, with clothbound covers, are also worth checking out.

LOOSE CHIPPINGS
NON-FICTION
The Paddocks, Back Ends, Chipping Campden, Gloucestershire GL55 6AU
01386 840435
contact@loosechippings.org
www.loosechippings.org
Editor: Arthur Cunynghame
Largely publishes non-fiction, including travel and memoir – but open to fiction submissions.

MAGIC OXYGEN ☆
NOVELS / SHORT STORY ANTHOLOGIES / NON-FICTION / MIXED-FORM ANTHOLOGIES / E-BOOKS
The Flat, 53 Broad Street, Lyme Regis DT7 3QF
01297 442824
editor@magicoxygen.co.uk
www.magicoxygen.co.uk
Editor: Simon West
Established 2012. Mainly publishes fiction, but also some poetry (see p47). Publications available direct from publisher website; from major chain and independent bookshops; at local literary events; and from amazon.com and other bookshop websites.
GENRES: Self-help; romance; comedy; sci-fi.
SUBMISSIONS: Submissions are usually by invitation only. Work should be sent to editor@magicoxygen.co.uk. Usually responds within one to

three months. Rejections may include occasional unsolicited feedback. Authors receive royalties.

WE SAY: We made use of the 'Look in the Book' feature in Magic Oxygen's online shop. The books usually have covers featuring photographic images with heavy, stylised fonts. The inner pages revert to standard serif. They seem a little stretched, but we suspect this is an effect of the online preview. We were particularly struck by Trish Vickers' *Grannifer's Legacy*, the story of which exudes the sort of personal warmth and community effort that seems to lie under much of Magic Oxygen's work.

See also: poetry publisher p47

MANDRAKE OF OXFORD
NON-FICTION / FICTION
mandrake@mandrake.uk.net
www.mandrake.uk.net
Fiction and non-fiction publisher, with wide-ranging interests but a particular focus on occultism, myths, legends, horror and true crime. Open submissions, but follow the guidelines closely please.

MANTLE LANE PRESS
NOVELS / SHORT STORY COLLECTIONS AND ANTHOLOGIES / NON-FICTION
01530 830811
matthew@red-lighthouse.org.uk
www.mantlelanepress.co.uk
Editor: Matthew Pegg
Established 2015. Also publishes scripts (see p279). Publications available direct from publisher website; from chain bookshops nationwide; from independent bookshops; at local literary events; and from Amazon and other bookshop websites.

GENRES: Literary; slipstream.

SUBMISSIONS: Open to all, during submission windows. Certain publication opportunities may only be available to Midlands writers. Submit online at www.greensubmissions. com/537/mantle-lane-press/ index.php. Guidelines at www. greensubmissions.com/537/ mantle-lane-press/terms.php?. Usually responds within one to three months. Rejections may occasionally include unsolicited feedback. Authors are paid a flat fee and receive free copies of the book.

WE SAY: We looked at a digital version of the 53-page story collection *A Far Cry* by Valentine Williams. It presents four short alluring stories about how change occurs in far-away communities. The book shows a beautifully illustrated cover, complementing one of the stories about a young girl finding a whale's valuable 'ambergris'. The book is pocket-sized, perfect to read on the move.

See also: script publisher p279

MARGŌ COLLECTIVE
E-BOOKS / NOVELS
hello@margocollective.com
www.margocollective.com
Established 2017. Indie publisher of writers and stories from the edges.

GENRES: Literary fiction, speculative fiction, experimental, non-conforming, cross-genre, YA

SUBMISSIONS: Open to all. Submit by email to submissions@ margocollective.com. Guidelines at www.margocollective.com/ submissions. Usually responds

134

within one to three months.
Authors receive royalties only or
a flat fee only (depending on the
type of book/funding), plus free
copies of the book.

MAYFLY PRESS
NOVELS
submissions@mayfly.press
www.mayfly.press
'Good books from the North of
England.' Mayfly and imprint Moth
(crime writing) look for work from

MONSTROUS REGIMENT PUBLISHING
NOVELS / SHORT STORY
ANTHOLOGIES / NON-FICTION
editor@monstrous-regiment.com
www.monstrous-regiment.com
Editors: Lauren Nickodemus,
Ellen Desmond

Established 2017. Also
publishes poetry in mixed-
form anthologies (see p49).
Publications available direct from
publisher website; by direct mail
and email orders; and at local
literary events.
GENRES: Non-fiction
commentary; confessional
essay; topical prose; creative
non-fiction; literary fiction.
SUBMISSIONS: Open to all,
during submission windows.
Submit by email (editor@
monstrous-regiment.com)
or online (www.monstrous-
regiment.com/contact).
Guidelines at www.monstrous-
regiment.com/submissions.
Usually responds within four
weeks, with feedback only if
requested. Authors are paid a
flat fee.
**See also: poetry publisher p49
and *Monstrous Regiment*
(mixed-form magazine) p209**

Monstrous Regiment

They say

Monstrous Regiment is an
independent micropublishing
initiative based in Edinburgh.
We publish a semi-annual
feminist literary magazine
of the same name, as well
as individual non-fiction
book projects. Our first book
publication, *The Bi-ble*, is an
anthology collection of original
voices on bisexuality. We
specialise in topics of gender,
sexuality, and feminism, and
are searching for bold new
content from established or
undiscovered writers. We have
a mild antiauthority streak
with an edgy literary twist,
and we're curating the kind
of content we want to see
in the world: intersectional,
unapologetic and diverse.

135

writers in the North of England,
and authors include Benjamin
Myers and Michael Donovan.
Check the website for details of
open submissions windows.

MERCIER PRESS
NON-FICTION / NOVELS
Unit 3B, Oak House, Bessboro Road,
Blackrock, Cork, Ireland
info@mercierpress.ie
www.mercierpress.ie
Established 1944. Publications
available direct from publisher
website; from chain bookshops
nationwide; from independent
bookshops; at local literary events;
and from Amazon and other
bookshop websites.
GENRES: History; lifestyle; food
and drink; current affairs; sport;
adult and YA fiction.
SUBMISSIONS: Open to all. Submit
by email to commissioning@
mercierpress.ie. Guidelines at
www.mercierpress.ie/submit.
Usually responds within one to
three months. Rejections may
occasionally include unsolicited
feedback. Authors are paid
royalties.

MIRA PUBLISHING
NON-FICTION / FICTION
Mira Publishing House cic,
Alfa House, 481A Otley Road,
Leeds LS16 7NR
info@mirapublishing.com
www.mirapublishing.com
Mira Publishing is part of Mira
Intelligent Read cic (Community
Interest Company) and publishes
fiction and non-fiction based on
contemporary topics. It aims to
enrich international literature
and looks to publish books from
different countries and in English
and other languages.

MUDFOG PRESS
SHORT STORY COLLECTIONS
c/o Beacon Guest, Chop Gate,
Stokesley TS9 7JS
contact@mudfog.co.uk
www.mudfog.co.uk
Editors: Pauline Plummer, Jo Heather,
Liz Geraghty, David Lynch
Established 1993. Mixed form:
also publishes poetry (see p50).
Publications available direct from
the publisher website.
GENRES: Short fiction /
environmental writing.
SUBMISSIONS: Favours writers
in the Tees Valley, stretching
from Whitby to Sunderland,
west to Darlington. However
also occasionally publishes
writers outside this area. Submit
by post (Beacon Guest, Chop
Gate, Stokesley TS9 7JS) or by
email (contact@mudfog.co.uk).
Guidelines at www.mudfog.co.uk/
submissions. Usually responds
within one to three months.
Rejections may occasionally
include unsolicited feedback.
Authors are able to buy a number
of their books at cost-price and sell
them at sales price.
WE SAY: *Invisible Sun* by
Jan Hunter is a short story
chapbook, A5 and 47 pages
long, with a cardboard cover
and staple spine. The materials
used are high quality. The matt
laminate cover has a simple
photographic design, and the
inner pages are satisfyingly thick.
It contains just three stories, which
are slice-of-life tales written with
pathos and humour, and the final
page includes a biography and
colour photo of the writer.
See also: poetry publisher p50

MURDER SLIM PRESS

NOVELS

22 Bridge Meadow, Hemsby, Norfolk
NR29 4NE
moonshine@murderslim.com

www.murderslim.com
Despite the name, not strictly
crime fiction. Established in 2004,
Murder Slim looks for 'writing at
the razor's edge'.

MOTHER'S MILK BOOKS ☆

NOVELS / SHORT STORY
ANTHOLOGIES / NON-FICTION /
E-BOOKS
teika@mothersmilkbooks.com
www.mothersmilkbooks.com
Editor: Dr Teika Bellamy

THE FORGOTTEN AND THE FANTASTICAL 3
Modern fables and ancient tales

EDITED BY TEIKA BELLAMY

Established 2011. Mixed form:
also publishes poetry (see p49).
Publications available direct
from publisher website; from
independent bookshops; at
national and local literary events;
and from Amazon.
Mother's Milk Books has won
numerous awards. Founder Teika
Bellamy received the Women in
Publishing's New Venture Award
for pioneering work on behalf
of under-represented groups
in society. Mother's Milk Books
title Baby X won the Commercial
Fiction category of the Eric
Hoffer Award in 2017.
GENRES: Commercial fiction;
literary fiction; fairy tales; fantasy;
sci-fi.
SUBMISSIONS: During
submission windows
only. Submit by email to
submissions@mothersmilkbooks.
com. Guidelines at www.
mothersmilkbooks.com/index.
php/submissions. Submitters are
required to buy a book from the
press. Usually responds within
one to three months. Rejections
may occasionally include
unsolicited feedback. Authors are
paid an advance/fee plus royalties
and receive free copies of the
book.
WE SAY: We looked at The
Forgotten and Fantastical 3, the
third in a series of short story
anthologies filled with 'modern
fables and ancient tales', which
is packed with 17 stories that
capture the imagination. With
elegant illustrations at the start of
every story, this anthology boasts
a stylish design. We also looked
at Baby X, a novel by Rebecca
Ann Smith, that continues the
sleek, high quality paperback style
and design of the press, which
is essentially – and admirably – a
one-woman operation.
See also: poetry publisher p49

MYRIAD EDITIONS
NOVELS / GRAPHIC NOVELS /
NON-FICTION
Myriad at New Internationalist,
The Old Music Hall,
106–108 Cowley Rd, Oxford OX4 1JE
01865 403345
info@myriadeditions.com
www.myriadeditions.com
Editors: Candida Lacey,
Corinne Pearlman, Linda McQueen,
Chris Brazier
Established 1993. Predominantly
publishes original fiction and
graphic novels. Publications
available direct from publisher
website; from chain bookshops
nationwide; from independent
bookshops; at national and local
literary events; and from Amazon
and other bookshop websites.
Myriad Editions titles *London
Triptych* by Jonathan Kemp
and *The Last Pilot* by Benjamin
Johncock won the Authors'
Club Best First Novel Award
respectively in 2010 and 2016.
Elizabeth Haynes' début novel,
Into the Darkest Corner, became a
bestseller.
GENRES: Literary fiction; crime;
graphic novels; feminist non-
fiction; graphic memoir; historical
fiction; graphic medicine.
SUBMISSIONS: Periodically
open to all. Submit by email to
submissions@myriadeditions.com.
Guidelines at www.myriadeditions.
com/about/submissions/. Usually
responds within one to three
months. Offers more detailed
feedback and consultation for a
fee. Authors are paid an advance
plus royalties, and receive free
copies of the book.
WE SAY: We considered a few
publications from the last four
years, each of which maintained
high-quality, contemporary cover
designs, on a size slightly smaller
than A5. The paperback covers
varied, with 2015's 312-page *The
Longest Fight* by Emily Bullock
moving to a slightly glossy finish,
but 2017's 474-page *The Favourite*
by S.V. Berlin returned to the
previous matt style. The pages also
changed in this latter to a softer,
more high-quality feel, with a
different perfect-binding that made
the book easier to peruse.

MYRMIDON BOOKS LTD
NOVELS / NON-FICTION / E-BOOKS
Rotterdam House, 116 Quayside,
Newcastle upon Tyne NE1 3DY
0191 206 4005
ed@myrmidonbooks.com
www.myrmidonbooks.com
Editor: Ed Handyside
Established 2006. Mainly publishes
fiction. Publications available
by post and email order; from
chain bookshops nationwide;
from independent bookshops; at
national and local literary events;
and from Amazon and other
bookshop websites.
Awards include winning the 2013
Man Asian Literary Prize and Walter
Scott Prize for Best Historical
Fiction.
GENRES: Crime/thriller/mystery;
fantasy/sci-fi; historical fiction;
literary fiction; romance; biography
and true stories; history; humour.
SUBMISSIONS: Open to all. Submit
by post (Myrmidon, Rotterdam
House, 116 Quayside, Newcastle
upon Tyne NE1 3DY) or by email
(ed@myrmidonbooks.com).
Guidelines on the website. Usually
responds in over six months. No
feedback offered with rejections.
Authors are paid royalties only, or
an advance/fee plus royalties.

WE SAY: Big Five publications from a small press. Myrmidon books come complete with the blurb, the marketing, the formatting and the materials to be at home in any bookshop. We particularly loved the cover of *Angel* by Jon Grahame, with its bolted-iron title and action-filled, yet ethereal, images.

NEGATIVE PRESS LONDON
TEXT-AND-ART BOOKS
07970 078862
info@neg-press.com
www.neg-press.com
Editor: Roelof Bakker
Established 2012. Publishes collaborative books mixing text and art (fiction, non-fiction, art and photography). Publications are available direct from publisher website; from independent bookshops; and at local literary events.
Negative Press was nominated for and came runner-up in the 2013 Saboteur Awards, Best Mixed Anthology category.
GENRES: Literary; non-fiction
SUBMISSIONS: Not accepting submission at time of going to press. Authors received free copies of the book and may be paid royalties.
WE SAY: The website for Negative Press gives the casual viewer a good gauge of the style of work produced by this publisher. The photographs displayed are emotive, and the writing that accompanies them explores domesticity, human nature, and hope and life. These are unique works, bringing writers and artists together in collaboration.

NEON BOOKS
E-BOOKS / NOVELS / SHORT STORY COLLECTIONS AND ANTHOLOGIES
info@neonbooks.org.uk
www.neonbooks.org.uk
Editor: Krishan Coupland
Established 2006. Also publishes poetry (see p51). Publications available direct from publisher website; by direct mail and email orders; from independent bookshops; at national literary events; and from Amazon and other bookshop websites.
Neon Books title *The Mesmerist's Daughter* won the 2015 Best Novellas Saboteur Award.
GENRES: Sci-fi; horror; slipstream; magical realism; surrealism.
SUBMISSIONS: Open to all, during submission windows. Submit by email to info@neonbooks.org.uk. Guidelines at www.neonbooks.org.uk/guidelines/. Usually responds within one to three months. Rejections may occasionally include unsolicited feedback for a fee. Submissions have a tip-jar option, but this does not affect publisher's decision. Authors are paid royalties only and receive free copies of the book.
See also: poetry publisher p51.
For further information, including what We Say, see *Neon Literary Magazine* (mixed-form magazine) p212

NEWCON PRESS
NOVELS / SHORT STORY COLLECTIONS AND ANTHOLOGIES / NON-FICTION / E-BOOKS
41 Wheatsheaf Road, Alconbury Weston, Cambridgeshire PE28 4LF
finiang@aol.com
www.newconpress.co.uk
Editor: Ian Whates
Established 2006. Also publishes

poetry (see p51). Publications available direct from publisher website; from chain bookshops nationwide; from Amazon; and at genre themed literary events. Jaine Fenn's short story 'Liberty Bird' from NewCon Press anthology *Now We Are Ten* won the BSFA Award for best short fiction in 2017.

GENRES: Sci-fi; fantasy; horror; slipstream; general criticism and review.

SUBMISSIONS: Submissions by invitation only. Author payment varies depending on the published work.

See also: poetry publisher p51

NEW ISLAND
NOVELS / NON-FICTION
16 Priory Office Park, Stillorgan, County Dublin
+ 353 1 278 42 25
info@newisland.ie
www.newisland.ie
New Island started out as Raven Arts Press In the 1980s and continues to commit to publishing 'exceptional literature and groundbreaking non-fiction'. It publishes various series, including Fiction Firsts, which focuses on début work.

See also: poetry publisher p51

NIGHTJAR PRESS
SHORT STORY CHAPBOOKS
63 Ballbrook Court, Wilmslow Road, Manchester M20 3GT
nightjarpress@gmail.com
nightjarpress.weebly.com
Editor: Nicholas Royle
Established 2009. Single-story chapbooks. Publications available direct from publisher website; by post and email order; from selected/local chain bookshops;

from independent bookshops; and at local literary events,

GENRES: Fantasy; horror; literary fiction; uncanny/gothic.

SUBMISSIONS: Open to all – but strongly encourages writers to research what the press does before submitting. Submit by post (63 Ballbrook Court, Wilmslow Road, Manchester M20 3GT) or by email (nightjarpress@gmail.com). Guidelines at nightjarpress.weebly.com/about.html. Usually responds within one to three months. Rejections may occasionally include unsolicited feedback. Authors are paid a flat fee.

WE SAY: Limited edition, single short story chapbooks of between 12–16 pages, the stories are published individually and designed to a consistent house style of textbook-ish covers and simple, well-formatted inner pages. The stories published are distinctly odd and uncanny – take a good look before you submit. Each chapbook is signed by the author, giving an exclusive, intimate feel. We liked the succinct author bios on the back covers.

NOSY CROW
NOVELS / PICTURE BOOKS / NON-FICTION
The Crow's Nest, 10a Lant Street, London SE1 1QR
020 7953 7677
submissions@nosycrow.com
www.nosycrow.com
Established 2011. Publisher of parent-friendly children's books for ages 0-14 yrs, both commercial fiction and non-fiction (YA or New Adult), and creates interactive multimedia apps.
Multi-award-winning publishers, including the 2016 IPG

Independent Publisher of the Year Award and Children's Publisher of the Year Award.

SUBMISSIONS: Open to all, preferably by email. Guidelines at www.nosycrow.com/contact/submission-guidelines. Tries to respond to all submissions within six months.

NOT BAD BOOKS
NOVELS / NON-FICTION
Port 57, 57 Albert Road,
Portsmouth PO5 2SF
ben@notbadbooks.co.uk
www.notbadbooks.co.uk
Editor: Ben Aitken

Fiction and non-fiction. A fairly new publisher, whose first book *Dear Bill Bryson: Footnotes from a Small Island* was well received.

NOTTINGHAM REVIEW, THE
SHORT STORY ANTHOLOGIES / E-BOOKS
thenottinghamreview@gmail.com
www.thenottinghamreview.com
Editor: Spencer Chou
Established 2015.
GENRES: Literary fiction.
SUBMISSIONS: Open to all. Submit by email to thenottinghamreview@gmail.com. Usually responds within four weeks. Rejections may occasionally include unsolicited feedback.

For a fuller description of this press, see *The Nottingham Review* (mixed-form literary magazine) p214

NOTTING HILL EDITIONS ☆
NON-FICTION ESSAYS
contact@nottinghilleditions.com
www.nottinghilleditions.com
Editor: Kim Kremer
Established 2011. Only publishes essays, but on any subject.
Publications available direct from publisher website; by post and email order; from chain bookshops nationwide; from independent bookshops; at national and local literary events; and from Amazon and other bookshop websites, including the *Guardian* bookshop. Notting Hill Editions won the 2011 Red Dot Design Award.

GENRES: Essays on art, fashion and photography; biography and true stories; history; science, technology and medicine; society, education and politics. No fiction.

SUBMISSIONS: Open to all. Submit by email to contact@nottinghilleditions.com. Usually responds within one to three months. Rejections may occasionally include unsolicited feedback. Authors are paid a flat fee or royalties only, and receive free copies of the book.

WE SAY: Notting Hill Editions publishes both print and e-book. The print books are stunning: hardback cloth-bound books with bright bold covers and thick high-quality paper, which look fantastic on a shelf. These are books that readers collect for decoration as much as for content – which is not to belittle the intelligent, thoughtful writing within.

O'BRIEN PRESS LTD, THE
NON-FICTION / CHILDREN'S FICTION AND NON-FICTION
12 Terenure Road East, Rathgar,
Dublin 6, Ireland
books@obrien.ie
www.obrien.ie

O'Brien Press's list covers a huge range, from biography to humour, photography to fiction, and is constantly expanding – but note that it strictly does not publish poetry, academic work or adult fiction. Hard copy submissions only.

OFFORD ROAD BOOKS
NOVELS / SHORT STORY COLLECTIONS AND ANTHOLOGIES / NON-FICTION
offordroadbooks@gmail.com
www.twitter.com/offordroadbooks
Editors: Martha Sprackland, Patrick Davidson Roberts
Established 2017. Also publishes poetry (see p52). Publications available by direct mail and email orders; from selected/local chain bookshops; from independent bookshops; at local literary events; and from Amazon.
GENRES: Literary fiction; essays.
SUBMISSIONS: Open to all. Submit by post (29a Womersley Road, Crouch End, London N8 9AP) or by email (offordroadbooks@gmail. com). Usually responds within four weeks. Rejections may occasionally include unsolicited feedback. Authors receive a small fee.
For further information, including what We Say, see also poetry publisher p52

OLDCASTLE BOOKS
NOVELS / NON-FICTION / E-BOOKS
PO Box 394, Harpenden AL5 1XJ
01582 766348
cqoldcastle@gmail.com
www.oldcastlebooks.co.uk
Editor: Clare Quinlivan
Established 1985. Publications available direct from publisher website; from chain bookshops nationwide; from independent bookshops; at national and local literary events; and from Amazon and other bookshop websites. Oldcastle Books title *Dodgers* by Bill Beverly has won four awards including the British Book Award for Best Crime & Thriller Novel 2017 and the *LA Times* Book Prize 2017.
GENRES: Crime; literary fiction; commercial fiction; historical fiction.
SUBMISSIONS: Open to all. Submit by post (Oldcastle Books, PO Box 394, Harpenden AL5 1XJ) or by email (cqoldcastle@ gmail.com). Guidelines at www. oldcastlebooks.co.uk/submissions. Usually responds within one to three months. Rejections may occasionally include unsolicited feedback. Authors are paid an advance/fee plus royalties.
WE SAY: Oldcastle Books directed us to their catalogue, where the wares of its imprints (No Exit Press, Pocket Essential, Kamera Books, Creative Essentials and Oldcastle) are on display. This publisher knows the market – the cover designs are professional and easily sit within genre conventions, so a casual browser instantly knows the type of book they are looking at. At a glance, we were able to peg No Exit Press as a crime/thriller imprint and Oldcastle as literary.

OLD STREET PUBLISHING
NOVELS / NON-FICTION / E-BOOKS
c/o Parallel.net, 8 Hurlingham Business Park, Sulivan Road, London SW6 3DU
020 8787 5812
info@oldstreetpublishing.co.uk
www.oldstreetpublishing.co.uk
An award-winning publisher, which won the IMPAC with Rawi Hage's De Niro's Game, and the BBC National Short Story Award.

ON STREAM
NON-FICTION
info@onstream.ie

142

www.onstream.ie
This Irish publisher focuses primarily on non-fiction, though has been known to publish some fiction. Also offers a service helping first-time authors to submit to other publishers.

ORENDA BOOKS
NOVELS
info@orendabooks.co.uk
www.orendabooks.co.uk
Publishes literary fiction and upmarket genre fiction (strictly no non-fiction, children's books or YA). Looking for new authors, and is also interested in authors who have been under-published in the past and have something to offer. Has a small list, so be sure your writing is good fit.

OUEN PRESS ☆
NOVELS / SHORT STORY COLLECTIONS AND ANTHOLOGIES / NON-FICTION / E-BOOKS
Suite One, Ingles Manor, Castle Hill Avenue, Folkestone, Kent CT20 2RD
info@ouenpress.com
www.ouenpress.com
Editor: Paula Comley
Mainly publishes fiction. Publications available by post and email order; in chain bookshops nationwide; at local literary events; and from various bookshop websites.
GENRES: Contemporary fiction; travel literature; biography.
SUBMISSIONS: Open to all. Submit by email to submissions@ouenpress.com. Guidelines at www.ouenpress.com. Usually responds within one to three months. No feedback offered with rejection. Authors are paid royalties and receive free copies of the book.

OWN IT!
NOVELS / IMMERSIVE DIGITAL BOOKS
www.ownit.london
Self-describer 'storytelling lifestyle brand, telling stories across books, music, fashion and film', with publishing just one of its branches. OWN IT! Novel *No Place to Call Home* by JJ Bola was longlisted for the *Guardian* Not The Booker Prize 2017. Looks for artists to collaborate with.

PALEWELL PRESS LTD
NOVELS / SHORT STORY COLLECTIONS AND ANTHOLOGIES / NON-FICTION / E-BOOKS
enquiries@palewellpress.co.uk
www.palewellpress.co.uk
Editor: Camilla Reeve
Established 2016. Mixed form: also publishes poetry (see p54). Publications available direct from publisher website; at local literary events; and from Amazon and other bookshop websites.
GENRES: Memoir; human rights and social history; environment.
SUBMISSIONS: Open to all, but must relate to subject areas. Submit by email (enquiries@palewellpress.co.uk) or by post (384 Upper Richmond Road West, London SW14 7JU). Usually responds within four weeks. Rejections may occasionally include unsolicited feedback. Authors are paid royalties only and receive free copies of the book. For authors in mainland UK, publisher shares cost of launch.
WE SAY: We looked at *Three Days in Damascus* by Kim Schultz, a 278-page A5 paperback with a glossy cover. The size and paper thickness meant the book was flexible, and the sparse inner design featured

143

wide margins and an increased line height. The memoir, following the author's time interviewing Iraqi refugees in the Middle East, also includes instant messaging conversations, dictionary entries, and emails featuring their own font and style.

See also: poetry publisher p54

PARALLEL UNIVERSE PUBLICATIONS

NOVELS / SHORT STORY COLLECTIONS AND ANTHOLOGIES / E-BOOKS
130 Union Road, Oswaldtwistle, Lancashire BB5 3DR
paralleluniversepublications@gmx.co.uk
www.parallelpublications.blogspot.co.uk
Editors: David A. Riley, Linden Riley
Established 2012. Also publishes poetry (see p56). Publications available direct from publisher website; by direct mail and email orders; from chain bookshops nationwide; from independent bookshops; and from Amazon and other bookshop websites.
GENRES: Horror; fantasy; sci-fi.
SUBMISSIONS: Open to all. Submit by post (Parallel Universe Publications, 130 Union Road, Oswaldtwistle, Lancashire BB5 3DR) or by email (paralleluniversepublications@gmx.co.uk). Guidelines at www.parallelpublications.blogspot.co.uk/p/submissions.html. Usually responds within one to three months. Rejections may occasionally include unsolicited feedback. Authors are paid royalties only.
WE SAY: We looked at a digital versions of the short story

collections *Parlour Tricks* by Carl Baker and *Radix Omnius Malus* by Mike Chinn. The covers of each are dark and ominous (fittingly), and both had cleanly laid out inner pages, with 15 stories from Baker and 16 from Chinn – notably stories in both collections have been previously published in anthologies and magazines. Both collections provide insight into the author and work: Chinn's collection includes a six-page introduction to his work by David A. Sutton, while Baker's work, however, has a section entitled 'Inner Circle' in which each story is compared to a parlour trick, and some insight into its writing is provided – a nice touch.

See also: poetry publisher p56

PARTHIAN BOOKS

NOVELS / SHORT STORY COLLECTIONS AND ANTHOLOGIES / NON-FICTION / E-BOOKS
022 Keir Hardie, Swansea University SA2 8PP
01792 606605
maria@parthianbooks.com
www.parthianbooks.com
Editor: Susie Wild
Established 1993. Also publishes poetry (see p56). Publications available direct from publisher website; from chain bookshops nationwide; from independent bookshops; at national and local literary events; and from Amazon and other bookshop websites. Parthian Books title *Pigeon* by Alys Conran was shortlisted for the International Dylan Thomas Prize 2017.
GENRES: Literary; Welsh; feminist/women's writing; historical.
SUBMISSIONS: Open to all. Submit by post to 022 Keir Hardie,

Swansea University SA2 8PP. Guidelines at www.parthianbooks. com/pages/contact-us. Usually responds within one to three months. No feedback offered with rejections. Author payment is dependent on deal but mostly fee/royalties.

For further information, including what We Say, see also: poetry publisher p56

PATRICIAN PRESS

NOVELS / SHORT STORY
COLLECTIONS / E-BOOKS
51 Free Rodwell House,
School Lane, Mistley, Manningtree
CO11 1HW
07968 288651
patricia@patricianpress.com
www.patricianpress.com
Editor: Patricia Borlenghi

Refugees and Peacekeepers
A Patrician Press Anthology

Established 2012. Mainly publishes fiction, but also some poetry books (see p56) and poetry-and-prose anthologies. Publications available direct from publisher website; from selected/ local chain bookshops; from independent bookshops; at local literary events; and from Amazon and other bookshop websites, including The Great British Bookshop website.
GENRES: Historical fiction; literary fiction; experimental fiction; children and teenagers; food and drink; society, education and politics.
SUBMISSIONS: Open to new and unpublished writers without agents. Submit during submissions windows, by email (patricia@patricianpress. com) or via the form at www. patricianpress.com/submissions (guidelines at the same address). Usually responds within one to three months. Rejections may occasionally include unsolicited feedback. Authors are paid royalties only.
WE SAY: We looked at a digital version of Patrician Press' *Refugees and Peacekeepers* anthology, which features work inspired by the recent refugee crisis. There is a lengthy introduction, which features remarks on pieces of work featured in the anthology, and thoughts on the subject matter. The tone manages to sidestep preachiness, focusing instead on human drama and poignancy. The design is very minimal, letting the work speak for itself.
See also: poetry publisher p56

PEEPAL TREE PRESS
NOVELS / SHORT STORY
COLLECTIONS AND ANTHOLOGIES
contact@peepaltreepress.com
www.peepaltreepress.com
Editors: Jeremy Poynting,
Kwame Dawes, Jacob Ross,
Kadija Sesay
Established 1986. Mixed form:
also publishes poetry (see p57).
Specialises in Caribbean and
Black British writing. Publications
available direct from publisher
website; by post and email
order; from chain bookshops
and independent bookshops
nationwide; at national and local
literary events; and from Amazon
and other bookshop websites.
Peepal Tree title *Sounding Ground*
by Vladimir Lucien was overall
winner for The OCM Bocas Prize
for Caribbean Literature 2015.
GENRES: Drama and criticism;
literary fiction; historical fiction;
biography and true stories; history;
music, stage and screen.
SUBMISSIONS: Open to all,
specialising in Caribbean and Black
British writing. Submit through
Submittable at peepaltreepress.
submittable.com (guidelines at
same address). Usually responds
within four to six months.
Rejections may occasionally include
unsolicited feedback, and some
manuscripts by UK-based authors
are offered a (free) in-depth reader
report through the press's Inscribe
Writer Development Programme.
Authors are paid royalties only.
WE SAY: We looked at *Come
Let Us Sing Anyway*, from Leone
Ross. This short story collection
has a bright, eye-catching cover
and tales inside that range from
one page palette-cleansers to
longer works. It's a richly written,
very sensual collection, beautifully
presented.
See also: poetry publisher p57

PEIRENE PRESS ☆
NOVELS / NOVELLAS /
SHORT STORY COLLECTIONS
020 7686 1941
meike.ziervogel@peirenepress.com
www.peirenepress.com
Editor: Meike Ziervogel
Established 2010. Fiction publisher.
Book-club subscription £35/year
for three books. Available direct
from publisher website; by post
and email order; from chain and
independent bookshops; at local
literary events; and from Amazon
and other bookshop websites.
Peirene Press translator Jamie
Bulloch won the 2014 Schlegel-
Tieck Prize for his translation of *The
Mussel Feast* by Birgit Vanderbeke.
GENRES: Literary; fiction in
translation.
SUBMISSIONS: For translation
proposals: submission any time.
For works written in English:
commissioned work only.
Usually responds within one to
three months. Rejections may
occasionally include unsolicited
feedback. Authors receive an
advance fee plus royalties.
WE SAY: The perfect-bound books
produced by Peirene feature matt
paperback covers with a cohesive
geometric design featuring
a photograph overlaid with a
rectangular colour block wrapping
around to the back. All publications
are less than 200 pages, and aim
to be able to be read in the time it
takes to watch a film. We saw *Her
Father's Daughter* by Marie Sizun,
which also featured hardcover-style
folds and a note about Peirene's
social activism; 50p of each sale

supports either Counterpoint Arts or the Maya Centre.

PENKHULL PRESS
NOVELS / SHORT STORY COLLECTIONS / E-BOOKS
penkhullpress@gmail.com
www.thepenkhullpress.wordpress.com
Editor: Peter Coleborn
Established 2015. Publications available direct from publisher website; by direct mail and email orders; at local literary events; and from Amazon.
GENRES: Literary; crime; women's; war stories; general.
SUBMISSIONS: By invitation only. Query by email to penkhullpress@gmail.com. Usually responds within one to three months. Rejections may occasionally include unsolicited feedback for a fee. Authors are paid royalties only and receives free copies of the book.
WE SAY: We looked at digital versions of *Fables and Fabrications* by Jan Edwards, a 187-page collection of stories and haikus about mystery, mirth and the macabre; and *Picking up the Pieces* by Misha Herwin, a 284-page story about three women who lose everything in life they took for granted. Both books are professionally designed, with relatively big serif fonts.

PENNED IN THE MARGINS
NOVELS / NON-FICTION / NOVELLAS / E-BOOKS
Toynbee Studios, 28 Commercial Street, London E1 6AB
020 7375 0121
info@pennedinthemargins.co.uk
www.pennedinthemargins.co.uk
Editor: Tom Chivers
Established 2006. Mixed form: also publishes poetry (see p58).

Publications available direct from publisher website; by post and email order; from selected/local chain bookshops; from independent bookshops; at local literary events; and from Amazon. Penned in the Margins' first published novel was shortlisted for the Gordon Burn Prize in 2015.
GENRES: Drama and criticism; literary fiction and non-fiction.
SUBMISSIONS: Publication history required. Submit by email to submissions@pennedinthemargins.co.uk. Usually responds within one to three months. Rejections may occasionally include unsolicited feedback. Authors are paid royalties only.
For a fuller description of this press, see poetry publisher p58

PENNILESS PRESS PUBLICATIONS
NOVELS / SHORT STORY COLLECTIONS
10 Albert Road, Grappenhall, Warrington WA4 2PG
editor@pennilesspress.co.uk
www.pennilesspress.co.uk
Editors: Alan Dent, Ken Clay
Established 2010. Mainly fiction, with some literary criticism. Publications available direct from publisher website; by post and email order; from independent bookshops; and from Amazon and other bookshop websites.
GENRES: Drama and criticism; literary fiction; literary criticism.
See also: *Penniless Press Magazine* **(mixed-form digital magazine) p216**

PENNYSHORTS ☆
SHORT FICTION SINGLE E-BOOKS
editor@pennyshorts.com
www.pennyshorts.com
Editor: Catherine Horlick

Established 2015. Short fiction of all genres. Digital publications available by post and email order – accessible by purchase only.

GENRES: Crime/thriller/mystery; fantasy/sci-fi; horror; historical fiction; romance; biography and true stories.

SUBMISSIONS: Open to all. Submit by email to editor@pennyshorts.com. Usually responds within four weeks. Rejections may occasionally include unsolicited feedback.

WE SAY: Lovely e-book nuggets to dip in and out of – we were impressed by the marketing strategy behind Pennyshorts, ensuring authors are paid. The e-books/pdfs are very simple – the illustrations for the stories that appear on the website don't carry over to the epubs we looked at. Tightly written and edited fiction straight to your device. Highly recommended.

PERISCOPE

NOVELS / NON-FICTION / E-BOOKS
info@periscopebooks.co.uk
www.periscopebooks.co.uk
Publisher and commissioning editor: Mitchell Albert

Established 2015. Mixed form: fiction and non-fiction. Publications available by post and email order; from chain bookshops nationwide; from independent bookshops; at national and local literary events; and from Amazon and other bookshop websites.

Periscope title *The Moor's Account* by Laila Lalami was long-listed for the 2015 Man Booker Prize.

GENRES: Crime/thriller/mystery; historical fiction; literary fiction; biography and true stories; food and drink; history; popular science and nature; society, education and politics.

SUBMISSIONS: Open to all. Submit by email to info@periscopebooks.co.uk. Usually responds within four to six months. Rejections may occasionally include unsolicited feedback. Authors are paid an advance/fee plus royalties and receive free copies of the book.

PETER OWEN PUBLISHERS

NOVELS / E-BOOKS
81 Ridge Road, London N8 9NP
020 8350 1775
info@peterowen.com
www.peterowen.com

One of the longest-established small presses, founded by Peter Owen (1927-2016) six years after the Second World War and instrumental in bringing the best international literature to the British market. Still publishing fiction and non-fiction, authors include seven Nobel Prize winners. A very highly regarded press.

PHAETON PUBLISHING LTD

NOVELS / NON-FICTION / SHORT STORIES
28 Leeson Park, Dublin 6
+353 1 498 1893
phaeton@iol.ie
www.phaeton.ie

Established 2017, and specialises in 'engaging books (both print and e-formats) of international interest for thoughtful readers'. Their catalogue includes a range of serious and entertaining non-fiction. Check the website for open submissions windows.

PHOENIX YARD BOOKS

CHILDREN'S BOOKS
Phoenix Yard, 65 King's Cross Road, London WC1X 9LW
020 7239 4968

info@phoenixyardbookscom
www.phoenixyardbooks.com
Children's fiction. Publications
available from chain bookshops
nationwide and from independent
bookshops.
Phoenix Yard Books won Best
Newcomer in the IPG Independent
Publishing Awards 2013.
GENRES: Children's fiction; YA. No
non-fiction.
SUBMISSIONS: Agented
submissions only.

PILRIG PRESS
NOVELS / E-BOOKS / NON-FICTION
32 Pilrig Street, Edinburgh EH6 5AL
0131 554 1857
enquiries@pilrigpress.co.uk
www.pilrigpress.co.uk
Founded in late 2010, and looking
for literary fiction and new crime
fiction, as well as historical fiction
and non-fiction with a focus on
Scotland. Wants to encourage new
Scottish talent, but not exclusively.

PINTER & MARTIN LTD
NON-FICTION / E-BOOKS
6 Effra Parade, London SW2 1PS
020 7737 6868
info@pinterandmartin.com
www.pinterandmartin.com
Established 1997. Publications
available direct from publisher
website; from chain bookshops
nationwide; from independent
bookshops; at local literary events;
and from Amazon and other
bookshop websites.
GENRES: Pregnancy, birth and
parenting; health and nutrition;
yoga; psychology.
SUBMISSIONS: Submissions only
accepted within specified themes.
Submit by email (submissions@
pinterandmartin.com). Guidelines
at www.pinterandmartin.com/

submissions.html. Usually responds
within four weeks. Rejections may
occasionally include unsolicited
feedback. Authors are paid an
advance/fee plus royalties and
receive free copies of the book.
WE SAY: *The Positive Birth Book*
we saw by Milli Hill was a larger
than A5 perfect-bound paperback
with 320 pages of information,
photographs, and illustrations
aimed at preparing parents and
helping them communicate their
wishes to healthcare providers.
Inside the bright, glossy cover, the
book is broken down into sections
by common questions or themes,
with many examples and first-hand
accounts to illustrate.

PLATYPUS PRESS
NOVELS / SHORT STORY
COLLECTIONS AND ANTHOLOGIES
/ NON-FICTION / E-BOOKS
enquiries@platypuspress.co.uk
www.platypuspress.co.uk
Editors: Michelle Tudor,
Peter Barnfather
Established 2015. Mainly publishes
poetry (see p58). Publications
available direct from publisher
website; at local literary events;
and from Amazon and other
bookshop websites.
GENRES: Literary.
SUBMISSIONS: Open to all.
Submit by email to submissions@
platypuspress.co.uk. Guidelines
at www.platypuspress.co.uk/
submit. Usually responds within
four weeks. No feedback offered
with rejections. Authors are paid
royalties only and receive free
copies of the book.
See also: poetry publisher p58 and
Wildness **(mixed-form magazine)**
p231

PLUTO PRESS

NON-FICTION / E-BOOKS
345 Archway Road, London N6 5AA
020 8348 2724
www.plutobooks.com
Editors: David Castle, David Shulman,
Anne Beech
Active for over 40 years, and
independent since 1979. One
of the world's leading radical
publishers, specialising in
progressive, critical perspectives
in politics and the social sciences.
Known for working very closely
with authors and open to
proposals.
SUBMISSIONS: See the extensive
submission information available
at www.plutobooks.com/page/
authors.

POOLBEG PRESS

NOVELS / CHILDREN'S /
NON-FICTION
+353 1 806 3825
info@poolbeg.com
www.poolbeg.com
One of Ireland's most established
presses (since 1976), and
particularly known for nurturing
new women's writing. Emphasis is
on fiction, with some non-fiction,
and children's fiction for ages six
to 12.
See also: Ward River Press p170

PORTOBELLO BOOKS

NOVELS / SHORT STORY
COLLECTIONS / NON-FICTION
12 Addison Avenue, London W11 4QR
020 7605 1380
info@portobellobooks.com
www.portobellobooks.com
Editors: Sigrid Rausing, Laura Barber,
Bella Lacey, Max Porter,
Anne Meadows, Ka Bradley
Established 2005. Mixed form:
publishes both fiction and
non-fiction equally. Publications
available from chain bookshops
nationwide; from independent
bookshops; at national and local
literary events; and from Amazon
and other bookshop websites.
Portobello Books was shortlisted
for the 2009 Independent Publisher
of the Year Award.
GENRES: Literary fiction; history;
popular science and nature;
technology and medicine; society,
education and politics; travel.
SUBMISSIONS: Agented
submissions only. Usually responds
within four weeks. Rejections may
occasionally include unsolicited
feedback. Authors are paid an
advance/fee plus royalties.
WE SAY: An imprint within Granta,
Portobello exhibits the same high
standards of publication, but with a
touch more elegance, worldliness
and experimentation. We looked
at *The End of Days* by Jenny
Erpenbeck: a 192-page paperback
available in print and digital
format, and comprising a number
of short stories documenting the
possible lives of the same woman.
We loved the 1920s-inspired cover.
Extremely engaging and highly
recommended.
**See also: Granta Books p118 and
Granta Magazine (mixed-form
literary magazine) p197**

PROLEBOOKS ☆

MIXED-FORM ANTHOLOGIES
01204 497726
admin@prolebooks.co.uk
www.prolebooks.co.uk
Editors: Brett Evans, Phil Robertson
Established 2010. Mainly publishes
poetry (see p61). Publications
available direct from publisher
website and by direct mail and
email orders.

GENRES: Literary; engaging; accessible; challenging; entertaining.
SUBMISSIONS: Work for anthology publication is usually selected from competition entries. Authors are paid royalties only.
See also poetry publisher p61 and *Prole* (mixed-form magazine) p218

PS PUBLISHING

NOVELS / SHORT STORY COLLECTIONS AND ANTHOLOGIES / NON-FICTION / E-BOOKS
Grosvenor House, 1 New Road, Hornsea, East Yorkshire
01964 537575
nickycrowther@pspublishing.co.uk
www.pspublishing.co.uk
Editor: Nicky Crowther
Established 1991. Mainly publishes fiction, but also some poetry (see p61). Publications available direct from publisher website; from Amazon and other bookshop websites; and at the British Science Fiction Convention and British Fantasy Convention.
PS Publishing won The Karl Wagner Award at the British Fantasy Awards 2012.
GENRES: Crime/thriller/mystery; fantasy/sci-fi; horror; literary fiction; biography and true stories.
SUBMISSIONS: Submissions welcome by invitation only or from agents, during submissions windows. Submit by email to nickycrowther@pspublishing. co.uk. Usually responds within one to three months. Rejections may occasionally include unsolicited feedback. Authors may be paid a flat fee; royalties only; or an advance/fee plus royalties; and/ or receive free copies of the book (depending on agreement).
See also: poetry publisher p61

PUSHKIN PRESS

NOVELS / NON-FICTION
Pall Mall Deposit, Unit 43, 124-128 Barlby Road, London W10 6BL
020 3735 9078
books@pushkinpress.com
www.pushkinpress.com
Managing director:
Adam Freudenhaim
Established 1997. One of the larger indie presses, with a wide range across fiction and non-fiction, including novels, essays, memoirs and children's book. Styles range from timeless classic to urgent contemporary. Includes imprint One.

RACK PRESS

NON-FICTION
The Rack, Kinnerton, Presteigne, Powys LD8 2PF
07817 424560
rackpress@nicholasmurray.co.uk
www.rackpress.blogspot.com
Editor: Nicholas Murray
Established 2005. Primarily publishes poetry (see p62). Publications available direct from publisher website; by post and email order; from chain bookshops and independent bookshops nationwide; at national and local literary events; and from bookshop websites.
Rack Press won the 2014 Michael Marks Award for Publisher of the Year.
GENRES: Poetry criticism.
SUBMISSIONS: Open to all. Submit by post (The Rack, Kinnerton, Presteigne, Powys, Wales LD8 2PF) or by email (rackpress@ nicholasmurray.co.uk). Guidelines at www.nicholasmurray.co.uk/ About_Rack_Press.html. Please check the publisher's website to confirm whether submissions are

currently being accepted. Usually responds within four weeks. Rejections may occasionally include unsolicited feedback. Authors receive free copies of the book, plus other copies at discount price for sale at readings etc.
For a fuller description of this press, see poetry publisher p62

RED SQUIRREL PRESS
NOVELS / SHORT STORY COLLECTIONS / NON-FICTION / E-BOOKS
Briery Hill Cottage, Stannington, Morpeth NE61 6ES
info@redsquirrelpress.com
www.redsquirrelpress.com
Editor: Sheila Wakefield
Established 2006. Mainly publishes poetry (see p62). Publications available direct from publisher website; by post and email order; from chain bookshops nationwide; from independent bookshops; at national and local literary events; and from Amazon and other bookshop websites; and from Inpress.com.
Red Squirrel was shortlisted for the Callum Macdonald Memorial Award 2015.
GENRES: Crime/thriller/mystery; wildlife (non-fiction).
SUBMISSIONS: Open to all. Submit by post to Briery Hill Cottage, Stannington, Morpeth NE61 6ES. Guidelines at www.redsquirrelpress.com/submissions. Usually responds in over six months. No feedback offered with rejections. Authors receive free copies of the book.
For a fuller description of this press, see poetry publisher p62

ROUTE PUBLISHING LTD
NOVELS / SHORT STORY

COLLECTIONS AND ANTHOLOGIES / NON-FICTION / E-BOOKS
01977 793442
info@route-online.com
www.route-online.com
Editor: Ian Daley
Established 2000. Primarily publishes non-fiction above other prose and poetry (see p64). Publications available direct from publisher website; by post and email order; from chain bookshops nationwide; from independent bookshops; at national and local literary events; and from Amazon and other bookshop websites. Route has been shortlisted for the Pen/Ackerley Prize (2008); the James Tait Black Memorial Prize for Fiction (2011); *NME* Book of the Year (2015); and the Penderyn Prize (Music Book of the Year) (2015).
GENRES: Literary fiction; biography and true stories; music, stage and screen; and sports and leisure.
SUBMISSIONS: Guidelines at www.route-online.com/submissions. Usually responds within four to six months, with feedback only if an SAE is provided. No feedback offered with rejections. Authors are paid a flat fee, or royalties only, or an advance/fee plus royalties.
WE SAY: *Rites* by Sophie Coulombeau is a contemporary thriller, looking at the false memories of childhood. A well-written and professionally presented 192-page publication that we saw in hardback, with a dust-jacket. A simple effective cover, the title made up of embroidered letters, with threads stretched taut across the page. High-quality materials.
See also: poetry publisher p64

RUFUS STONE LIMITED EDITIONS

NON-FICTION
mark@rufuspublications.com
www.rufuspublications.com
Editor: Mark Smith
Established 2011. Publications available direct from publisher website.
GENRES: Art, fashion and photography; music, stage and screen.
SUBMISSIONS: Open to all. Submit by email to mark@rufuspublications.com. Usually responds within four weeks. Rejections may occasionally include unsolicited feedback. Authors are paid an advance/fee plus royalties.

SACRISTY PRESS

NOVELS / NON-FICTION / E-BOOKS
PO Box 612, Durham DH1 9HT
01913 038313
enquiries@sacristy.co.uk
www.sacristy.co.uk
Editor: Thomas Ball
Established 2011. Also publishes poetry (see p64). Publications available direct from publisher website; from independent bookshops; and from Amazon and other bookshop websites.
GENRES: History; theology; historical fiction.
SUBMISSIONS: Open to all. Guidelines at www.sacristy.co.uk/info/authors. Usually responds within one to three months. Rejections may occasionally include unsolicited feedback. Authors contribute to editorial/publication/marketing costs and are paid royalties only.
WE SAY: We looked at digital editions of novel *The Summer of '39* by David Lowther and

non-fiction book *The Evil That Men Do: Faith, Injustice and the Church*, by Marcus K Paul, a defence of the Church's history and ideas. Both are cleanly designed. The contents of *Evil* are easy to follow, and the book ends with clear notes. The cover is standard non-fiction – banded top and bottom, with an illustration framed in the middle. *'39* has a more creative design, using both script and 'typewriter' fonts for chapter titles. The cover features a block colour sketch of Berlin under Nazi Germany.
See also: poetry publisher p64

SALÒ PRESS

NOVEL / SHORT STORY COLLECTIONS AND ANTHOLOGIES
85 Gertrude Road, Norwich NR3 4SG
editorsalopress@gmail.com
www.salopress.weebly.com
Editor: Sophie Essex
Established 2015. Mainly publishes poetry (see p65). Publications available direct from publisher website.
GENRES: Literary; experimental.
SUBMISSIONS: Open to all. Submit by email to editorsalopress@gmail.com. Guidelines at www.salopress.weebly.com. Usually responds within one to three months. Feedback not offered with rejections. Authors are paid royalties only.
For what We Say, see also: poetry publisher p65

SALT PUBLISHING LTD

NOVELS / SHORT STORY COLLECTIONS AND ANTHOLOGIES / E-BOOKS
12 Norwich Rd, Cromer NR27 0AX
01263 511011
sales@saltpublishing.com
www.saltpublishing.com

Editors: Jen Hamilton-Emery, Nicholas Royle

Established 1999. Primarily publishes fiction. Publications available direct from publisher website; by post and email order; from chain bookshops nationwide; from independent bookshops; at national and local literary events; and from Amazon and other bookshop websites.

Salt title *The Redemption of Galen Pike* by Carys Davies won the International Frank O'Connor Short Story Prize, while *The Many* by Wyl Menmuir was longlisted for the 2016 Man Booker Prize.

GENRES: Literary fiction.

SUBMISSIONS: Only during open submissions windows. Guidelines at www.saltpublishing.com/pages/submissions. Usually responds within four to six months, with feedback only if requested. Authors are paid royalties only, or an advance/fee plus royalties, and receive free copies of the book.

WE SAY: A major player in the indie publishing world, Salt's perfect-bound paperbacks are of an exceedingly high quality: cool crisp cover designs, big-name blurb quotes and beautifully edited stories on cream paper. The sleek website, stellar reputation and faultless social media presence (160,000 Twitter followers) put Salt in the same league as the heavy hitters of the industry.

SANDSTONE PRESS

FICTION / NON-FICTION / E-BOOKS
7 Dochcarty Road, Sandstone Press, Dingwall IV15 9UG
moira@sandstonepress.com
www.sandstonepress.com
Editorial Director: Moira Forsyth
Established 2002. Publishes around 50% fiction and 50% non-fiction. Available direct from publisher website; from chain and independent bookshops; at literary events; and from amazon.com and other bookshop websites.

A Sandstone Press author won Society of Authors' 2017 Betty Trask Prize.

GENRES: Literary; memoir; outdoors; crime; women's fiction.

SUBMISSIONS: Open to all. Submit by email to submissions@sandstonepress.com. Guidelines at www.sandstonepress.com/contact/submissions. Usually responds within four weeks. Rejected authors may be offered feedback. Authors receive an advance and royalties.

WE SAY: We saw a digital proof of Addison Jones' *Wait for Me, Jack.* With a simple and clean design, the 342-page novel centres around moments in the lives of a long-married husband and wife, reflected in the photo of a swimming couple in old-fashioned garb on the cover.

SAQI BOOKS

NOVELS / SHORT STORY COLLECTIONS AND ANTHOLOGIES / NON-FICTION / E-BOOKS /
26 Westbourne Grove, London W2 5RH
020 7221 9347
elizabeth@saqibooks.com
www.saqibooks.com
Publisher and Managing Director: Lynn Gaspard
Editor and Marketing Manager: Elizabeth Briggs

Established 1983. Mixed form: also publishes mixed poetry/prose anthologies and collections (see p66), and widely publishes work from and about the Middle East and North Africa. Publications available from chain bookshops nationwide; from independent bookshops; at national and local literary events; and from Amazon and other bookshop websites. Saqi Books won the IPG Diversity Award in 2013, the Arab British Culture and Society Award in 2008 and the British Book Industry Award for Diversity in Literature in 2009.

GENRES: Literary; gender studies; literature in translation; non-fiction; history.

SUBMISSIONS: Open to all. Guidelines at www.saqibooks. com/contact/submissions. Usually responds within one to three months. Rejections may occasionally include unsolicited feedback. Authors are paid an advance/fee plus royalties.

See also: poetry publisher p66

SARABAND

NON-FICTION / NOVELS / E-BOOKS
Digital World Centre, 1 Lowry Plaza, The Quays, Salford M50 3UB
hermes@saraband.net
www.saraband.net
Editors: Sara Hunt, Craig Hillsley
Established 1994. Available from chain and independent bookshops; at literary events; from amazon. com and other bookshop websites. Saraband has won and been shortlisted for several awards, including Man Booker Prize 2016 (shortlist); IPG Independent Publisher of the Year 2016 (shortlist); Saltire Society Literary Awards 2016 (winner Best Fiction Book and Best First Book, and shortlisted Best History Book. Also in shortlisted the Research Book category in 2014); winner of the Striding Edge Award (Lakeland Awards) 2016; and winner of the

Saltire Society Publisher of the Year 2013 (shortlisted 2015 and 2016).

GENRES: Literary fiction; crime fiction; nature writing; memoir.

SUBMISSIONS: Open to all. Submit by email to hermes@saraband.net. Guidelines at www.saraband.net/ about-us. Due to high numbers, Saraband is unable to respond to most submissions. Authors are paid an advance, plus royalties.

WE SAY: We looked at the digital version of Ramaswamy's memoir *Expecting: the inner life of pregnancy*, which features a striking red cover with a drawing of two hands resting over a pear-shape, signifying a pregnant woman's body. Well laid out, the book aims to be an account of pregnancy that goes 'above and beyond a manual', and begins with a dedication and quotes from Sylvia Plath, Margaret Atwood and James Joyce, as well as praise for the book.

SEA LION PRESS

NOVELS / NOVELLAS / SHORT STORY COLLECTIONS AND ANTHOLOGIES
www.sealionpress.co.uk
Established 2015. A niche publisher of alternate history. May also consider sci-fi as 'future history' qualifies as a form of alternate history in the eyes of the editors, but strictly no other genres.

SELFMADEHERO

GRAPHIC NOVELS
info@selfmadehero.com
www.selfmadehero.com
Established 2007. A 'quirky' publishing house looking for groundbreaking graphic novels. Highly Commended for the 2011 FutureBook Digital Innovation

Awards, and champions both independently minded commercially successful work and graphic novels in translation. Open to submissions – see www.selfmadehero.com/submissions.php for details.

SEREN BOOKS

NON-FICTION / NOVELS / SHORT STORY COLLECTIONS AND ANTHOLOGIES / E-BOOKS
57 Nolton Street, Bridgend, Wales CF31 3AE
01656 663018
seren@serenbooks.com
www.serenbooks.com
Established 1963. Mixed form: also publishes poetry (see p66). Publications available direct from publisher website; by post and email order; from chain bookshops nationwide; from independent bookshops; at national and local literary events; and from Amazon.
GENRES: Drama and criticism; literary fiction; poetry; art, fashion and photography; biography and true stories; history; travel; books about Wales.
SUBMISSIONS: Non-fiction is open to all; fiction currently open only to authors previously published by Seren (check the website for updates). Submit by post to 57 Nolton Street, Bridgend CF31 3AE. Guidelines at www.serenbooks.com/seren/submissions-policy. Usually responds within one to three months. Rejections may occasionally include unsolicited feedback. Authors are paid an advance/fee plus royalties and receive free copies of the book, as well as other copies at a discount price.
For a fuller description of this press, see poetry publisher p66 and *Poetry Wales* (poetry magazine) p250

SHOESTRING PRESS

NOVELS / SHORT STORY COLLECTIONS / NON-FICTION
19 Devonshire Avenue, Beeston, Nottingham NG9 1BS
info@shoestring-press.com
www.shoestring-press.com
Editor: John Lucas
Mainly publishes poetry (see p67), but also some prose. Publications available direct from publisher website; by post and email order; from independent bookshops; at national and local literary events; and from Amazon.
Shoestring titles have been shortlisted for Vondel Prize for Translation and for the Cricket Club Writers' Book of the Year.
GENRES: Historical fiction; literary fiction; biography and true stories.
SUBMISSIONS: Submit by invitation only.
For a fuller description of this press, see poetry publisher p67

SILHOUETTE PRESS

NOVELS / SHORT STORY COLLECTIONS AND ANTHOLOGIES / NON-FICTION
adam.steiner@silhouettepress.co.uk
www.silhouettepress.co.uk
Editor: Adam Steiner
Established 2012. Mainly publishes poetry (see p68). Publications available direct from publisher website; by direct mail and email orders; from independent bookshops; and at national literary events.
GENRES: No genres specified.
SUBMISSIONS: Open to all, although publication history, covering letter, and/or completed manuscript will be advantageous. Submit online at www.silhouettepress.submittable.com/submit. Usually responds in over six

156

months. Some but limited feedback offered with rejections. Authors receive free copies of the book.
For further information, including what We Say, see also poetry publisher p68

SIX MINUTES TO MIDNIGHT
NOVELS / SHORT STORY COLLECTIONS AND ANTHOLOGIES / E-BOOKS
www.6ixminutes.co.uk
Established 2016. Publications available direct from publisher website; by direct mail and email orders; and from Amazon.
GENRES: Speculative fiction.
SUBMISSIONS: By invitation only. Usually responds within one to three months, with feedback only if requested. Authors are paid royalties only and receive free copies of the book.
WE SAY: We looked at a digital version of *This Twisted Earth*, a 287-page anthology of twelve sci-fi stories. The book is designed with straight letters, here and there alternating with different 'alien'-styled fonts. These nicely match the stories and illustrate the out-of-this-world characters speaking. This first volume will be followed by two others, both planned to be released in 2018.

SNOWBOOKS LTD
NOVELS / SHORT STORY / ANTHOLOGIES / E-BOOKS
info@snowbooks.com
www.snowbooks.com
Established 2003. Mainly publishes genre fiction. Publications available direct from publisher website; by post and email order; from chain bookshops nationwide; from independent bookshops; at national and local literary events;

and from Amazon and other bookshop websites.
Snowbooks won Futurebook Best Innovation of the Year 2013.
GENRES: Fantasy/sci-fi; horror.
SUBMISSIONS: Open to all. Submit using the online submissions form at snowbooksltd.submittable.com/submit. Guidelines at www.snowbooks.com/pages/submissions. Requires a small fee of £2, with 50% of each fee going to Save the Children. Usually responds within four to six months or more. No feedback offered with rejections. Authors are paid royalties only, and receive free copies of the book.
WE SAY: Snowbooks publishes a wide range of books – up to and including colouring books and choose-your-own-adventure – and in a number of formats, including hardback, paperback, clothbound and e-book (though not every book is available in all formats). We were particularly impressed with the production values of *Alice's Nightmare in Wonderland* by Jonathan Green, which includes beautiful illustrations and an Afterword by the author.

SOARING PENGUIN PRESS
GRAPHIC NOVELS AND COMICS / E-BOOKS
4 Florence Terrace, London SW15 3RU
07985 201621
submissions@soaringpenguinpress.com
www.soaringpenguinpress.com
Publisher: John Anderson
Established 2012. Publishes graphic novels, both fiction and non-fiction. Publications available direct from publisher website; by post and email order; from selected/local chain bookshops;

from independent bookshops; national literary events; and from Amazon and other bookshop websites. Publications distributed by Turnaround Distribution (UK/Europe) and SCB Distributors (USA/Canada); digital editions available from Comixology and Sequential.

Title *To End All Wars* was nominated for two Eisner Awards: Best Anthology and Best Non-fiction Title. Title *The Black Feather Falls* was nominated for Ignatz for Outstanding Series.

GENRES: Fantasy/sci-fi; graphic/comics; horror.

SUBMISSIONS: Open to all. Submit by post (4 Florence Terrace, London SW15 3RU) or by email (submissions@soaringpenguinpress.com). Guidelines at www.soaringpenguinpress.com/submissions. Usually responds within four to six months or more. Rejections may occasionally include unsolicited feedback. Authors are paid royalties only, and receive free copies of the books and a discount purchase price on future copies.

WE SAY: We looked at Soaring Penguin's catalogue, which gave us a great overview of the work it produces, particularly the graphic novels. High-quality drawing in a range of styles, which bold, striking covers and judicious use of colour in the comics in the inner pages. The work featured includes LGBTQ YA fiction, politics, time travel and translated work (Boulet's *Notes* is almost meta, chronicling the artist pulling together his first comics collection), all under the umbrella of graphic books. We were captivated and wanted to read more.

See also: *Meanwhile* **(mixed-form magazine) p208**

SPIRIT DUPLICATOR
CHAPBOOK/PAMPHLETS / ANTHOLOGIES
touch@spiritduplicator.org.uk
www.spiritduplicator.org
Pamphlets and books are printed using digital or risograph. Publishes *The British Esperantist* alongside other titles and is interested in the interface between design and writing. Always looking for collaborations, commissions and submissions.
See also: poetry publisher p71

STINGING FLY PRESS, THE
SHORT STORY ANTHOLOGIES AND COLLECTIONS
PO Box 6016, Dublin 1, Ireland
stingingfly@gmail.com
www.stingingfly.org
Editors: Thomas Morris, Declan Meade
Established 1997. Mainly fiction. Publications available direct from publisher website; from selected/local chain bookshops; from independent bookshops; and at national and local literary events. Stinging Fly title *Young Skins* by Colin Barrett won the 2014 Guardian First Book Award and the 2014 Frank O'Connor Short Story Award.
GENRES: Irish literary fiction.
SUBMISSIONS: By invitation.
For a fuller description of this press see *The Stinging Fly* **(mixed-form magazine) p225**

STONEWOOD PRESS
SHORT STORY COLLECTIONS
Diversity House, 72 Nottingham Road, Arnold Nottingham NG5 6LF

158

0845 456 4838
stonewoodpress@gmail.com
www.stonewoodpress.co.uk
Editor: Martin Parker
Established 2011. Also publishes
poetry (see p71). Publications
available direct from publisher
website; from chain bookshops
and independent bookshops
nationwide; and from Amazon and
other bookshop websites.
GENRES: Literary fiction; fantasy/
sci-fi
SUBMISSIONS: See guidelines at
www.stonewoodpress.co.uk/about/
submissions. Usually responds
within four months. Rejections may
occasionally include unsolicited
feedback. Authors are paid
royalties only and receive free
copies of the book.
WE SAY: We looked at a digital
version of Krishan Coupland's
When You Lived Inside the Walls,
a 41-page book which contains
three short stories. The design is
well thought out and executed
nicely: each chapter starts with a
big, illustrated letter, matching the
story themes. The inside cover is
illustrated with rat traps, the topic of
the first story. The type is a relatively
big serif style. Different chapters
within the story are divided by stars.
See also: poetry publisher p71

STORGY ☆
SHORT STORY ANTHOLOGIES /
E-BOOKS
www.storgy.com
Editors: Tomek Dzido, Anthony Self,
Ross Jeffery, Alice Kouzmenko
Established 2013. Anthologies
printed as part of the e-zine and
competitions.
GENRES: Literary fiction.
SUBMISSIONS: Open to all. Submit
by email to submit@storgy.com.

Guidelines on website. Usually
responds within one to three
months. No feedback offered
with rejections. Authors receive
free copies of the book. No fee or
royalties paid.
WE SAY: We looked at Storgy's
2014 *Short Story Competition
Anthology*, 173 pages of
short stories. The design has a
contemporary aesthetic with full-
colour illustrations. Interviews with
the winner and runners up provide
information on their writing
process. A nice touch.
**See also: *Storgy Magazine* (prose
magazine) p270**

STRANGE ATTRACTOR PRESS
NON-FICTION / NOVELS / SHORT
STORY COLLECTIONS AND
ANTHOLOGIES / E-BOOKS
contactee@strangeattractor.co.uk
www.strangeattractor.co.uk
Editors: Mark Pilkington,
Jamie Sutcliffe
Established 2004. Primarily
publishes non-fiction. Publications
available direct from publisher
website; from chain bookshops
nationwide; at national and local
literary events; and from Amazon
and other bookshop websites.
GENRES: Fantasy/sci-fi; horror; art
and photography; history; popular
science and nature; science,
technology and medicine; and
spirituality and beliefs.
SUBMISSIONS: Open to all. Submit
by post (BM SAP, London WC1N
3XX) or by email (proposals@
strangeattractor.co.uk). Usually
responds in up to six months.
Rejections may occasionally
include unsolicited feedback.
Authors are paid royalties only and
receive free copies of their book.

STRUCTO PRESS

STORY COLLECTIONS AND NOVELS
editor@structomagazine.co.uk
www.structopress.co.uk
Editor: Euan Monaghan
Established 2015. First book due early 2018. Mixed form: also publishes poetry chapbooks (see p72). Publications available direct from publisher website; from bookshops; and from bookshop websites.
GENRES: Literary fiction; literature-in-translation; slipstream; short stories.
SUBMISSIONS: Open to all via email enquiry.
For a fuller description of this press, see *Structo* (mixed-output magazine) p225 and poetry publisher p72

SWAN RIVER PRESS

NOVELS / SHORT STORY COLLECTIONS AND ANTHOLOGIES
www.swanriverpress.ie
Editor: Brian J. Showers
Established 2003. Publications available direct from publisher website; by post and email order; from independent bookshops; at national and local literary events; and from independent online retailers.
Swan River Press title *Dreams of Shadow and Smoke: Stories for J.S. Le Fanu* won the Ghost Story Award for best book.
GENRES: Supernatural; ghost stories; horror; literary fiction; literary criticism.
SUBMISSIONS: By invitation only. See guidelines at www.swanriverpress.ie. Usually responds within four weeks. Rejections may occasionally include unsolicited feedback. Authors are paid a flat fee.

See also: *The Green Book* (prose magazine) p265

SYLPH EDITIONS

NOVELS / SHORT STORY COLLECTIONS / NON-FICTION
020 7625 3223
info@sylpheditions.com
www.sylpheditions.com
Established 2006. Primarily publishes fiction. Publications available direct from publisher website and from independent bookshops.
GENRES: Literary fiction; art, design, photography and culture.
SUBMISSIONS: Open to all. Submit by email to info@sylpheditions.com. Usually responds within four weeks. Authors receive free copies of the book. No fee or royalties paid.
WE SAY: We looked at the *Cahiers* series, a staple-spine, folded paper series of essay pamphlets. Around 40 pages long, with dust jackets over the thick textured paper covers. The essays are thoughtful and accessible, and illustrated with full-colour images.

SYNCHRONISE WITCHES PRESS

SHORT STORY ANTHOLOGIES
cherrystyles@hotmail.co.uk
www.cherrystyles.co.uk
Editor: Cherry Styles
Established 2012. Mixed form: also publishes poetry (see p72). Publications available direct from publisher website; by post and email order; from independent bookshops; at national and local literary events; at zine fairs; and in art bookshops.
The press was shortlisted for the Turn The Page artists' book award, 2015.

GENRES: Literary fiction; poetry; art, fashion and photography; biography and true stories; music, stage and screen; society, education and politics.
SUBMISSIONS: Open to women writers only. Submit by email (thechapess@gmail.com) or via online form (www.cherrystyles.co.uk/the-chapess). Usually responds within one to three months. Rejections may occasionally include unsolicited feedback.
For a fuller description of this press, see *The Chapess* (mixed-form magazine) p189. See also poetry publisher p72

TANGENT BOOKS
NOVELS / NON-FICTION / SHORT STORY ANTHOLOGIES
Unit 5.16, Paintworks, Bristol BS4 3EH
0117 972 0645
richard@tangentbooks.co.uk
www.tangentbooks.co.uk
Founded in 2004, Tangent's mission statement is 'to publish interesting stuff' and provide 'quality books for the discerning punter' – their range is extensive. Resolutely independent and supportive of local businesses.

TANGERINE PRESS
NOVELS / SHORT STORY ANTHOLOGIES / NON-FICTION
18 Riverside Rd, Garratt Business Park, London SW17 0BA
michael@eatmytangerine.com
www.eatmytangerine.com
Editor: Michael Curran
Established 2006. Mainly publishes fiction, but also some poetry (see p73). Publications available direct from publisher website; by post and email order; from major chain and independent bookshops; and

at local literary events.
Tangerine Press was longlisted for *3AM Magazine*'s Publisher of the Year (2010) and the inaugural Republic of Consciousness Award 2016. Author Chris Wilson (*The Glue Ponys*) was longlisted for the Edgehill Short Story Prize 2017.
GENRES: Autobiographical fiction.
SUBMISSIONS: No feedback offered with rejections.
See also: poetry publisher p73

TARTARUS PRESS
NON-FICTION / SHORT STORY ANTHOLOGIES AND COLLECTIONS / NOVELS / E-BOOKS
Coverley House, Carlton, Leyburn, North Yorkshire DL8 4AY
01969 640399
tartarus@pavilion.co.uk
www.tartaruspress.com
Editors: Rosalie Parker, Raymond Russell
Established 1990. Mainly publishes fiction. Available direct from publisher website; by post and email order; in selected chain bookshops; and in independent bookshops.
Tartarus Press won the 2015 World Fantasy Award (Non-professional).
GENRES: Supernatural; literary.
SUBMISSIONS: Open to all. Submit by email to rosalieparker@btinternet.com. Guidelines at www.tartaruspress.com/submissions.html. Usually responds within four weeks. No feedback offered with rejection. Authors are paid an advance and royalties.
WE SAY: We looked at digital editions of *The Autobiography Of Arthur Machen: Far Off Things Near And Far* and *A Country Still All Mystery* by Mark Valentine. The covers of the books had a uniform style: a pale yellow background,

with a small image in the lower middle of the cover. Both covers featured a landscape image; Machen's was a dark church-like building, with trees in the foreground and a dark orange sky, while Valentine's was a high-rise-style building on a green hill, with a grey-blue sky. The books supplied to us were both non-fiction, but Tartarus Press also accepts supernatural fiction.
See also: *Wormwood* (prose magazine) p271

TEAM ANGELICA PUBLISHING

NOVELS / SHORT STORY COLLECTIONS AND ANTHOLOGIES / E-BOOKS
51 Coningham Road, London W12 8BS
john@teamangelica.com
www.teamangelica.com
Editor: John R Gordon
Established 2011. Predominantly publishes queer-of-colour centred fiction. Also produces film and theatre projects. Publications available from independent bookshops; and from Amazon and other bookshop websites.
Team Angelica title *Fairytales for Lost Children* by Diriye Osman won the Polari Prize for Best First Book (2014). *Tiny Pieces of Skull* by Roz Kaveney won the Lambda Best Trans Fiction award (2015).
GENRES: Self-help/inspirational; graphic/comics; literary fiction; biography and true stories; health and lifestyle.
SUBMISSIONS: Submissions by invitation only. Email contact john@teamangelica.com. Usually responds within four weeks. No feedback offered with rejections, but they may occasionally include unsolicited feedback. Writers are paid an advance/fee plus royalties.
WE SAY: We looked at the award-winning *Fairytales for Lost Children* by Diriye Osman. A black-and-white image of the author in an Elizabethan gown adorns the cover, which has a slightly rubbery matt laminate feel, and there are ornate drop-cap letters at the beginning of each story, as befits the fairytale title. Set in Kenya, Somalia and South London, the stories explore identity in terms of gender, sexuality, family and country. A prime example of the important work Team Angelica is publishing.

TELOS PUBLISHING LTD

NOVELS / SHORT STORY COLLECTIONS AND ANTHOLOGIES / NON-FICTION / E-BOOKS
david@telos.co.uk
stephen@telos.co.uk
www.telos.co.uk
Editors: David J Howe, Stephen James Walker, Sam Stone
Established 2000. Publications available direct from publisher website; from chain bookshops nationwide; from independent bookshops; and from Amazon and other bookshop websites. In 2006, the founders of Telos Publishing won a World Fantasy Award for the company's work. Telos Publishing also won the British Fantasy Award for Best Publisher in 2010 and 2011.
GENRES: Sci-fi/fantasy/horror; film and television; crime fiction; self-help guides.
SUBMISSIONS: Open to all. Submit by email to david@telos.co.uk or stephen@telos.co.uk. Guidelines at www.telos.co.uk/submissions-3. Usually responds within four weeks. No feedback offered with

rejections. Authors are paid either: an advance plus royalties; or a flat fee depending on the project. All authors receive free copies of their book.

WE SAY: We looked at a digital version of *Nights of Blood Wine* by Freda Warrington: a 215-page collection of fifteen vampire stories. It contains formerly published stories as well as new ones. The first part is made up of ten 'Blood Wine' stories, where the second part covers five further pieces, such as a journal extract and a sequel to a previous publication. The design is plain: black and white print, serif type and justified text. The stories are intriguing, sometimes elaborating on earlier stories with the same characters.

TEST CENTRE

MIXED-FORM COLLECTIONS AND ANTHOLOGIES
71 Oriel Road, London E9 5SG
admin@testcentre.org.uk
www.testcentre.org.uk
Editors: Jess Chandler, Will Shutes
Established 2011. Mainly publishes poetry (see p74). Publications available direct from publisher website; from selected/local chain bookshops; from independent bookshops; and at local literary events.
Test Centre was nominated for Most Innovative Publisher at the Saboteur Awards 2015.
GENRES: Experimental fiction; spoken word audio/musical collaborations.
SUBMISSIONS: During submission windows only. Submit by post (71 Oriel Road, London E9 5SG) or by email (admin@testcentre.org. uk). Guidelines at www.testcentre. org.uk/about/submissions.

Usually responds within one to three months. Rejections may occasionally include unsolicited feedback. Authors are paid a flat fee and receive free copies of the book.
For more information see also: poetry publisher p74 and mixed-form magazine p227

THISTLE PUBLISHING

PAPERBACKS / NOVELS / NON-FICTION / E-BOOKS
020 7222 7574
info@thistlepublishing.co.uk
www.thistlepublishing.co.uk
Editors: David Haviland, Andrew Lownie
Established 1996. Publications available direct from publisher website; from chain bookshops nationwide; from independent bookshops; at national and local literary events; and from Amazon and other bookshop websites. Thistle Publishing won the People's Book Prize 2017.
GENRES: Crime; thriller; literary; reading group; women.
SUBMISSIONS: Open to all. Submit by email to info@thistlepublishing. co.uk. Non-fiction authors should provide a synopsis, author profile, sample chapter, and brief chapter summaries. Fiction authors should provide a synopsis and three sample chapters. Guidelines at www.thistlepublishing.co.uk/about. html. Usually responds within four weeks. Rejections may occasionally include unsolicited feedback. Authors are paid an advance/fee plus royalties.
WE SAY: We looked at a digital version of *Rickshaw*, a 260-page story about a homeless Irish character who rides a rickshaw in London. This is a fascinating, sharp

and humorous story from the very first page. The writing is direct and to-the-point, and the design simple with a classical font and justified text.

THREE DROPS PRESS

SHORT STORY COLLECTIONS / NOVELLAS / MIXED-FORM ANTHOLOGIES
www.threedropspress.co.uk
Editor: Kate Garrett
Established 2015. Also publishes poetry (see p74). Publications available by direct mail and email orders; from independent bookshops; from Amazon and other bookshop websites; and from Lulu.
GENRES: Mythology; folklore; fairytales; literary.
SUBMISSIONS: During submission windows only. Submit by email to threedropspoetry@gmail.com. Usually responds within one to three months. Rejections may occasionally include unsolicited feedback. Anthology authors are paid royalties only. Authors of single books get five free copies and a royalty share, and pay a discounted price if they wish to sell copies at readings, etc.
See also: poetry publisher p74. For what We Say, see *Three Drops from a Cauldron* (mixed-form magazine) p228

TINY TREE CHILDREN'S BOOKS

CHILDREN'S PICTURE BOOKS / CHILDREN'S FICTION
Unit 46, Goyt Mill, Marple, Stockport SK6 7AW
01614 278329
james.shaw@matthewjamespublishing.com
www.matthewjamespublishing.com

Editor: James Shaw
Established 2016. Publications available direct from publisher website; by direct mail and email orders; from selected/local chain bookshops; from independent bookshops; at national and local literary events; and from Amazon and other bookshop websites.
GENRES: Children's fiction.
SUBMISSIONS: Open to all. Submit by email to submissions@matthewjamespublishing.com. Guidelines at www.matthewjamespublishing.com/submissions-and-permissions. Usually responds within four weeks. Rejections may occasionally include unsolicited feedback. Authors receive an advance/fee publish royalties and receive free copies of the book.

TIRGEARR PUBLISHING

NOVELS / SHORT STORY COLLECTIONS AND ANTHOLOGIES / NOVELLAS / E-BOOKS
info@tirgearrpublishing.com
www.tirgearrpublishing.com
Established 2012. Commercial adult and cross-genre fiction. Publications available by post and email order, and from Amazon and other bookshop websites, and by request from most bookshops.
GENRES: Commercial adult genre and cross genre fiction: mystery; horror; thrillers; suspense; detective/PI; police procedurals; romance; romantic suspense; erotic romance; historical fiction; historical romance; sci-fi/fantasy.
SUBMISSIONS: Open to all. Submit via online form at www.tirgearrpublishing.com/submissions (guidelines at the same address). Usually responds within one to three months, and provides

feedback with all rejections. Authors are paid royalties only and receive free copies of book.

WE SAY: An e-book-only publisher, Tirgearr has an extensive list of genre fiction. We took a look at their online catalogue, where the cover designs echo those of big commercial print publishers (passionate gazing-into-the-distance for romance; chrome and planets for sci-fi, etc). The stories are well edited and entertaining.

TOLLINGTON PRESS
NOVELS / SHORT STORY COLLECTIONS / NON-FICTION / E-BOOKS
helensandler@gmail.com
www.tollingtonpress.co.uk
Editor: Helen Sandler
Established 2008. Mixed form: also publishes poetry (see p75). Publications available from chain bookshops nationwide; from independent bookshops; at local literary events; and from Amazon. Tollington Press titles have been longlisted (2015) and shortlisted (2011) for the Polari Prize.
GENRES: Literary; memoir; lesbian/LGBT interest; Jewish interest.
SUBMISSIONS: Open to all. Submit by query only to helensandler@gmail.com. Guidelines at www.tollingtonpress.co.uk/about.html. Usually responds within four weeks. Rejections may occasionally include unsolicited feedback. Authors contribute to editorial/publication/marketing costs.
WE SAY: We looked at PDF versions of three prose books, in which the page design is more standard than the press's poetry offering (see p75). The contents

of the books all seem to look at being true to oneself. The 75-page *Rights of Passage*, for example, is a script-style piece (with plenty of monologues) looking at LGBTQ experiences in societies where this is not accepted, while *Out On A Limb* is a selection of sermons, presenting the 'revolutionary religion', as the author sees it, 'of the prophets and Jesus.' A look through *Not In Our Hands* reveals a coming-of-age story set in Italy, with characters of various religions facing a world less-than-tolerant of their friendships and upbringings.
See also: poetry publisher p75

TRAMP PRESS
NOVELS / CREATIVE NON-FICTION / SHORT STORY COLLECTIONS AND ANTHOLOGIES / E-BOOKS
info@tramppress.com;
submissions@tramppress.com
www.tramppress.com
Publishers/editors: Lisa Coen, Sarah Davis-Goff
Established 2014. Publications available direct from publisher website; at chain and independent bookshops nationwide and internationally; at national and local literary events; and from Amazon and other bookshop websites and e-book providers. Some online content freely available to all. Tramp Press authors have won the Goldsmiths Prize, four Irish Book Awards, the Rooney Prize, the Geoffrey Faber Memorial Award, the Waterstones Book of the Year and the Kate O'Brien Award. They've been nominated for many others including the Kerry Group, the IMPAC, the Republic of Consciousness Prize, the Costa, the Warwick Prize, the Guardian First Book Award, the Man Booker and

the Desmond Elliot Prize.

GENRES: Crime/thriller/mystery; fantasy/sci-fi; horror; literary fiction; YA.

SUBMISSIONS: Open to all. Submit by email to submissions@tramppress.com. Guidelines at www.tramppress.com/submissions. Usually responds within four weeks. Rejections may occasionally include unsolicited feedback. Authors are paid an advance/fee plus royalties.

WE SAY: Tramp Press hit headlines in 2015 with an article in the Irish Times about sexism in publishing; their books are equally bold and outspoken. The perfect-bound paperbacks we saw feel like Big Five titles – indeed Mike McCormack's *Solar Bones* was longlisted for the Man Booker Prize. The covers are eye-catching, such as the droplet-strewn feathers of a blue bird featured on Sara Baume's *A Line Made by Walking*. The novel follows a young artist who, having dropped out of college and moved in with her grandmother in rural Ireland, begins a series photographing everything from road-kill to kitchen curios, documenting the beauty and destruction around her.

TTA PRESS
NOVELS / SHORT STORY COLLECTIONS AND ANTHOLOGIES / NOVELLAS / E-BOOKS
5 Martins Lane, Witcham, Ely, Cambridgeshire CB6 2LB
www.ttapress.com
Editor: Andy Cox
Established 1994. Fiction. Publications available direct from publisher website; by post and email order; from chain bookshops nationwide; from independent

bookshops; at national and local literary events; and from Amazon and other bookshop websites. All online content available to all.

GENRES: Crime/thriller/mystery; fantasy/sci-fi; horror; literary fiction.

SUBMISSIONS: Open to all. Submit via tta.submittable.com/submit. Usually responds within four weeks. Rejections may occasionally include unsolicited feedback. Authors are paid a flat fee and receive free copies of the book.

For fuller descriptions of this press, see also *Interzone* (sci-fi prose magazine) p265, *Black Static* (horror prose magazine) p259, and *CrimeWave* (crime prose magazine) p262

TWO RIVERS PRESS
NON-FICTION
7 Denmark Road, Reading RG1 5PA
tworiverspress@gmail.com
www.tworiverspress.com
Editor: Sally Mortimore
Established 1994. Publishes mainly non-fiction. Publications available direct from publisher website; by post and email order; from selected/local chain bookshops; from independent bookshops; at local literary events; and from Amazon and other bookshop websites.

GENRES: Books about Reading and the Thames Valley; art books.

UKAUTHORS/UKAPRESS
NOVELS / SHORT STORY ANTHOLOGIES / NON-FICTION
ukauthors@ukauthors.com
www.ukapress.com
Fiction and non-fiction unrestricted by genre or style. Looking for quality writing with 'originality, sparkle and the promise of something unexpected'.

UNBOUND

NOVELS / SHORT STORY
COLLECTIONS AND ANTHOLOGIES
/ NON-FICTION / E-BOOKS
Unit 18, Waterside, 44-48 Wharf Road,
London N1 7UX
020 7253 4230
www.unbound.co.uk

Established 2011. Mixed form:
also publishes poetry (see p75).
Publications available direct
from publisher website; by
post and email order; at chain
and independent bookshops
nationwide; at national and local
literary events; and through
Amazon and other bookshop
websites. Publications are
subsidised by crowdfunding.
Multi-award-winning: Unbound title
The Wake won Book of the Year
at the 2015 Bookseller Industry
Awards and the 2014 Gordon Burn
Prize; was shortlisted for the 2014
Goldsmiths Prize; and longlisted
for the Man Booker Prize 2014, the
Desmond Elliott Prize 2014, and
the Folio Prize 2014. Unbound won
Best Publisher Website 2014 at the
FutureBook Innovation Awards and
British Book Design and Production
Awards, and Best Start-Up at
the 2011 FutureBook Innovation
Awards. Also won the Literature
Award 2013, for 26 Treasures,
at the British Book Design and
Production Awards.
GENRES: Crime/thriller/mystery;
fantasy/sci-fi; graphic/comics;
historical fiction; literary fiction;
biography and true stories; food
and drink; history; popular science
and nature; society, education and
politics.
SUBMISSIONS: Open to all.
Submit via the online form at www.
unbound.co.uk/authors/work-with-
us. Guidelines at the same address.
Usually responds within one to
three months. Rejections may
occasionally include unsolicited
feedback. Authors are paid
royalties: a 50/50 profit share from
crowdfunding.
WE SAY: We looked at *The Wake*
by Paul Kingsnorth: a prime
example of an indie taking a
punt on a risky book. *The Wake*
is a post-apocalyptic novel, set
in 1066, and written in a version
of Old English. The production
values on this book are impressive,
from the textured cover to the
wonderfully thick paper. Unbound's
crowdfunding approach to
publishing means it can afford to
get the best materials possible,
knowing future readers have
already covered the cost. And
with *The Wake* already a modern
classic, the editors clearly have an
eye for the market.
See also: poetry publisher p75

UNIFORMBOOKS

NON-FICTION
info@uniformbooks.co.uk
www.uniformbooks.co.uk
Editor: Colin Sackett

Established 2011. Mixed form:
also publishes poetry (see p76).
Publications available direct from
publisher website; by direct mail
and email orders; from chain
bookshops nationwide; from
independent bookshops; and from
Amazon.
GENRES: Visual and literary arts;
cultural geography and history;
music and bibliographic studies.
SUBMISSIONS: Open to all. Submit
by email to info@uniformbooks.
co.uk. Usually responds within four
weeks. Rejections may occasionally
include unsolicited feedback.
Authors are paid royalties only and

UNTHANK BOOKS

NOVELS / SHORT STORY
COLLECTIONS AND ANTHOLOGIES
/ NON-FICTION / E-BOOKS
PO Box 3506, Norwich NR7 7QP
information@unthankbooks.com
www.unthankbooks.com
Editor: Ashley Stokes

Established 2010. Publications
available direct from publisher
website; by direct mail and email
orders; from chain bookshops
nationwide; from independent
bookshops; at local literary events;
and from Amazon and other
bookshop websites. Unthank Books
was shortlisted in the Saboteur
Awards 2017 for Most Innovative
Publisher and Best Anthology.
GENRES: Literary.
SUBMISSIONS: Open to all.
Submit by post (PO Box 3506,
Norwich NR7 7QP). Guidelines at
www.unthankbooks.com/contacts.
html. Usually responds within one
to three months. Rejections may
include occasional unsolicited
feedback. Authors are paid royalties
only and receive free copies of the
book.
WE SAY: We looked at *Some of
us glow more than others: stories*
by Tania Hershman. The cover
features an ethereal image of
jellyfish and marked with 'As heard
on Radio 4' – which indicates the
high quality of writing Unthank
looks for. Hershman's work blurs
the story/poetry line, and the
stories are divided into groups,
'Fight or Flight', 'Grounded' etc,
and the title pages of each section
feature poetry.

They say

Unthank Books was born in
Norwich and London but
operates globally. We remain
deeply committed to offering
a platform to aspiring authors
of any format of the human
species, or other species when
they're ready. Basically, we
believe in the transformative
power of literature and are
not fussed where we find
it. We think we're fun to
know and be around and
relish giving birth to books,
both print and digital,
and providing them a life
everlasting. We teach writing
creatively through our sister,
the Unthank School, and our
alumni are beginning to make
wakes on earth and beyond.

168

receive free copies of the book.
See also: poetry publisher p76 and
Uniformagazine **(prose magazine)**
p271

UNSUNG STORIES

NOVELS / SHORT STORY
COLLECTIONS AND ANTHOLOGIES
/ NON-FICTION / E-BOOKS
info@unsungstories.co.uk
www.unsungstories.co.uk
Editor: George Sandison
Established 2014. Publications
available direct from publisher
website; from chain bookshops
nationwide; from independent
bookshops; and from Amazon and
other bookshop websites.
Unsung Stories titles have
been nominated for the John
W. Campbell Award, Shirley
Jackson Award, James Tiptree
Jr Awards, BSFA Awards, BFS
Awards, Saboteur Awards and the
Guardian's Not the Booker.
GENRES: Speculative fiction; sci-fi;
fantasy; horror; weird fiction.
SUBMISSIONS: Open to all, during
submission windows. Submit
online at www.unsungstories.co.uk/
submissions. Guidelines at www.
unsungstories.co.uk/submissions.
Usually responds within four
to six months. Rejections may
occasionally include unsolicited
feedback. Authors are paid
royalties on sales and receive free
copies of the book.
WE SAY: Unsung publish a number
of short stories on their website,
which is where we looked to get
a feel for its publications. The site
certainly gives enough information
on their books to pique interest.
Cover designs are professional: all
fit the Unsung template (a jagged
slice of colour across the bottom
containing the author/title). The

cover images are disquieting:
almost ordinary at first glance, only
for the viewer to be unsettled by
an out-of-the-ordinary detail, as is
fitting for an imprint specialising in
high-quality speculative fiction.

V. PRESS

COLLECTIONS, ANTHOLOGIES AND
CHAPBOOKS/PAMPHLETS
vpresspoetry@hotmail.com
vpresspoetry.blogspot.co.uk
Editor: Sarah Leavesley
Established 2013. Publishes poetry
and flash fiction. Publications
available direct from publisher
website; at national and local
literary events; and from Amazon.
SUBMISSIONS: Submit by email
to vpresspoetry@hotmail.com,
but only when the submissions
window is open. Guidelines at
vpresspoetry.blogspot.co.uk/p/
submissions.html. Usually responds
within three months. Rejections
may occasionally include feedback.
Authors receive initial free copies
of the book, followed by copies at
a discount rate.
WE SAY: As with their poetry entry
(p76) V. Press shared a favourite
piece of fiction with us, with the
caveat that their 'tastes are quite
eclectic'. 'Wild green fig jam' is
taken from Jude Higgin's flash
fiction pamphlet *The Chemist's
House* – the cover of which is in
black and white, and features a
photo within a photo. The piece is
evocative and almost poetic in its
use of repetition and the senses,
even as it relays the harsh realities
of illness and loss. As an example
of the standard published by V.
Press, this is setting the bar very
high indeed.
See also: poetry publisher p76

169

VALLEY PRESS

NOVELS / SHORT STORY
COLLECTIONS AND ANTHOLOGIES
/ NON-FICTION / E-BOOKS
Woodend, The Crescent,
Scarborough YO11 2PW
01723 332077
office@valleypressuk.com
www.valleypressuk.com
Editor: Jamie McGarry
Established 2008. Mainly publishes
poetry (see p77). Publications
available direct from publisher
website; from chain bookshops
nationwide; from independent
bookshops; at national and local
literary events; and from Amazon
and other bookshop websites.
In 2017, Valley Press title
Remembering Oluwale won
the Saboteur Award for Best
Anthology.
GENRES: Short stories; literary
fiction; anthologies; memoir.
SUBMISSIONS: Open to all. Submit
online at www.valleypressuk.com/
submissions. Usually responds
within one to three months.
Rejections may occasionally
include unsolicited feedback.
Submitters are required to buy a
magazine/book from the press.
Authors are paid a flat fee and
royalties only and receive free
copies of the book.
**For further information, including
what We Say, see also: poetry
publisher p77**

VANE WOMEN PRESS

SHORT STORY PAMPHLETS AND
ANTHOLOGIES
low.down@vanewomen.co.uk
www.vanewomen.co.uk
Editors: SJ Litherland,
Marilyn Longstaff (assistant editor),
Pat Maycroft (art editor)
Established 1993. Mainly publishes
poetry (see p77). Publications
available direct from publisher
website; by post and email order;
at local literary events; and at Vane
Women events and workshops.
Vane Women title *The Spar Box* by
Pippa Little was the 2006 Poetry
Book Society Pamphlet choice.
SUBMISSIONS: Open to previously
unpublished women in North
East England. Contact by email
(submissions@vanewomen.co.uk)
in the first instance, and a postal
address to send poems and
short stories to will be provided
if appropriate. Full submission
guidelines at www.vanewomen.
co.uk/submissions.html. Usually
responds in up to six months.
Rejections may occasionally
include unsolicited feedback.
Authors receive free copies of their
book.
**For a fuller description of this press,
see poetry publisher p77**

VOIDERY APERTURE, THE

NOVELS
information@thevoideryaperture.com
www.thevoideryaperture.com
Editor: Christopher Pickard
Established 2016. Mixed form:
also publishes poetry (see p78).
Publications available from chain
bookshops nationwide; from
independent bookshops; and
from Amazon and other bookshop
websites.
GENRES: Literary; experimental.
SUBMISSIONS: Submissions by
invitation only. Rejections may
occasionally include unsolicited
feedback. Authors are paid
royalties only.
WE SAY: We looked at the Voidery
Aperture website, where cover
images and extracts from its
publications can be accessed.

Covers designs are simple –
plain colour backgrounds, with
contrasting title-and-author text in
a serif font, and the publisher logo
clearly displayed. The inner page
design is clean and professional.
The types of writing seems to err
on the side of experimental, for
example Neil Godsell's *Crump
Redivivus*, which is fiction written
almost as script, but without any
stage directions.
See also: poetry publisher p78

WARD RIVER PRESS
NOVELS
+353 1 806 3825
info@poolbeg.com
www.poolbeg.com
The literary imprint of Poolbeg
Press, one of Ireland's most
established presses (since 1976),
which is particularly known for
nurturing new women's writing.
See also: Poolbeg Press p148

WARD WOOD PUBLISHING
NOVELS / SHORT STORY
COLLECTIONS / MIXED-FORM
ANTHOLOGIES / E-BOOKS
6 The Drive, Golders Green, London
NW11 9SR
07504 863024
adele@wardwoodpublishing.co.uk
www.wardwoodpublishing.co.uk
Editor: Adele Ward
Established 2010. Mixed output
– also publishes poetry (see p78),
as well as the Bedford Square
MA Anthology from from Royal
Holloway, University of London,
with work by graduates of the
poetry and fiction courses.
Publications available direct from
publisher website; from major
chain and independent bookshops;
at literary events; and from Amazon
and other bookshop websites.

Ward Wood author Joe Stein was
on the longlist of 10 for the Crime
Writers' Association Dagger in the
Library award 2016.
GENRES: Literary; crime; comedy;
LGBT.
SUBMISSIONS: By invitation only,
to adele@wardwoodpublishing.
co.uk. Please check
www.wardwoodpublishing.co.uk/
manuscripts.htm for submissions
information. Usually responds
within one to three months.
Rejections may occasionally
include unsolicited feedback.
Authors are paid royalties.
WE SAY: Of the digital versions
we saw, *Mr Oliver's Object
of Desire* by V G Lee had the
most interesting cover, with a
watercolour-styled outline of the
London skyline. Lee's novel, along
with *Through Another Night* by
Joe Stein and the collection by
Royal Holloway Creative Writing
Programme, *Bedford Square
10*, were clearly formatted for
print, but translated well to PDF
form. *Bedford Square 10*, which
leads with a description of the
programme, sets out the varied
work of its students, ranging
from fiction time-travel from the
1930s to psychological mystery,
encompassing prose and poetry.
See also: poetry publisher p78

WAYWISER PRESS, THE ☆
NOVELS / SHORT STORY
COLLECTIONS / NON-FICTION /
ILLUSTRATED WORKS / E-BOOKS
Christmas Cottage, Church Enstone,
West Oxfordshire OX7 4NN
www.waywiser-press.com
Editors: Philip Hoy, Joseph Harrison,
Dora Malech, V Penelope Pelizzon,
Eric McHenry, Greg Williamson,
Clive Watkins, Matthew Yorke

Established 2001. Mainly publishes poetry (see p79). Publications available direct from publisher website; by post and email order; at chain bookshops and independent bookshops nationwide; and via Amazon and other bookshop websites, including Inpress Books.

GENRES: Fantasy/sci-fi; graphic/comics; horror; biography and true stories; literary criticism; literary history.

SUBMISSIONS: Prose can be submitted year round. Submit by post to Christmas Cottage, Church Enstone, Chipping Norton OX7 4NN. Guidelines at www.waywiser-press.com/authors.html. Usually responds within one to three months, no feedback offered if rejected. Authors receive royalties and free copies of the book.

For a fuller description of this press see poetry publisher p79

WILD WOLF PUBLISHING
NOVELS
editor@wildwolfpublishing. com
www.wildwolfpublishing.com
'Fiction with teeth.' Looks for full-length fiction of a dark nature: thriller, horror or sci-fi.

WINTER GOOSE PUBLISHING
NOVELS / CREATIVE NON-FICTION
www.wintergoosepublishing.com
Editors: James Logan Koukis, Sherry Foley
Works closely with authors, publishing action/adventure, suspense, fantasy, mystery, romance, YA and general fiction, as well as creative non-fiction. Strongly suggest writers read work by the press's authors to get a feel for preference.
See also: poetry publisher p79

WRECKING BALL PRESS ☆
NOVELS / SHORT STORY COLLECTIONS AND ANTHOLOGIES / NON-FICTION / E-BOOKS
5 Theatre Mews, Egginton Street, Hull HU2 8DL
01482 211499
editor@wreckingballpress.com
www.wreckingballpress.com
Editors: Shane Rhodes, Russ Litten
Established 1997. Mainly publishes poetry (see p79). Publications available direct from publisher website; by post and email order; at chain and independent bookshops nationwide; at literary events; and on Amazon. Some online content available to all. Wrecking Ball Press title *The Scene of My Former Triumph* by Matthew Caley was nominated for Best First Collection, The Forward Prize 2005.

GENRES: Drama and criticism; fantasy/sci-fi; literary fiction; biography and true stories.

SUBMISSIONS: Open to all. Submit by post (Wrecking Ball Press, 5 Theatre Mews, Egginton Street, Hull HU2 8DL) or by email (editor@wreckingballpress.com). Guidelines on the website. Usually responds within one to three months. Rejection may occasionally include unsolicited feedback. Authors are paid royalties and receive free copies of the book.

See also: poetry publisher p79

Y LOLFA
NOVELS / NON-FICTION / E-BOOKS
Talybont, Ceredigion, Wales SY24 5HE
01970 832304
ylolfa@ylolfa.com
www.ylolfa.com
Editors: Lefi Gruffudd, Eirian Jones
Established 1967. Mainly publishes non-fiction. Publications available

direct from publisher website; by post and email order; at chain and independent bookshops; at local literary events; and through bookshop websites.

Titles from Y Lolfa have been shortlisted for British Sports Book of the Year and won Welsh Book of the Year.

GENRES: Welsh interest; biography and true stories; history; sports and leisure; travel.

SUBMISSIONS: Open to all. Submit by post (Y Lolfa, Talybont, Ceredigion SY24 5HE) or email (edit@ylolfa.com). Guidelines at www.ylolfa.com/en/cyhoeddi.php. Usually responds within four weeks. Rejection may occasionally include unsolicited feedback. Authors are paid royalties or an advance/ fee plus royalties. Some titles may require crowdfunding or author contribution.

WE SAY: We looked at *The Shadow of Nanteos* by Jane Blank, a weighty perfect-bound paperback publication that connects the matt finish of the professional design to the dark plot within the novel. The quality continues within with high-quality cream paper. This dark historic novel provides a gripping gothic chill and oozes Welsh history: a great read for anyone who wants to find more about Welsh heritage.

YLVA PUBLISHING
NOVELS / SHORT STORY COLLECTIONS AND ANTHOLOGIES / E-BOOKS
astrid.ohletz@ylva-publishing.com
www.ylva-publishing.com
Editor: Astrid Ohletz
Established 2012. Publisher of lesbian and bi fiction. Publications available direct from publisher

website; from chain bookshops nationwide; from independent bookshops; at local literary events; and from Amazon and other bookshop websites.

Two Ylva Publishing titles have been finalists in the 2016 and 2017 Lambda Awards, with Andrea Bramhall's *Collide-O-Scope* and Lee Winter's *Requiem for Immortals*. Ylva have also won several other awards over the past five years with the GCLS and the Rainbow Awards.

GENRES: Lesbian or bi: romance; crime/mystery; sci-fi/fantasy; YA; erotica.

SUBMISSIONS: Women writers only. Submit by email to astrid.ohletz@ylva-publishing.com. Guidelines at www.ylva-publishing.com/submissions-guidelines. Usually responds within one to three months. No feedback offered with rejections. Authors are paid royalties only.

WE SAY: We saw a variety of examples, from the A5 *Collide-o-Scope* by Andrea Bramhall, featuring a misty photo of a lake on its matt cover, and containing the tale of a murder mystery set on the North Norfolk Coastal Path; to the larger *Defensive Mindset* by Wendy Temple, which features a line drawing of two female football players tussling on its glossy cover, and is a drama focused on a footballer/businesswoman who must learn to play with her foil. Quality materials, with the lesbian focus of Ylva writ proudly in the cover designs.

ZED BOOKS
NON-FICTION
The Foundry, 17 Oval Way, London SE11 5RR

editorial@zedbooks.net
www.zedbooks.co.uk
Editors: Ken Barlow, Kim Walker,
Kika Sroka-Miller

Non-fiction only. An independent, scholarly publishing house, Zed Books caters to academics and students, and more widely, activists and policy-makers. It promotes diversity, alternative voices and progressive social change through critical and dynamic publishing.

GENRES: Politics and international; relations; economics; development studies; gender studies; area studies (Africa, the Middle East, Asia and Latin America); environment.

SUBMISSIONS: Open to all. Extensive guidelines are available at www.zedbooks.net/publishing-with-zed.

Part 2:
Literary magazines
and e-zines

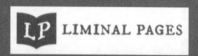

Literary magazines:
an ever-changing sector

The world of independent book publishers and literary magazines is a precarious one, and our research for this expanded and updated edition of the *Indie Press Guide* revealed that the magazines were especially vulnerable to the slings and arrows of outrageous fortune.

Twenty five of the magazines that we included in first edition had shut up shop by the time we went to press with the second edition – with another five teetering on the brink. But just as fast as they close down, so new magazines are being launched to take their place – we've added 56 completely new titles to the catalogue. And some of the zines that were new on the scene in the first edition have gone on to thrive beyond our (and presumably their) wildest dreams.

Running a literary magazine, let alone launching a completely new title, is a labour of love. Editors' evenings and weekends are spent sifting through submissions, laying out pages, untangling code, talking to printers, marketing – and editing, of course. Add in the day job, getting their own writing done (the majority of editors are writers too), and trying to spend time with family and friends, and it's not surprising that some editors eventually start to feel ground down and exhausted. Some presses and magazines are supported by regional Arts Councils and local government; others are subsidised by their founders, or their founders' generous benefactor(s). In a few rare cases, such as *Granta*, a wealthy sponsor has stepped in. Very few are able to survive on income from subscriptions and single sales alone.

So bear this in mind when submitting to magazines. The editors love good writing, and want to share it with the world – but they are almost certainly working for nothing, can often afford to pay very little (if at all) for the writing they publish (though there are some high payers in these listings), and are scrabbling for the time to get the work into the world. They rarely have time to tailor individual rejection letters – don't underestimate just how many submissions even the smallest publication receives.

As a writer, you can help by sticking to submission guidelines, ensuring your work matches their aesthetic, and being patient as you wait for a reply (see p11 where we've laid all of this out in exhaustive detail!). If you do receive a rejection, take it on the chin (or go and have a little cry), but don't lash out at the poor editor.

As a reader, you can help by actually supporting the magazines you are submitting to. Buy a single copy, at least. If you love it, take out a subscription. If it's an online-only publication, share the love. Spread the word about items you've enjoyed and alert people when there's a new issue out. In particular, try to share beyond your immediate circle and help break the cycle of writers who only read in order to be published. There are some amazing stories, heart-stopping poems and beautiful accessible e-zines and magazines out there, and they deserve to be read by everyone.

As Debbie wrote in her introduction to the first edition of this Guide, 'Independent presses are literature's Amazon rainforest, the oxygen that sustains new voices and helps them rise to the top of the mainstream's slush pile. Yet many presses teeter constantly on the brink of extinction, sustained mainly by the hard work and self-sacrifice of those who run them. If we don't buy what they publish, they will disappear. They need us as much as we need them. It's as simple as that.'

Mixed-form literary magazines

By 'mixed form', we mean magazines that publish both poetry and prose (fiction and/or non-fiction), as opposed to focusing exclusively on either poetry or prose, as in the later sections of this Guide. Some magazines may have a bias towards one form, such as poetry, but also mix in a few short stories and/or reviews – or vice versa. And some feature poetry and prose in a particular genre, such as fantasy or science fiction. Whatever you write, you're sure to find a place to submit here.

3:AM MAGAZINE
DIGITAL
www.3ammagazine.com
Co-Editors-In-Chief: Andrew Gallix,
David Winters, Tristan Foster
Publishes a wide range of fiction,
flash fiction, poetry, interviews
and criticism, all to-the-point,
funny and whip-smart. Tagline:
'Whatever it is, we're against it'.

404 INK
PRINT, DIGITAL AND E-ZINE
hello@404ink.com
www.404ink.com
Editors: Heather McDaid, Laura Jones
Established 2016. Mixed form. $10
subscription per issue, via Patreon,
or available via the publisher
website. Only subscribers/
purchasers can read all content,
though some pieces are made
available to all via the website.
GENRES: Fiction, non-fiction,
poetry; comics.
SUBMISSIONS: Open to all.
Submit by email to hello@404ink.
com. Guidelines are available
www.404ink.com/submissions.
Usually responds in one to three
months. Rejections are to a
standard template and include an
overview of main points as to why
pieces were not published in the
issue. Contributors are paid a set
rate, and receive free copies of
magazine.
WE SAY: This hefty 194-page A5
literary magazine more closely
resembles a collection with its
clean, black and white format.
We saw a digital version, though
it's also available in print. Tying

into the press' name – 404 being
the error message received when
a server cannot find a requested
webpage – the editor's letter
begins, 'You found us.' Each
piece is preceded by a brushed
chrome facing page, with the
title in all caps running vertically
down the edge. Included work
ranges from essays to fiction
and poetry, illustrations to comics.
**See also: 404 Ink (prose publisher)
p86**

AFRICAN WRITING
PRINT AND E-ZINE
398-400 Holdenhurst Road,
Bournemouth BH7 7JQ
editor@african-writing.com
www.african-writing.com
Editor: Chuma Nwokolo
Mixed form, including poetry,
essays, fiction, memoir and
other prose. Its 'natural
constituency of writers and
material are African or Diasporan'
but any writer who publishes into
the African Condition will
be considered.

ALLITERATI
DIGITAL AND E-ZINE
editor@alliteratmagazine.com
www.alliteratimagazine.com
Senior Editor: Adam Thompson
With roots and an editorial
team based at Newcastle
University, this magazine has
grown to international popularity
since moving online in 2010.
Accepts poetry, fiction, and visual
creative work and other media
(art, music and film).

ALL-NEW SWIMMERS CLUB, THE

E-ZINE
www.all-new.swimmersclub.co.uk
Editors: Victoria Brown,
Richard Brammer
Established 2015. Mixed form. All online content available to all.
GENRES: Short stories; literary interviews.
SUBMISSIONS: Open to all. Submit by email to email.swimmersclub@gmail.com. Guidelines at www.all-new.swimmersclub.co.uk/sub-

A3 REVIEW, THE ☆

PRINT
PO Box 65016, London N5 9BD
020 7193 7642
a3@writingmaps.com
www.TheA3Review.com
Editors: Shaun Levin, KM Elkes

Established 2014. Mixed form, including comics/graphics.
GENRES: Graphic / comics; literary fiction; biography and true stories.
SUBMISSIONS: Open to all, during submission windows. Submit via Submittable at writingmaps.submittable.com/submit (guidelines at the same address); a reading fee is charged for submissions. Usually responds in one to three months. No feedback offered with rejections. Contributors receive a print copy of the magazine, and the top three contributors per issue receive cash prizes.
WE SAY: Microfiction, poetry and illustrations printed on both sides of one piece of thick, coloured A3 paper, with the creases acting as page dividers. The illustrations pull the page as a whole together. It's an ingenious design idea; the fiction and poetry are nuggets of strong writing, whole narratives in just a few words.

They say

The A3 Review comes out every six months, with 12 contributions sourced from our monthly themed contest. We're a magazine that behaves like a map. We believe in words and images, and love a combination of the two. We're looking for prose, poetry, graphic stories, photography, paintings, drawings, and other visual and word-based creations and various combinations of the above. Three overall winners are chosen per issue to win cash prizes. 1st = £175, 2nd = £100, 3rd = £75 (approx $220, $130, $95).

missions. Usually responds within four weeks. Unpaid.
WE SAY: This is a graphics-led site, with the home page contents a grid of linked photographic images leading to articles and stories. Each photo includes a subhead with the author or subject name and a category header (e.g. Subterraneans are interviews within

ALL THE SINS
E-ZINE
allthesinssubmissions@gmail.com
www.allthesins.co.uk
Editors: Lisa Davison, Sinéad Keegan

Established 2016. Mixed form, published quarterly, with additional long and short features on arts-related topics published on the website. All online content is available to all, with additional editorial feedback and behind-the-scenes information available to patrons (see the magazine's Patreon page at www.patreon.com/allthesins).
GENRES: Literary; experimental; slipstream; collaborative.
SUBMISSIONS: Open to all. Submit via email to allthesinssubmissions@gmail.com. Guidelines at www.allthesins.co.uk/submissions. Usually responds in one to three months. To date the editors have been able to offer basic feedback to every submitter, and offer extended, guaranteed feedback to patrons. Unpaid.
WE SAY: We looked at Issue 2 and two features. The 'cover page' consists of a beautiful drawing illustrating the title on the left of the screen. The contents page and editorial note are to the right, and each issue item has its own page. We loved the editors' piece 'Why theatre shouldn't be safe'.

They say

all the sins is a quarterly digital magazine that encourages writers and artists to sin against staid storytelling. Break rules, push boundaries and tell new stories in new ways. Just tell a good story. The magazine is a blend of visual, digital and written art that takes storytelling to new limits, asks questions and explores the worlds in which art is made. Through poetry and short fiction, essays, photography and digital art, we encourage artistic engagement and discourse. We are digital by design and are particularly interested in work that makes use of the form.

subcultures and independent culture; Treading Water leads to short fiction). Offerings include audio as well as text, and the photographic images add a lot to the experience. Biogs are short, with author/interviewee info offered as a 'factfile'. There's much to explore here.

See also: Dostoyevsky Wannabe (poetry publisher p28 and prose publisher p109)

AMBIT MAGAZINE ☆

PRINT AND DIGITAL
Staithe House, Main Road, Brancaster Staithe, Norfolk PE31 8BP
07503 633 601
contact@ambitmagazine.co.uk
www.ambitmagazine.co.uk
Editors: Briony Bax, Kate Pemberton, Declan Ryan
Established 1959. Mixed form. Subscription £29.99 per annum. Available direct from publisher website; by post and email order; from selected/local chain bookshops; from independent bookshops; and at local literary events. Only subscribers/purchasers can access online content.
GENRES: Drama and criticism; literary fiction; poetry.
SUBMISSIONS: Open to all, during submissions windows. Submit by post (Staithe House, Main Road, Brancaster Staithe, Norfolk PE31 8BP) or through Submittable (ambit.submittable.com/submit). Guidelines available at www.ambitmagazine.co.uk/submit. Usually responds within one to three months. Rejections may include occasional unsolicited feedback. Contributors can choose between receiving payment (set rate), a discount subscription, or print copies.
WE SAY: At 96 pages and slightly larger than A5, *Ambit*'s contents are entirely selected from unsolicited submissions. The magazine's plain white cover is wrapped with a funky jacket sleeve. Each full-colour issue has a different atmosphere – the one we read (Issue 221) combined writing from established names like Carolyn Jess-Cooke with newer artistic talents in photography, illustration and graphics. We loved the way the various mediums were creatively interspersed throughout.

AMORIST, THE

PRINT AND DIGITAL
Moray House, 23-31 Great Titchfield Street, London W1W 7PA
020 7436 8801
editorial@theamorist.co.uk
www.theamorist.co.uk
Editor: Rowan Pelling
Features, fiction and poetry, articles and reviews, exploring sexual love. Looking for discursive, romantic, philosophical writing, with historical perspective and touching on science and technology.

A NEW ULSTER ☆

PRINT AND DIGITAL
g.greig3@gmail.com
anuanewulster.wixsite.com/anewulster
Editors: Amos Greig, Arizahn, E V Greig
Established 2012. Print copies available direct from publisher website. All online content is freely available to all.
GENRES: Literary; humour; fiction.
SUBMISSIONS: Open to all. Submit by email to anu.anewulster@gmail.com. Guidelines at anuanewulster.wixsite.com/anewulster/submission-guidelines. Usually

responds within four weeks. Feedback on request. Contributors receive a digital copy of the magazine.

WE SAY: We looked at a digital version of *A New Ulster* (Issue 53), which champions the work of Northern Irish writers, as well as welcoming global writers. Also available in print, it has a neatly presented design – plain, with minimal artwork – and includes biographies of its featured writers. It also showcases their work well, allowing for a good number of poems for each poet, interspersed with stories. Clearly dedicated and filling the gaps left by *The Honest Ulsterman* and *Fortnight* magazines.

ARCHIPELAGO
PRINT
PO Box 154, Thame OX9 3RQ
info@clutagpress.com
www.clutagpress.com/archipelago
Non-fiction prose and verse.
An occasional magazine – no fixed publication dates.
See also: Clutag Press (poetry publisher) p24

ARETÉ MAGAZINE
PRINT
8 New College Lane, Oxford OX1 3BN
01865 289194
aretebooks@gmail.com
www.aretemagazine.com
Editor: Craig Raine
Established 1999. Mixed form. Annual subscription costs: £27 UK individual; £30 library; $65 overseas; $85 overseas library. Issues available direct from the publisher website; in selected/local chain bookshops; in independent bookshops; and on Amazon. Some online content available to all.

GENRES: Drama and criticism; literary fiction; poetry; art, fashion and photography; biography and true stories; music, stage and screen.

SUBMISSIONS: Open to all. Submit by post to *Areté*, 8 New College Lane, Oxford, OX1 3BN. Guidelines at www.aretemagazine.co.uk/about-arete/. Usually responds within one to three months. Rejections may include occasional unsolicited feedback. Contributors receive a print copy of the magazine.

WE SAY: We looked at Issue 43, which is a beautifully produced perfect-bound paperback: 157 thick, bright white pages contained in a dark grey matt, French-flap cover with a smart wraparound design and a pink cardboard inner cover. The brightly coloured titles look appropriately sophisticated and scholarly. The quantity of closely-typed text inside is rather daunting, but the reviews, poetry and fiction are actually very accessible.
See also: Areté Books (poetry publisher) p18

BANIPAL
PRINT
1 Gough Square, London EC4A 3DE
editor@banipal.co.uk
www.banipal.co.uk
Editor: Samuel Shimon
Primarily translated literature, exclusively featuring authors from the modern Arab world. Each issue is themed and includes poems, short stories or excerpts of novels, plus interviews with authors, publishers and translators, and book reviews.

BANSHEE

PRINT AND DIGITAL
bansheelit@gmail.com
www.bansheelit.com
Editors: Laura Jane Cassidy,
Claire Hennessy, Eimear Ryan
Established 2014. Mixed
form. Issues available direct
from publisher website and at
independent bookshops and
local literary events. Some online
content available to all.
GENRES: Literary fiction; memoir
and personal essays.
SUBMISSIONS: Open to all, during
submissions windows. Submit
by email to bansheelit@gmail.
com. See guidelines at bansheelit.
tumblr.com/submissionsguidelines.
Usually responds within one to
three months. Rejections may
occasionally include unsolicited
feedback. Contributors are paid a
set rate and receive a print copy of
the magazine.
WE SAY: We looked at Issues 1
to 3 of *Banshee*. All score points
for design. It's a 98-page A5
magazine, with striking photo
image covers – often featuring
depictions of figures dwarfed
within natural spaces. The materials
used are of high quality: a thick,
matt cover and heavy white pages.
The design is clean and neatly
presented, alternating stories
with poems. The writing is bold
and engaging – we recognised
several emerging names in the
contributors list.

BARE FICTION MAGAZINE ☆

PRINT AND DIGITAL
177 Copthorne Road, Shrewsbury
SY3 8NA
info@barefiction.co.uk
www.barefictionmagazine.co.uk
Editor: Robert Harper

Established 2013. Mixed form.
Annual subscriptions cost £20
print/£12 digital (both include
digital access to all back issues).
Issues available direct from
publisher website; by post and
email order; and from independent
bookshops. Most online content
is only accessible to subscribers/
purchasers, with some available to
all. Shortlisted for Best Magazine
in Saboteur Awards 2014; runner-
up for Best Magazine in Saboteur
Awards 2015.
GENRES: Drama and criticism;
literary fiction; poetry.
SUBMISSIONS: Open to all,
during submissions windows.
Submit through Submittable at
www.barefictionmagazine.co.uk/
submissions/. Usually responds
within one to six months. No
feedback offered with rejections.
Contributors receive a print copy of
the magazine.
WE SAY: A4 and perfect bound on
quality paper, *Bare Fiction* uses a
two-column layout, with effective
chunky design quirks that reflect
the logo. The cover images vary
within the banded blue and white
framing: sometimes cool and
futuristic, sometimes busy black-
and-white, sometime bright art.
Containing poetry, reviews, short
stories and even scripts, this is a
contemporary, recognisable brand
that has rapidly built a name for
itself.
**See also: Bare Fiction (poetry
publisher) p19**

BLACK MARKET RE-VIEW

DIGITAL
Edge Hill University, Lancashire
blackmarketreview@googlemail.com
blackmarketre-view.weebly.com
Mixed-form magazine in PDF

format, publishing short stories, flash fiction, poetry, and art and photography. The magazine is edited exclusively by Creative Writing undergraduate and postgraduate students at Edge Hill University.

BRITISH JOURNALISM REVIEW
PRINT AND E-ZINE
SAGE Publications, 1 Oliver's Yard, 55 City Road, London EC1Y 1SP
020 7324 8500
editor@bjr.org.uk
www.bjr.org.uk
Editor: Kim Fletcher
Non-fiction magazine with a focus on society, education and politics. According to its website, it is 'designed as a forum of analysis and debate, to monitor the media, submit the best as well as the worst to scrutiny, and to raise the level of the dialogue'.

BRITTLE STAR ☆
PRINT AND DIGITAL
Diversity House, 72 Nottingham Road, Arnold, Nottingham NG5 6LF
0845 456 4838
brittlestarmag@gmail.com
www.brittlestar.org.uk
Editors: Martin Parker, Jacqueline Gabbitas
Established 2000. Poetry and short stories, articles and reviews of first full collections. Subscription £15 (UK) or £25 (world) for two issues. Available direct from publisher website, and by post and through bookshops. Digital edition available at www.0s-1s.com/brittle-star. Some online content available to non-subscribers.
GENRES: Literary fiction; poetry.
SUBMISSIONS: Open to all new and emerging writers (no established writers from major

presses, please). Submit by post to *Brittle Star*, Diversity House, 72 Nottingham Road, Arnold, Nottingham NG5 6LF. Guidelines at www.brittlestar.org.uk/submissions. Usually responds within one to six months, no feedback offered on rejections. Contributors receive a print copy and a discount purchase price. Please refer to website for up-to-date information.
WE SAY: *Brittle Star* is a bit smaller than A5 and perfect bound. The PDF issue we looked at (Issue 37) was 86 pages long. The cover is striking – *Brittle Star* seems to go for images with texture, in this case a repeated pattern of grey cells (or are they pebbles?). Detailed line drawings are placed at the start of each story. The writing is punchy and in some cases rather experimental, blurring the line between poetry and prose.

BUNBURY MAGAZINE
DIGITAL AND E-ZINE
5 Chester Street, Bury, Lancashire BL9 6EU
07446 025630
admin@bunburymagazine.com
www.bunburymagazine.com
Editors: Christopher Moriarty, Keri Moriarty
Established 2013. Mixed form. All content available to all.
GENRES: Crime/thriller/mystery; fantasy/sci-fi; horror; literary fiction; poetry; art, fashion and photography; biography and true stories; humour; music, stage and screen; society, education and politics.
SUBMISSIONS: Open to all. Submit by email to submissions@bunburymagazine.com. Guidelines

at www.bunburymagazine.com/submit-to-us/. Usually responds within one to three months. Rejections may include occasional unsolicited feedback. Contributors receive a digital copy.

WE SAY: *Bunbury* makes the most of being a digital magazine: full-colour and plenty of design, including page backgrounds (faded wallpaper for poems; lined paper for stories). The cover is an image taken from featured illustrator Iñaki Oñate's work. There's a warning to readers about any violence, sexual content or explicit language in the work published. Poems come first, interviews follow (with plenty of photos); then flash fiction (single column) and short stories (two columns). The stories run straight on from each other rather than starting on new pages, which can feel slightly relentless. A busy, bright publication.

CADAVERINE MAGAZINE
E-ZINE
thecadaverine@hotmail.com
www.thecadaverine.com
Publishes only work by emerging writers under age 30. Poetry, prose, and non-fiction. 'Showcasing contemporary, innovative and original new writing from the next generation of talent.'

CAKE MAGAZINE
PRINT
English and Creative Writing Department, County Main, Lancaster University, Lancashire LA1 4YD
themixingbowl@hotmail.co.uk
www.cake-magazine.co.uk
Short fiction, poetry, comment/essays, reviews and artwork. Set up by students at Lancaster University

in 2009, every issue of this perfect-bound journal is named after a type of bake.

CAMBRIDGE LITERARY REVIEW
PRINT
Trinity Hall, Cambridge CB2 1TJ
cambridgeliteraryreview@gmail.com
www.cambridgeliteraryreview.org
Editors: Lydia Wilson, Rosie Snajdr
Established 2009. Mixed form. Subscription £25/€40/$60. Available direct from publisher website and in independent bookshops. Some content is available to view as a taster online.
GENRES: Drama and criticism; literary fiction; poetry; history; and essays on a variety of subjects but mostly in the humanities, and mostly on some aspect of literature.
SUBMISSIONS: Open to all. Submit by post (Trinity Hall, Cambridge CB2 1TJ) or by email (cambridgeliteraryreview@googlemail.com). Usually responds within four to six months. Rejections may include occasional unsolicited feedback. Contributors receive a print copy of the magazine.
WE SAY: *Cambridge Literary Review* is a fairly high-brow affair, which warrants attention from *TLS*. We looked at the available online content (the website reflects the print design and is easy to navigate), which includes poetry, short fiction, essays and criticism. The creative work is contemporary and accessible; the essays and criticism weighted with theoretical knowledge, but not so intellectual as to be alienating.

CARDIFF REVIEW, THE
PRINT, DIGITAL AND BLOG
John Percival Building, Colum Dr,
Cardiff CF10 3EU
hello@cardiffreview.com
www.cardiffreview.com
Editors: Jamie Gillingham,
Rebecca Lawn, Callum McAllister
Established 2015. Mixed form.
Subscription £25/year for four
issues. Publications available direct
from publisher website; from
selected/local chain bookshops;
and from independent bookshops.
All online content available to all.
GENRES: Literary.
SUBMISSIONS: Precedence given
to students currently on a related
postgraduate course (i.e. Creative
Writing, English Literature or
Journalism) or, alternatively, who
have recently graduated and
have yet to publish a major work.
Submit by email to submissions@
cardiffreview.com. Guidelines at
www.cardiffreview.com/submit.
Usually responds within one to
three months. Rejections may
occasionally include unsolicited
feedback. Contributors are paid a
set rate and receive a print copy.
WE SAY: The 72-page, perfect-
bound eighth instalment of *The
Cardiff Review* begins with two
poems printed vertically down the
pages, rather than horizontally, to
preserve line length. Prose pieces
are headed by a large-font title set
low from the top of the page, with
the text beginning in single-column
width in the bottom third. The
magazine is stylish, wrapped in a
high quality coloured matt cover.

CARILLON MAGAZINE
PRINT
19 Godric Drive, Brinsworth,
Rotherham, South Yorkshire S60 3JB
editor@carillonmag.co.uk
www.carillonmag.org.uk
Editor: Graham Rippon
Mixed form: stories, articles,
fillers, news, and poetry. A long-
established magazine, with a great
reputation. UK residents must
submit by post (overseas may
use email). Subscribers are given
preference.

CATERPILLAR, THE ☆
PRINT
Ardan Grange, Belturbet, Co. Cavan,
Ireland
editor@thecaterpillarmagazine.com
www.thecaterpillarmagazine.com
Editor: Rebecca O'Connor
Sibling magazine to *The Moth* (see
p210). Mixed form: poetry, stories
and art aimed at children between
the ages of 7 and 11.
Annual subscription €28.
SUBMISSIONS: Open to
all. See guidelines at www.
thecaterpillarmagazine.com/a1-
page.asp?ID=4150&page=5.
WE SAY: Slightly less than
letter-sized, this saddle-stitched
magazine includes various styles
of colourful art, including collage,
pencil drawing and digital art.
In 27 pages of matt paper, the
copy we saw of Issue 17, Summer
2017, showcased such work as a
fun poem rhyming eight lines with
'octopus' and another about a
sheep feeling better after 'a good
baaaa' with his friend.
**See also: *The Moth* (mixed-form
magazine) p210**

CHAPESS, THE
PRINT
thechapess@gmail.com
www.cherrystyles.co.uk/the-chapess
Editor: Cherry Styles
Established 2012. Mixed form.

Available direct from publisher website; by post and email order; and at zine fairs and art bookshops. Shortlisted for the 'Turn The Page' artists' book award 2015.

GENRES: Literary fiction; poetry; art, fashion and photography; biography and true stories; music, stage and screen; society, education and politics.

SUBMISSIONS: Open to women writers and artists only. Submit by email (thechapess@gmail.com) or through the online submissions manager at www.cherrystyles. co.uk/the-chapess (guidelines at same address). Usually responds within one to three months. Rejection may occasionally include unsolicited feedback. Contributors receive digital copies.

WE SAY: A 44-page quarterly magazine with a controversial artistic design. Black and white images punctuate the articles and poetry. A magazine with a spontaneous feel and urban edge.
See also: Synchronise Witches Press (poetry publisher p72 and prose publisher p159)

CŌNFINGŌ

PRINT AND DIGITAL
2 Stonecraft, Parkfield Road South, Didsbury, Manchester M20 6DA
www.confingopublishing.uk
Editors: Tim Shearer, Zoe McLean
Established 2014. Fiction and poetry focus. Subscription £15 per annum. Available direct from publisher website; from selected/ local chain bookshops; from independent bookshops; and at local literary events. Some online content available to all.
GENRES: Literary fiction; poetry; art.
SUBMISSIONS: Open to all, during submissions windows. Submit by email to tim@confingopublishing. uk. Guidelines at www. confingopublishing.uk/form. Usually responds within one to three months. Rejections may occasionally include unsolicited feedback. Contributors are paid a set rate and receive a print copy of the magazine.
WE SAY: Perfect bound and featuring full-colour bright, contemporary images, *Cōnfingō* gives an impression of spaciousness, with cutting-edge art and writing framed in plenty of white space, interspersed with contemporary poetry and fiction.
See also: prose publisher p102

CRYSTAL MAGAZINE

PRINT
3 Bowness Avenue, Prenton, Birkenhead CH43 0SD
0151 608 9736
christinecrystal@hotmail.com
www.christinecrystal.blogspot.com
Editor: Christine Carr
Established 2001. Poems, stories, articles. Subscription £18 UK/£22 overseas for six issues. Sample £2. PayPal buttons on website or cheque payable to Mrs C Carr.
GENRES: Stories, true and fiction. No erotica.
SUBMISSIONS: Open to subscribers only. Submit by post to 3 Bowness Avenue, Prenton, Birkenhead CH43 0SD or by email to christinecrystal@hotmail. com. Usually responds within two weeks. No feedback offered with rejection. Will accept handwritten contributions.
WE SAY: A 42-page A4 wiro-bound monthly magazine, with a warm informal community aesthetic. Editor Christine Carr addresses

subscribers as 'Crystallites' and her Editor's Letter includes personal news as well as the usual introduction to the issue's contents.

It publishes (mostly rhyming) poetry, short stories, comment, prose poems and personal anecdotes, with occasional

CRANNÓG
PRINT
editor@crannogmagazine.com
www.crannogmagazine.com
Editors: Sandra Bunting, Ger Burke, Jarlath Fahy, Tony O'Dwyer

Established 2002. Fiction and poetry. Annual subscription €22.50 for three issues. Publication available at major bookshops nationwide; at independent bookshops; on bookshop websites; direct from the publisher 's website; and from Amazon (including by Kindle).
GENRES: Literary.
SUBMISSIONS: Open to all, during submissions windows. Submit via email only to editor@crannogmagazine.com. Guidelines at www.crannogmagazine.com/submissions.htm. Usually responds in eight weeks from closing date. No feedback offered with rejection. Contributors are paid a set rate and receive a print copy of the magazine.
WE SAY: A 96-page A5 perfect-bound magazine with a matt cover. In Issue 45, the titles of the pieces are framed by an upper and lower line the width of the text area; prose pieces are also started with a drop-cap. The page margins are somewhat small, but the design remains stylish. A statement from the cover image's artist is included just before the writers' biographies.

They say

Crannóg's mission is to publish the work of Irish writers alongside the best available worldwide and to show how well such writing sits with the best available internationally. We look for writing that is well structured with an original voice and well developed characterisation. We think a fine balance between style, character, and plot is important. In poetry we look for some awareness of form however loose, structure and strong fresh imagery. We like writing that is aware of its ancestry while being contemporary. Our target readership is those with an interest in quality literature.

colour photographic and clip-art illustrations. The subject matter is mainly autobiographical. A three-page Readers' Letters section comments on the contents of the previous magazine ('kind comments or none at all').

CUCKOO CHRONICLE ☆
PRINT AND E-ZINE
3 Ellison Terrace, University of Northumbria, Newcastle upon Tyne NE1 8ST
0191 204 8850
cuckoo@newwritingnorth.co.uk
chronicle.cuckoowriters.com
Editors: a committee of young people
Presented by Cuckoo Writers and established in 2012. Primarily fiction focus. Available in independent bookshops, at local literary events and distributed with *NARC* magazine. All online content openly available to all.
GENRES: Literary fiction; poetry; YA; art and photography; children and teenagers; music, stage and screen; society, education and politics.
SUBMISSIONS: Open to young writers aged 15-21, during submissions windows. Submit by email to cuckoochroniclenwn@gmail.com. Guidelines at chronicle.cuckoowriters.com/submit. Usually responds within one to three months. Rejections may occasionally include unsolicited feedback. Contributors are paid a set rate and receive a print copy of the magazine.
WE SAY: A literary magazine written and edited by young writers of the North East. We looked at the e-zine. With a bold orange and cream palette and an art-deco font logo, *Cuckoo Chronicle* has an uncluttered contemporary design

that is easy to navigate. Clicking on an issue link takes you to the editors' letter and contents page (ordered poetry; shorts; theme; non-fiction; periodicals), where the link to each piece is highlighted with a cartoon of a cuckoo. This is for a younger audience, and the standard of writing is very high.

DAWNTREADER MAGAZINE, THE
PRINT
24 Forest Houses, Halwill, Beaworthy, Devon EX21 5UU
publishing@indigodreams.co.uk
www.indigodreams.co.uk
Editor: Dawn Bauling
Established 2007. Mainly poetry, some stories and articles under 1,000 words. Subscription £17/year for four issues. Available direct from publisher website; and by post and email order. Indigo Dreams editors won the Ted Slade Award for Services to Poetry 2015 (organised by Poetry Kit).
GENRES: Myth; legend; in the landscape; nature; spirituality and love; the mystic, the environment.
SUBMISSIONS: Open to all. Submit by post (IDP, 24 Forest Houses, Halwill, Beaworthy, Devon EX21 5UU) or by email (dawnidp@gmail.com). Guidelines at www.indigodreams.co.uk. Usually responds within four weeks. No feedback offered with rejection.
WE SAY: One of the Indigo Dreams' publications, *The Dawntreader* is an A5, 52-page monthly magazine, perfect bound with a (rare, these days) glossy full colour cover. We looked at Issue 039. IDP encourage comment on the included work, and welcome environmental, spiritual, folklorish etc work, which is described by

one reader as 'poetry for the soul'. The magazine has an international readership and IDP foster a community of readers.

For what They Say, see Indigo Dreams Publishing Ltd (poetry publisher) p43. See also: *Sarasvati* (mixed-form magazine) p220 and *Reach Poetry* (poetry magazine) p251

DISSECTIONS
E-ZINE
CLT, University of Brighton, Falmer, Brighton BN1 9PH
01273 643115
www.simegen.com/writers/dissections
Editors: Gina Wisker, Michelle Bernard
Established 2006. Mainly fiction. All online content available to all.
GENRES: Fantasy/sci-fi; horror; literary fiction; poetry; non-fiction (horror, literary criticism).
SUBMISSIONS: Open to all. Submit by post (CLT, University of Brighton, Falmer, Brighton BN1 9PH, to Gina Wisker) or by email (ginwskr@aol.com and michelle. bernard2@ntlworld.com). Usually responds within three to four months. Rejections do not include feedback. Unpaid.
WE SAY: An annually updated e-zine that focuses on the horror genre. Line drawings illustrate each piece, and it has a dark palette. It's easy to navigate to poems, short stories and reviews, which are contemporary and must have a fresh take on any horror tropes. The poetry we saw was mainly narrative and lyrical in style, and the prose was gripping. No writer biographies were offered.

DNA MAGAZINE
DIGITAL
hello@dnamag.co.uk
www.dnamag.co.uk
Editor: Katie Marsden
Established 2017. Only accepts non-fiction prose. All online content available to all.
GENRES: Twitterature; creative flash non-fiction; poetry.
SUBMISSIONS: Open to all, during submission windows. Submit by email to submissions@dnamag. co.uk. Guidelines at www.dnamag. co.uk. Usually responds within one to three months. Rejections may occasionally include unsolicited feedback. Unpaid.
WE SAY: We looked at Issue 2, digitally available through Issuu. The cover features an arresting photograph with a bright yellow background. The inner pages make strong use of graphics, sometimes provided by contributors, to accentuate the writing. Items are rarely over one page long, and include 'twitterature' (flash non-fiction), experimental non-fic, and straightforward autobiographical texts. Each piece is a glimpse into someone else's life. An engaging and stylish magazine, we loved 'Divine Delivery': twitterature about a package, styled to appear in the 'bottom' of a box.

ELBOW ROOM
PRINT
5 Veales Rd, Kingsbridge, Devon TQ7 1EX
admin@asyetuntitled.org
www.asyetuntitled.org
Editor: Rosie Sherwood
Established 2012. Mixed form: short stories, poetry, visual arts. Annual subscription £10 excluding P&P (two issues). Available direct from publisher website; in selected/local chain bookshops

and independent bookshops; and at local literary events including Artists' Book Fairs (national) and the Small Publishers Fair. Some tasters of content available online.
GENRES: Unrestrained by genre – work selected is what's liked by the Editors, regardless of genre, medium or type of fiction/poetry.
SUBMISSIONS: Open to all during submissions windows. Submit by email to elbowroomsubmissions@gmail.com. Guidelines at www.elbow-room.org/submissions. Usually responds within one to three months. Due to the number of submissions we cannot offer feedback. Contributors receive a print copy of the magazine.
WE SAY: We looked at Volume 9, a sewn-spine, 14-page magazine with a chapbook aesthetic. The cover is dark green textured card hand-stamped with the logo and issue number. Inner pages are thick and cream; the ink is a rather lovely dark cyan. This is an artisan publication. The text is laid out with an eye to the space around the words, and interspersed with full-colour art images. The final page is marked with a limited edition counter (26/50), and a confirmation that 'Submissions are (VERY) welcome'. The published writing is achingly lyrical.
See also: As Yet Untitled (prose publisher p91 and poetry publisher p18)

EROTIC REVIEW
E-ZINE
editorial@ermagazine.org
www.eroticreviewmagazine.com
Editor: Jamie Maclean
Aims to 'take a lively, intelligent approach to erotica and sexuality', and publishes fiction, articles, photography, art portfolios and reviews, as well as videos and podcasts.

ESC ZINE
PRINT AND DIGITAL
escpeople@gmail.com
esczine.wordpress.com
Editors: Jessica Maybury, Aine Belton
Established 2011. Mixed form, including 'pocket ESC', which are small poetry and micro-fiction digital anthologies and chapbooks. Print publications available direct from publisher website and at national and local literary events. All online content is available to all.
GENRES: Literary fiction; poetry; slipstream; experimental; art, fashion and photography.
SUBMISSIONS: During submissions windows, submit by email to escpeople@gmail.com. Guidelines at esczine.wordpress.com/submissions/. Usually responds within four weeks. Rejection may occasionally include unsolicited feedback. Contributors receive a print copy of the magazine; otherwise unpaid.
See also: poetry publisher (p31) and prose publisher (p111)

FAR HORIZONS ☆
DIGITAL
info.far.horizons@gmail.com
farhorizonsmagazine.wordpress.com
Editors: Susan Horsnell, Valery Riddle
Established 2014. Mainly publishes fiction. Publication available direct from publisher website.
GENRES: Sci-fi; fantasy; horror.
SUBMISSIONS: Open to all. Submit by email to info.far.horizons@gmail.com. Guidelines at farhorizonsmagazine.wordpress.com. Usually responds within four weeks. Rejections may occasionally

include unsolicited feedback. Unpaid.

WE SAY: We looked at a digital copy of Issue 27. After the bright, galactically illustrated cover (complete with the futuristic font of the masthead) and the alien landscape background of the contents page, each story and poem in *Far Horizons* is given its own background design. Prose is split into an easy-to-read two columns (poems centralised), and interspersed with bright, fantastic art and book adverts. The stories range from long and involving to near-flash. We didn't see any authors biogs, and submission info is in green text on a discreet black-background page.

See also: Far Horizons Press (poetry publisher p33 and prose publisher p113)

FAR OFF PLACES

PRINT, DIGITAL AND PODCAST
Flat 14, 24 East Parkside, Edinburgh EH16 5XN
words@faroffplaces.org
www.faroffplaces.org
Editor: Annie Rutherford
Established 2013. Mixed form. Available at local literary events and from the publication website. Only subscribers/purchasers can access all of the online content, though some of it is freely available to all.

GENRES: Children's fiction; drama and criticism; literary fiction; poetry; creative non-fiction.

SUBMISSIONS: Open to all during submissions windows. Submit by email to submissions@ faroffplaces.org. Guidelines at www.faroffplaces.org/submissions. Usually responds within one to three months, and regularly offers free feedback on submissions. Contributors receive a digital copy of the magazine and 'a drink, if we meet them'.

WE SAY: A 64-page themed magazine – we looked at a PDF of Volume III, Issue 1, which contains poetry and short stories on the theme of 'The Second Breakfast.' It's a straightforward mono design, the only illustration being a line-drawing on the cover. However the theme is strong: the editors provide a recipe rather than a letter, and a 'menu' rather than contents. Poetry and stories mingle, divided into 'Aperitif', 'All-Day Breakfasts', etc, and the writing is, literally, mouthwatering: this issue made us hungry. The biography pages at the end are funny and whimsical.

FIREWORDS

PRINT AND DIGITAL
info@firewords.co.uk
www.firewords.co.uk
Editors: Dan Burgess, Jen Scott
Established 2014. Mainly fiction. Publication available direct from publisher website and at independent bookshops.

GENRES: Short stories and poetry. Artwork. No non-fiction.

SUBMISSIONS: Open to all during submissions windows. Submit via online submissions form at www.firewords.co.uk/submit (guidelines found at the same place). Responses take up to three months, with feedback only if requested. Contributors receive a copy of the magazine.

WE SAY: You'd never guess this perfect-bound, full-colour literary magazine wasn't produced by a full-time team. Smaller than A5 and full of bold design, it's an innovative 48-page affair printed on matt paper. The writing is thought-provoking, unique and contemporary, but it was the unexpected design quirks that had us hooked, from the striking illustrations to the contents laid out on the back cover like a rock album.

FIVE DIALS
DIGITAL
craig@fivedials.com
www.fivedials.com
Established 2008 – a free literary magazine offering from publishing house Hamish Hamilton. Mixed form, including literary fiction; poetry; general essays and literary criticism. All online content is freely available to all.

FOR BOOKS' SAKE
E-ZINE
jane@forbookssake.net
www.forbookssake.net
Editor: Jane Bradley
Mainly fiction, reviews, interviews, articles, including the Weekend Read fiction slot. All online content available to all.
GENRES: Literary fiction; poetry; YA; biography and true stories; music, stage and screen; society, education and politics.
SUBMISSIONS: Submit during submissions windows. Open to self-identifying women and especially encouraged from women of colour, disabled women, queer women, trans women and women from low-income backgrounds. Submit through Submittable at forbookssake. submittable.com/submit. Pitches for reviews/features can be emailed to reviews@forbookssake. net / features@forbookssake.

net. Guidelines at forbookssake. submittable.com/submit. Usually responds within four weeks.
For a fuller description of this press, see poetry publisher p36 and prose publisher p115

FUNHOUSE MAGAZINE
PRINT AND DIGITAL
info@funhousemagazine.com
www.funhousemagazine.com
Editor: Oliver Zarandi
A perfect-bound colour-illustrated magazine, containing poems, short stories, essays and comics. Issue 1 sold out (but is still available digitally), and the press's ethos is to 'make reading fun again' and create a magazine for writers and artists who 'feel like outsiders' or who 'feel their work is too strange for other magazines'.

GOLD DUST MAGAZINE
PRINT AND DIGITAL
55 Elmsdale Road, Walthamstow, London E17 6PN
mailtallulah@gmail.com
www.golddustmagazine.co.uk
Editors: Omma Velada,
David Gardiner
Established 2004. Mixed form. Also releases 'best of' anthologies containing the best short stories and poetry. Available direct from publisher website. All online content is freely available to all.
GENRES: Crime/thriller/mystery; drama and criticism; fantasy/sci-fi; literary fiction; romance; writing.
SUBMISSIONS: Open to all. Submit by email to sirat@davidgardiner.net or bramwith22@aol.com. Usually responds within one to three months. Includes feedback with rejection. Unpaid.
WE SAY: *Gold Dust* offers its 50-page magazine in three formats:

as digital (free), black-and-white print (cheapish), and full-colour print (less cheap). We looked at the digital version of Issue 28 on www.issuu.com. Alternating features, reviews, stories and poems throughout, the magazine is liberally scattered with photo illustrations. Its layout is closer to a lifestyle magazine than your average literary magazine. The contents are well curated – we think most people would find something to enjoy here.

GOOD JOURNAL, THE

www.thegoodjournal.co.uk
Editor: Nikesh Shukla
Announced just before this edition of the *Indie Press Guide* was due to go to press, *The Good Journal* is the natural successor to the important and successful anthology *The Good Immigrant* (Unbound, ed. Nikesh Shukla). Slated to launch Spring 2018, it will include essays, short stories, poems, novel extracts and illustrations from British writers of colour, offering a space for the BAME 'stars of tomorrow' to be showcased alongside already established writers. Writers in the first four issues include Kamile Shamsie, Niven Govinden, Sunny Singh, Bolu Babalola and Bridget Minamore. Check the website for further information.

GORSE

PRINT AND E-ZINE
info@gorse.ie
www.gorse.ie
Established 2014. Mixed form. Subscription: two issues €35 (Ireland); €45 (rest of the world). Available direct from the publisher website; from independent

bookshops; and at local literary events, with some online content available to all, updated on a rolling basis.
Gorse was shortlisted for the Association of Illustrators awards, Book Category, 2014.
GENRES: Literary fiction; poetry; essays; interviews.
SUBMISSIONS: During submissions windows, submit by email to info@gorse.ie. Usually responds within one to three months, with a standard rejection (no feedback). Contributors are paid a set rate, and receive a print copy and a discount purchase price on the magazine.
WE SAY: Thick enough to be an anthology, *Gorse* features beautiful matt covers with regular artist Niall McCormack's bold, textured paintings. Containing essays, poems and stories, this is a high-quality publication in every sense of the word. The writing is sharp, sometimes traditional, sometimes experimental (see the poems from Kimberly Campanello in Issue 4, available online).

GRANTA MAGAZINE

PRINT AND DIGITAL
12 Addison Avenue, London W11 4QR
020 7605 1360
info@granta.com
www.granta.com
Editor-in-Chief: Sigrid Rausing
Established 1979. Mixed form. Annual subscription £32 (print and digital); £12 (digital only). Available direct from publisher website; by post and email order; at chain bookshops nationwide; in independent bookshops; at national literary events; at local literary events; and from Amazon and other bookshop websites.

Only subscribers/purchasers can access all of the online content, but some online content is freely available to all.

GENRES: Literary fiction; poetry; biography and true stories; history; popular science and nature; society, education and politics; travel.

SUBMISSIONS: During submissions windows, submit via Submittable to granta.submittable.com/submit (guidelines at the same address). Agented submissions also welcome. Usually responds within one to three months. A rejection may occasionally include unsolicited feedback. Contributors are paid a set rate.

WE SAY: A literary magazine available in print and online, *Granta* is one of the writing world's heavy weights: hard to get your work into, but worth the effort. Your work would be rubbing shoulders with some big names. The style of writing leans towards the literary, but is always entertaining and readable. Work tends to have an international slant as well.

See also: Granta Books p118 and Portobello Books p149 (prose publishers)

GULL, THE
E-ZINE
thegull_cornwell@outlook.com
thegullmagazine.wordpress.com
Editor: The Gull, Sarah Reynolds, Chris Cornwell

Wales-based publication, accepting submissions of poetry, creative prose, artwork, photography and articles.

GUTTER MAGAZINE
PRINT AND DIGITAL

Freight Books, 49 Virginia Street, Glasgow G1 1TS
info@guttermag.co.uk
www.guttermag.co.uk
Editor: Henry Bell

Established 2011. Mainly fiction. Annual subscription £12. Available direct from publisher website; from some chain and independent bookshops; and at literary events. Some online content is available to all.

GENRES: Crime/thriller/mystery; historical fiction; literary fiction; poetry; YA; art, fashion and photography; food and drink; humour; society, education and politics; travel.

SUBMISSIONS: Open to all. Submit by email to info@guttermag.co.uk. Guidelines at www.guttermag.co.uk/submissions/. Usually responds in over six months, with feedback only if requested. Contributors receive a print copy of the magazine.

WE SAY: Perfect-bound 184-page magazine with the feel of an anthology, that highlights new Scottish writing. Features eye-catching designs on high quality cream paper; the cover images are bright and modern. The magazine publishes literary poetry and prose, plus interviews and reviews.

See also: Freight Press (poetry publisher p37 and prose publisher p116)

HAM FREE PRESS, THE
PRINT AND DIGITAL
thehamfreepress@gmail.com
www.thehamfreepress.com

Aims to provide a platform for writers and artists that are under-represented. Looks for short fiction and poetry by writers still developing their careers. As part of distribution, 25% of the printed copies of *The Ham* are left 'on public transport and in pubs and clubs where you might not expect to find literary and arts journal'.

HAVERTHORN
PRINT
haverthorn@gmail.com
www.hvtn.co.uk
Editor: Andrew Wells
Established 2014. Mixed-form magazine. Available direct from publisher website; and at local literary events.
SUBMISSIONS: Open to all. Submit by email to haverthorn@gmail.com. Guidelines at www. hvtn.co.uk/submission. Usually responds within four weeks, but please note that response times are usually faster in January and August. Feedback offered only if requested. Contributors receive a print copy of the magazine.

HERE COMES EVERYONE
PRINT AND DIGITAL
ICE, Parkside, Coventry CV1 2NE
raef@herecomeseveryone.me
matt@herecomeseveryone.me
www.herecomeseveryone.me
Editors: Raef Boylan, Matthew Barton
Established 2012. Mixed form. Publication available by direct post and email order; local literary events; and from independent bookshops and bookshop websites.
GENRES: No fixed genres. (Poetry, short stories, creative non-fiction, visual artwork.)
SUBMISSIONS: Open to all. Submit through Submittable at: herecomeseveryone.me/submit/submission-guidelines. Usually responds within four to six months.

Rejection may occasionally include unsolicited feedback. Unpaid.
WE SAY: We looked at two issues, very different in theme: 'Toys & Games' (resplendent with building blocks, a maze and a dildo on the cover) and 'East & West' (political leaders), in PDF format. In the 58 pages per issues, you'll rarely find white space: pages feature backgrounds appropriate to their theme. The layout alternates between prose and poetry, with regular insertions of bright, modern artwork. The writing is superb: contemporary, self-aware with a touch of humour, as in-your-face as the design.
See also: Silhouette Press (poetry publisher p68 and prose publisher p155)

HOAX
PRINT AND DIGITAL
hoaxpublication@gmail.com
www.hoaxpublication.co.uk
Editor: Lulu Nunn
Established 2012. Mixed form. Print publications available by post and email order; in independent bookshops and art galleries worldwide; and at national and local literary events. All online content is freely available to all.
GENRES: No non-fiction.
SUBMISSIONS: *HOAX* is currently on hiatus. Check the website for more details.

HOGS BACK BOOKS LTD
CHILDREN'S BOOKS
34 Long Street, Devizes, Wiltshire SN10 1NT
enquiries@hogsbackbooks.com
www.hogsbackbooks.com
Bright and beautiful children's picture books and non-fiction books up to age 10. Also reviews

YA and non-fiction. Welcomes submissions both directly from authors and through agents.

IDLE INK
ZINE
idleink@outlook.com
www.twitter.com/_idleink_
Editor: JL Corbett
Established 2017. Mixed form. Publication available at local literary events and on Etsy (link on Twitter page).
GENRES: Literary; sci-fi; horror; introspective.
SUBMISSIONS: Open to all, during submission windows. Submit by email to idleink@outlook.com. Guidelines at www.twitter.com/_idleink_/status/881103424728817664. Acknowledgement of submission within 24 hours. Usually responds with a decision within one to three months, with feedback only if requested. Contributors receive print copies.
WE SAY: Issue 1 of *Idle Ink* has the title 'Madness'. The publishing style is simple: staple spine, folded green cardboard cover reminiscent of pamphlets; 20 thick white paper inner pages. The front cover is illustrated with a pen-and-ink drawing of a face made up of four different characters; the issue contains four stories, and the back cover gives a tagline for each story, though there is a standard contents page as well. Every story is also illustrated with a line drawing. The stories in this issue skirt the edges of genre fiction: madness, aliens, psychic gifts and robots abound.

INK SWEAT & TEARS ☆
E-ZINE
www.inksweatandtears.co.uk

Editor: Helen Ivory
Established 2007. Primarily poetry. All online content available to all.
GENRES: Poetry; word and image work; flash and short fiction (under 750 words); reviews of poetry books.
SUBMISSIONS: Open to all. Guidelines at www.inksweatandtears.co.uk/pages/?page_id=23. Usually responds within one to three months. No feedback with rejection. Unpaid, but readers vote for Pick of the Month and the winning writer receives a £10 gift card.
WE SAY: Clearly signposted and publishing new content each day. The magazine focuses mainly on poetry and reviews and takes a contemporary approach to its content, with a fair amount of free verse and prose-poetry, but without stepping into the realms of the wildly experimental. There's a clear sense of curation and selection. Each piece of creative writing includes a brief biography of the contributor. Given that the site's set up makes it a satisfying read, this is a good site for a poet's CV, allowing easy access, a welcoming way for readers to discover your work.
See also: Ink Sweat & Tears Press (poetry publisher) p42

INTERPRETER'S HOUSE, THE ☆
PRINT
36 College Bounds, Old Aberdeen, Aberdeen, Scotland AB24 3DS
01224 487094
theinterpretershouse@aol.com
www.theinterpretershouse.com
Editors: Martin Malone, Charles Lauder Jnr (Deputy Editor)
Established 1984. Mainly poetry.

Annual subscription £15. Available direct from publisher website; by post and email order; and at independent bookshops and local literary events.

GENRES: Poetry; short stories on all subjects; reviews.

SUBMISSIONS: Open to all, during submissions windows (though past contributors are asked to wait three issues after appearing in the magazine before submitting again). Submit by post (36 College Bounds, Old Aberdeen, Aberdeen, Scotland AB24 3DS) or by email (theinterpretershouse@aol.com). Guidelines at www.theinterpretershouse.com/submissions. Please note that a new editorial team will be coming

---

IRISH PAGES

PRINT
129 Ormeau Road, Belfast,
Northern Ireland BT7 1SH
028 9043 4800
editor@irishpages.org
www.irishpages.org
Editors: Chris Agee,
Cathal Ó Searcaigh

Established 2003. Mixed form. Annual subscription £16 for one year, £32 for two years and £48 for three years. Available direct from publisher website; by direct mail and email orders; from selected/local chain bookshops; from independent bookshops; at national and local literary events; and from Amazon.

GENRES: Poetry; short fiction; essays; creative non-fiction; photography.

SUBMISSIONS: Open to all. Submit by post to 129 Ormeau Road, Belfast, Northern Ireland BT7 1SH. Guidelines at www.irishpages.org/submissions. Usually responds in over six months. No feedback offered with rejections. Contributors receive a print copy of the magazine.

IRISH PAGES
A JOURNAL OF CONTEMPORARY WRITING

They say

Ireland's premier literary journal, combining a large general readership with outstanding writing from Ireland and overseas. Widely considered the Irish equivalent to *Granta* in Britain, or *The Paris Review* in the United States. Offering an unrivalled window on the literary and cultural life of these islands – and further afield. Order now our celebrated Heaney memorial issues, 'Heaney' (Vol 8, No 2) and 'After Heaney' (Vol 9, No 1).

into effect from Summer 2018. Usually responds within one to three months. Rejections may include occasional unsolicited feedback. Contributors receive a print copy of the magazine.
WE SAY: We looked at Issue 59, a perfect-bound 108-page A5 publication, professionally designed and printed on high-quality paper. The work published has a confident contemporary literary aesthetic. The issue we looked at included the winning poems from the 2015 Open House Poetry Competition, followed by selected poetry submissions and a (very) few short stories, arranged in alphabetical order by author. The Editor's Letter is a bracing plea for 'poetry that is different', specifically poetry that deviates from the autobiographical topics that 'zillions of other poets' are writing about.

IRIS
PRINT
www.hurststreetpress.co.uk
Editors: Beth Sparks, Shoshana Kessler
Established 2016. Mixed form. Publication available direct from publisher website; from selected/local chain bookshops and independent bookshops.
GENRES: No fixed genres.
SUBMISSIONS: Open to all. Usually responds within four weeks. Rejection may occasionally include unsolicited feedback. Contributors receive a print copy of the magazine.
For a fuller description of this press see Hurst Street Press (poetry publisher p42 and prose publisher p124)

IRISH LITERARY REVIEW
E-ZINE
editor@irishliteraryreview.com
www.irishliteraryreview.com
Editor: Catherine Higgins-Moore
A mixed-form magazine, publishing poetry, flash fiction, short stories and interviews. Welcomes submissions from Ireland and around the world

ISLAND REVIEW, THE
E-ZINE
mail@theislandreview.com
www.theislandreview.com
Editors: Jordan Ogg, Malachy Tallack
Established 2013. Mixed form. All online content freely available to all.
GENRES: Crime/thriller/mystery; fantasy/sci-fi; historical fiction; literary fiction; poetry; art, fashion and photography; biography and true stories; history; popular science and nature; travel.
SUBMISSIONS: Open to all. Submit through Submittable at theislandreview.submittable. com/submit (guidelines at same address). Usually responds in up to six months. Usually no feedback if rejected, but may include occasional unsolicited feedback. Unpaid.
WE SAY: A clean, heavily illustrated website, featuring writing inspired by islands. It's a niche subject with great potential. One story we particularly liked imagines Glasgow as a city of islands. The site is updated regularly, with work well curated and presented.

JOTTERS UNITED LIT-ZINE ☆
E-ZINE
unitedjotters@gmail.com
jottersutd.wix.com/jotters-united
Editor: Nick Gerrard

Established 2014. Mainly fiction. Free access – all online content available to all.

GENRES: Literary fiction; poetry; biography and true stories; travel.

SUBMISSIONS: Open to all. Submit by email to unitedjotters@gmail.com. Guidelines at jottersutd.wixsite.com/jotters-united/submit. Usually responds within four weeks. Rejections may occasionally include unsolicited feedback. Unpaid.

WE SAY: Bold and bright, *Jotters United* combines bright illustration and surreal artwork with videos, music, slideshows and, of course, writing. The menu starts at Issue 1, so it's a bit of a scroll to get to the most recent work, but once you find it, it's clearly laid out, with six writers per issue. The writing itself is in a clear large-ish font; the stories very much slices of life.

LABLIT.COM
E-ZINE
editorial@lablit.com
www.lablit.com
Editor: Dr Jennifer Rohn
Mixed lab-lit genre writing – fiction, non-fiction, reviews, interviews etc. Note: lab lit is not sci-fi. The magazine is 'dedicated to real laboratory culture and to the portrayal and perceptions of that culture', so stick to realistic science, please, written to inform, entertain and surprise non-scientists as well as scientists.

LAMPETER REVIEW, THE
DIGITAL
The Journal of the Lampeter Creative Writing Centre
info@lampeter-review.com
www.lampeter-review.com
The online magazine of Lampeter Creative Writing Centre (part of the University of Wales, Trinity St David), this publication accepts submissions of prose, poetry and screenplays/plays. Contributors receive a hard copy of the magazine.

LEARNED PIG, THE
E-ZINE
tom@thelearnedpig.org
www.thelearnedpig.org
Editor: Tom Jeffreys
Established 2013. Mixed form. All online content available to all.

GENRES: Art; nature writing; philosophy; poetry; creative non-fiction.

SUBMISSIONS: Open to all. Submit by email to tom@thelearnedpig.org. Guidelines at www.thelearnedpig.org/contact. Usually responds within four weeks. Individual feedback is provided in all rejections. Unpaid.

WE SAY: This is a graphics-heavy zine, with every article heralded by a photo banner. The contents are divided into the categories 'art', 'thinking', 'nature' and 'writing', which is slightly unclear to the reader (as the first three categories all contain writing), but is explained on the 'about' page. The site runs themed editorial seasons, rather than obvious issues, the most recent being 'Wolf Crossing', which makes for some eye-catching art and intense reading.

LETTERS PAGE, THE
DIGITAL
School of English, University of Nottingham, Nottingham NG7 2RD
editor@theletterspage.ac.uk
www.theletterspage.ac.uk
Editor: Jon McGregor
Established 2013. Mixed form.

Available direct from publisher website, with all online content freely available to all.

GENRES: Literary and poetry correspondence.

SUBMISSIONS: Open to all. Submit by post to *The Letters Page*, School of English, University of Nottingham, Nottingham NG7 2RD. Guidelines at www.theletterspage.ac.uk/letterspage/submissions.aspx. Usually responds within one to three months. No feedback is offered with rejections. Contributors are paid a set rate.

WE SAY: The art of letter writing turned into a lit-zine, *The Letters Page* consists of handwritten letters that have been transcribed into a simple and effective layout. These letters appear in the magazine 'illustrated' by scanned images of the original letter. There's something voyeuristic and satisfying about the resulting reading experience. The tone varies – sad, humorous, matter-of-fact – and it's almost impossible to distinguish between memoir, essay and invention. A unique idea, presented well.

LIARS' LEAGUE

E-ZINE & LIVE EVENT WITH VIDEO AND PODCAST
07808 939535
liars@liarsleague.com
www.liarsleague.com
Editor: Katy Darby

Established 2007. Fiction suitable for performance. All online content available to all. Liars' League won the 2014 Saboteur Award for Best Regular Spoken Word Event and was named one of *The Guardian*'s 10 Great Storytelling Nights.

GENRES: Crime/thriller/mystery; fantasy/sci-fi; horror; historical fiction; literary fiction; romance. No YA or children's fiction.

SUBMISSIONS: Open to all. Submit by email to liars@liarsleague.com. Guidelines at www.liarsleague.com/liars_league/writers.html. Usually responds within eight weeks. Offers feedback only on shortlisted stories. Contributors are offered payment in kind (books, and/or free ticket and drinks).

WE SAY: Including Liars' League in this Guide is something of an anomaly, as they are primarily known for performances. Submitted stories are chosen to be performed by a professional actor in front of an appreciative audience; those same stories are also published on the website in an easy-to-browse archive, along with the performances on videos and audio (there are podcast and YouTube channels). The League is noted for great taste in fiction and looks for surprising, unique work that fits themes that are announced well in advance. A great way to get your name known and your work performed.

LIGHTHOUSE

PRINT
32 Grove Walk, Norwich, NR1 2QG
admin@gatehousepress.com
www.gatehousepress.com/lighthouse
Editors: Meirion Jordan,
Andrew McDonnell, Julia Webb,
Philip Langeskov, Anna de Vaul,
Jo Surzyn, Angus Sinclair,
Scott Dahlie, Molly-Sue Moore,
Sharlene Teo

Established 2012. A journal for new writers. Poetry and short fiction. Subscription £22.50 per year (four issues); single issue £5 plus postage. Available direct from publisher website; at selected/local

chain bookshops and independent bookshops; and at national and local literary events.
Lighthouse won the Saboteur Award for Best Magazine 2015.
GENRES: Literary fiction; poetry, art. Essays by request.
SUBMISSIONS: Submit during submissions windows by email to submissions@lighthouse. gatehousepress.com. Usually responds within one to three months. No feedback offered on submissions. Contributors receive a print copy of the magazine, and a discount purchase price on further copies.
WE SAY: We looked at a PDF of Issue 9, a 96-page A5 quarterly magazine is printed in a font that reminded us of old novels (in a good way). Stories are laid out as if in a book, without much white space, and both stories and poems are interspersed with artwork that looks like line drawings of slanted sunlight. Poetry, prose and prose poetry is gathered here, all very high quality. Features are saved for last, and are very in-depth.
See also: Gatehouse Press (poetry publisher p37 and prose publisher p117)

LITRO MAGAZINE
PRINT AND DIGITAL
020 3371 9971
info@litro.co.uk
www.litro.co.uk
Editors: Eric Akoto, Precious Williams
Established 2005. Mainly publishes fiction, in print, online and as a podcast. For subscription information see www.litro.co.uk/join. Available direct from publisher website; at chain bookshops nationwide; at independent bookshops; and at national and local literary events. Only subscribers/purchasers can access all online content, although some is available as a preview. *Litro* has been shortlisted for awards.
GENRES: Crime/thriller/mystery; drama and criticism; literary fiction; poetry; art, fashion and photography; food and drink; music, stage and screen; science, technology and medicine; society, education and politics; travel.
SUBMISSIONS: Submit across all *Litro*'s platforms via Submittable. Guidelines and link at www.litro. co.uk/submit.
WE SAY: Perfect-bound 40-page magazine featuring fiction, essays, interviews and culture. Matt finish, striking cover design (we looked at Issue 144: 'Transgender'), and full-colour inside, printed on thick quality paper. *Litro* has its roots in the city, and this is reflected in its aesthetic, which is contemporary and edgy. The expansive website features a large number of articles, interviews, weekly flash fiction etc., as well as the contents of the print version of the magazine. The sheer scale of the site was somewhat difficult to navigate – there's a lot going on – but the content is interesting and well-written.
See also: Litro Magazine Ltd (prose publisher) p131

LONDON MAGAZINE, THE ☆
PRINT AND DIGITAL
11 Queen's Gate, London SW7 5EL
020 7584 5977
admin@thelondonmagazine.org
www.thelondonmagazine.org
Editor: Steven O'Brien
Established 1732. Mixed form. Annual subscription £33. Available direct from publisher website; by

post and email order; from chain bookshops; and from independent bookshops. Some online content is freely available to all.

GENRES: Literary fiction; poetry; art, fashion and photography; biography and true stories; history; music, stage and screen; society, education and politics; travel.

SUBMISSIONS: Open to all. Submit by post (to 11 Queen's Gate, London SW7 5EL), by email (admin@thelondonmagazine. org) or through Submittable (thelondonmagazine.submittable. com/submit). Sometimes charges a reading fee. Usually responds within one to three months. Rejections may occasionally include unsolicited feedback. Contributors are paid (rate by negotiation) and receive print copies and a digital copy of the magazine.

WE SAY: A long-established perfect-bound 118-page magazine with a contemporary aesthetic. The cover design is eye-catching; the materials high quality. The publication takes an intellectual, literary approach in its critical essays and reviews, and is strict about the quality of the free verse it publishes – the poems must have a purpose and no word should be wasted. The creative writing is engaging and tightly written, somewhat traditional and often London-focused.

LONELY CROWD, THE
PRINT AND E-ZINE
johnlavin@thelonelycrowd.org
www.thelonelycrowd.org
Editor: John Lavin

Billed as 'the new home of the short story', but does also publish a small amount of poetry. Founded by *Wales Arts Review*'s Fiction Editor, Dr John Lavin, a thick print publication that looks for artwork, and pays for print contributions. Printed stories are accompanied by online work, including essays giving behind-the-scenes accounts of how the published stories were written.

LOW LIGHT MAGAZINE
PRINT
contact@hi-vispress.com
www.hi-vispress.com/low-light-magazine
Editors: Sophie Pitchford, Jim Gibson, Ben Williams

Established 2017. Mixed form. Publications available direct from publisher website; from selected/local chain bookshops; from independent bookshops; and at national literary events.

GENRES: Social realism; literary fiction; working class writing; experimental form poetry and prose.

SUBMISSIONS: During submission windows only. Submit by email to contact@hi-vispress.com. Guidelines at www.hi-vispress. com/low-light-magazine. Usually responds within one to three months, with feedback only if requested. Contributors receive a free print copy and prize money is awarded for best prose/poetry contribution and best photography contribution.

WE SAY: *Low Light* is beautifully designed, with plenty of soft light, darkly emotive photography (in black and white, and colour), accompanying poetry and prose laid out with an eye to space. The occasional splash of bold red is used judiciously. All attributions include the writers'/artists' twitter handle or website. At 82 pages,

LOSSLIT MAGAZINE

DIGITAL MAGAZINE / E-ZINE
losslituk@gmail.com
www.losslit.com
Editors: Kit Caless, Aki Schilz,
Jonny Keyworth

Established 2014. Welcomes poetry, short stories, and creative non-fiction. All online content freely available to all. *LossLit* was shortlisted for the Saboteur Awards: Best Collaborative Work 2015 and runs alongside the #LossLit digital literature project on Twitter.

GENRES: Literary; genre; poetry; short story; creative non-fiction (essay).

SUBMISSIONS: Open to all. No fee. Submit by email to losslituk@gmail.com during submission periods: January (for April issue), May (for August issue) and September (for December issue). Aims to respond within two months and will always get in touch if interested in seeing more work, or if they have feedback. However may not always be able to get back to everyone. Unpaid.

WE SAY: *LossLit* consists of an easily navigated website, the home page of which takes you straight to the most recent issue. It's a plain, almost austere site, appropriate for its content, which focuses on all forms of loss. In addition to the website, there is the collaborative *LossLit* Twitter project, on the first Wednesday night of the month. Writers share microfiction about loss (#LossLit) and respond to

They say

LossLit is an attempt by its creators, Kit Caless and Aki Schilz, to explore the various influences of loss in literature. Collating original fiction, poetry, audio and essays by contributing writers as well as building a canon of important existing LossLit titles, LossLit Magazine will produce a body of work that will look at loss from all angles, alongside its online micro-project, the #LossLit hashtag on Twitter. A Twitter writeclub is hosted every first Wednesday of the month between 9 and 11pm GMT. The writeclub is online and open to all, with updates and RTs on @LossLit.

each other's work. The result is archived to be read at leisure. *LossLit* is an interesting read, with a truly original use of social media.

there's plenty to read, including interviews, in-depth essays, experimental poetry, and even includes a Lit Zine round-up. We looked at a PDF proof, but in our dreams, this is printed on textured, matt paper.
See also: Hi Vis Press (poetry publisher p41 and prose publisher p120)

LUCIFER MAGAZINE
PRINT
luciferpress@gmail.com
www.lucifermagazine.co.uk
Editors: David Sillitoe, Neil Fulwood
A 'high literary and culture' magazine published twice a year. Features photograph, poetry, fiction and non-fiction (travel writing, pop culture articles, reportage, memoir). Also looking for contributors to two regular columns: Postcards from the Edge and Dispatches from the Front Line. The editors request that submitters 'tell us something we don't know'.

MANCHESTER REVIEW, THE
E-ZINE
Centre for New Writing, Samuel Alexander Building, University of Manchester M13 9PL
0161 2753167
manreviewsubmissions@gmail.com
www.themanchesterreview.co.uk
Editors: John McAuliffe, Lucy Burns
Established 2007. Mixed form. Two issues a year, plus rolling reviews. All online content available for free.
GENRES: Literary fiction; poetry; creative non-fiction.
SUBMISSIONS: Open to all during submissions windows. Submit by email to manreviewsubmissions@gmail.com. Usually responds within four to six months. Rejections may

occasionally include unsolicited feedback. Contributors are paid (by negotiation).
WE SAY: The front page of this online magazine is very sleek and minimal in design. At the top of the page, we have a gallery of the images to scroll through, with links to each story. Then, moving down, the images appear again as thumbnails accompanying the first paragraph of each story. The art varies in style, but is always eye-catching. The aim of the magazine is to feature international writers, both established and up-and-coming, and to '[document] the constantly evolving cultural landscape of our beloved Manchester'.

MEANWHILE...
PRINT AND DIGITAL / E-BOOKS
4 Florence Terrace, London SW15 3RU
07985 201621
submissions@soaringpenguinpress.com
www.soaringpenguinpress.com
Editor: John Anderson
Established 2012. Graphic fiction. Annual subscription £39.99 (UK). Available direct from publisher website; by post and email order; at selected/local chain and independent bookshops; at national literary events; and via Amazon and other bookshop websites (including Diamond Comics Distributors). Digital editions available from Comixology and Sequential.
GENRES: Fantasy/sci-fi; graphic/comics; horror; poetry.
SUBMISSIONS: Open to all. Submit by post (4 Florence Terrace, London SW15 3RU) or by email (submissions@soaringpenguinpress.com). Usually responds within four to six

months or more. Rejections may occasionally include unsolicited feedback. Contributors are paid (set rate or by negotiation), and receive print copies and a discount purchase price on the magazine. **See also: Soaring Penguin Press (prose publisher p156)**

MECHANICS' INSTITUTE REVIEW, THE
E-ZINE
editor@mironline.org
www.mironline.org
Established 2010 (previously Writers' Hub). Mixed form. All online content available to all.
GENRES: Literary fiction; poetry; features; reviews; biography and true stories.
SUBMISSIONS: Open to all, during submissions windows. Submit by email to editor@mironline.org. Guidelines at www.mironline.org/submissions. Usually responds within four to six months. Rejections may include occasional unsolicited feedback. Unpaid.
WE SAY: *MIRonline* is the online publication from Birkbeck University, which also produces the high-quality *MIR* print publication (which contains work only by Birkbeck students and well-known authors). The site is clean and easy to navigate – fiction, poetry, features and reviews are all separately signposted, so readers in the mood for a long read can just work their way down the backlist or easily search the archives. There's even some audio, if you prefer your poetry to go straight to the ear. It's a professional, organised, easy-on-the-eye site – and as the student editorial staff rotates annually, never a place to cross off as 'not

for my work', because the tastes and design change with the staff.

MINOR LITERATURE[S]
E-ZINE
www.minorliteratures.com
Editor: Fernando Sdrigotti, Tomoe Hill, Kevin Mullen, Eli Lee, Martin Dean, Thom Cuell, Yanina Spizzirri, Daniela Cascella
Established 2013. Published three times a week. All online content is freely available to all.
GENRES: Literary fiction; essays; poetry; experimental prose; book reviews.
SUBMISSIONS: Open to all, must be anonymous. Submit via minorliteratures.submittable.com/submit – guidelines available at the same address. Usually responds within one to three months. No feedback offered with rejection.
WE SAY: The *Minor Lits* zine website is simple to navigate, with bold photography and large serif font headers announcing the work. Essays, features, fiction, experimental prose and poetry, all are available. We particularly looked at the evocative essay 'Cocktail napkin: Chateau Marmont' by Liska Jacobs, an exploration of family and heredity as explored through the doors of Hotel Chateau Marmont in Los Angeles, combining imagined glamour with memories.

MONSTROUS REGIMENT
PRINT
editor@monstrous-regiment.com
www.monstrous-regiment.com
Editors: Lauren Nickodemus, Ellen Desmond
Established 2017. Mixed form. Publications available direct from publisher website; by direct mail

and email orders; and at local literary events.

GENRES: Short literary fiction; poetry; creative non-fiction; illustrations/photography; short genre fiction.

SUBMISSIONS: Open to all, during submission windows. Submit by email to editor@monstrous-regiment.com. Guidelines at www.monstrous-regiment.com/submissions. Usually responds within four weeks, with feedback only if requested. Contributors are paid a set rate and receive print copies.

For further information, including what They Say, see also Monstrous Regiment Publishing: poetry publisher p49 and prose publisher p134

MOTH, THE ☆
PRINT

Ardan Grange, Belturbet, County Cavan, Ireland
editor@themothmagazine.com
www.themothmagazine.com
Editor: Rebecca O'Connor

Established 2010. Mixed form. Annual subscription €28. Available direct from publisher website; by post and email order; at independent bookshops; and in Eason and newsagents in Ireland. *The Moth* features work from new writers as well as from the likes of Billy Collins, John Boyne and Sara Baume; a poem published in *The Moth* was shortlisted for the Forward Prize for Best Single Poem. They also publish a children's version called *The Caterpillar* (see p189).

GENRES: Literary fiction; poetry; interviews.

SUBMISSIONS: Open to all. Submit by post (*The Moth*, Ardan Grange, Belturbet, Co. Cavan, Ireland) or by email (editor@themothmagazine.com). Guidelines at www.themothmagazine.com/a1-page.asp?ID=1972&page=18. Usually responds within four to six months. Rejections may occasionally include unsolicited feedback. Contributors receive a print copy of the magazine.

WE SAY: Aesthetically striking, this 35-page magazine features literature, interviews and art. Contents are published on high quality matt paper with artwork throughout and a cover-image which continues onto the back. We looked at Issue 29, Summer 2017, which showcased compelling fiction and a high-quality array of poetry ('Brezhenv's Daughter' by Carole Braverman was particularly captivating).

See also: *The Caterpillar* (literary magazine) p189

MOVING WORLDS
A Journal of Transcultural Writings
PRINT

School of English, University of Leeds, Leeds LS2 9JT
mworlds@leeds.ac.uk
www.movingworlds.net
Editors: Shirley Chew, Stuart Murray

Established 2001. Mixed-form output. Subscriptions £32/year for two issues (individuals); £14/year (students/unwaged); £62/year (institutions). Available direct from publisher website; by post and email order; and from bookshop websites including Neilsens and EBSCO.

SUBMISSIONS: Open to all. Submit by email to mworlds@leeds.ac.uk. Guidelines at www.movingworlds.net/submissions. Usually responds within one to three months. Rejections may occasionally include unsolicited feedback. Contributors receive print copies of the magazine and a discount purchase price on further copies. Creative work (poetry) is paid.

MYTHS OF THE NEAR FUTURE (NAWE)
DIGITAL
www.nawe.co.uk/young-writers-hub/myths/about-myths.html

MSLEXIA ☆
PRINT AND DIGITAL
PO Box 656, Newcastle upon Tyne NE99 1PZ
0191 204 8860
postbag@mslexia.co.uk
www.mslexia.co.uk
Editor: Debbie Taylor

Established 1999. Mixed form. Subscription £34.75 (UK) a year for four issues. Available direct from publisher website; by post and email order; at selected chain bookshops and independent bookshops; and at national and local literary events. Only subscribers/purchasers can access all of the online content, although some content is available to read freely.
GENRES: Literary fiction; poetry; script; features; biography and true stories; history; society, education and politics.
SUBMISSIONS: Open to all. Submit by post (PO Box 656, Newcastle upon Tyne NE99 1PZ), by email (submissions@mslexia.com) or via online form. Guidelines at www.mslexia.co.uk/submit-your-work/. Usually responds within one to six months. Feedback overview of all entries offered with rejections (for creative work). Contributors are paid a set rate and may receive a copy of the magazine.

They say

No other magazine provides *Mslexia*'s unique mix of debate and analysis, advice and inspiration; news, reviews, interviews; competitions, events, courses, grants. All served up with a challenging selection of new poetry and prose. *Mslexia* is read by top authors and absolute beginners. A quarterly masterclass in the business and psychology of writing, it's the essential magazine for women who write. We are a vibrant, ambitious and growing organisation, and we aim to provide a high-profile platform for new and established voices with every copy of the magazine.

For writers aged between 16 and 25. 'Tread[s] the tightrope between demanding quality and encouraging talent.'

NEON LITERARY MAGAZINE
PRINT AND DIGITAL
info@neonmagazine.co.uk
www.neonmagazine.co.uk
Editor: Krishan Coupland
Established 2006. Mixed form. Annual subscription £12 (three issues). Publications available direct from publisher website; by direct mail and email orders; from independent bookshops; at national literary events; and from Amazon and other bookshop websites. Only subscribers/purchasers can access all online content, although some content is available to read freely.
GENRES: Sci-fi; horror; slipstream; magical realism; literary fiction.
SUBMISSIONS: Open to all, during submission windows. Submit by email to subs@neonmagazine.co.uk. Guidelines at www.neonmagazine.co.uk/guidelines. Usually responds within four to six months. Rejections may occasionally include unsolicited feedback for a fee. Submissions hold a tip-jar option, but this does not affect publisher's decision. A reading fee is required for expedited response times. Contributors are paid a set rate and receive a free digital copy, print copy and discount purchase price on further copies.
WE SAY: We saw a digital version of Issue 43, which featured a black-and-white photo of patterned fabric on the front and back cover, with further black-and-white photos throughout the publication. The design is simple and crisp, the photos used for atmospheric purposes alongside each piece of work. Coupled with the decision to leave the writers' bios until the end, there is a definite choice to let the work speak for itself, with very little to influence your mood while reading except the text itself. There is a mix of poetry and prose in this issue – the tone is dark and melancholic, presented in a very stylish magazine.
See also Neon Books (poetry publisher p51 and prose publisher p138)

NEW WELSH READER ☆
FORMERLY NEW WELSH REVIEW
PRINT
PO Box 170, Aberystwyth SY23 1WZ
01970 628410
admin@newwelshreview.com
www.newwelshreview.com
Editor: Gwen Davies
Established 1988 as *New Welsh Review*, and rebranded as *New Welsh Reader* in 2015. Now contains creative content only, with all review content appearing online as part of the e-zine, which is still *New Welsh Review*. Subscription £16.99 a year. Available direct from publisher website; by post and email order; at chain bookshops nationwide and independent bookshops; at national and local literary events; and from Amazon. Only subscribers/purchasers can access all of the online content, although some content is available to read freely (see *New Welsh Review*).
GENRES: Drama and criticism; literary fiction; poetry; art, fashion and photography; biography and true stories; history; popular science and nature; society, education and politics.

SUBMISSIONS: Open to all. Submit by post (Submissions, PO Box 170, Aberystwyth SY23 1WZ) or by email (editor@newwelshreview.com). Guidelines at www.newwelshreview.com/submissions.php. Usually responds within one to three months. No feedback offered with rejections. Contributors are paid a set rate and receive a discount purchase price on the magazine.

WE SAY: A perfect-bound 80-page magazine, *New Welsh Reader* boasts a high-quality glossy design, with a mixture of grey-scale and colour images. It is packed with contemporary writing, all connected to Wales, well presented to readers.

See also: *New Welsh Review* (mixed-form e-zine), below

NEW WELSH REVIEW ☆
E-ZINE

PO Box 170, Aberystwyth SY23 1WZ

01970 628410

admin@newwelshreview.com

www.newwelshreview.com

Editor: Gwen Davies

Established 1988. Mainly reviews, with previews of *New Welsh Reader* fiction and articles. Only subscribers/purchasers can access all content, although some content is available to read freely.

GENRES: Drama and criticism; literary fiction; poetry; art, fashion and photography; biography and true stories; history; popular science and nature; society, education and politics.

SUBMISSIONS: Open to all. Submit by post (Submissions, PO Box 170, Aberystwyth SY23 1WZ) or by email (editor@newwelshreview.com). Guidelines at www.newwelshreview.com/submissions.php. Usually responds within one to three months. No feedback offered with rejections. Contributors are paid a set rate and receive a discount purchase price on the magazine.

WE SAY: *New Welsh Review* is bright and easy-to-navigate e-zine packed with features, articles, commentary and reviews. The website also features video interviews. There's no indication, though, as to which content is free and which requires subscription, so we'd suggest you subscribe.

See also: *New Welsh Reader* (mixed-form literary magazine), above

NEW WRITING SCOTLAND
PRINT

ASLS, 7 University Gardens, Glasgow G12 8QH

0141 330 5309

office@asls.org.uk

www.asls.org.uk

Editors: Susie Maguire, Samuel Tongue

Established 1983. Fiction, non-fiction and poetry. Subscription: Annual anthology – copies can be purchased direct from the publisher or from booksellers.

GENRES: Any and all genres of short fiction; prose work on all topics; poetry.

SUBMISSIONS: Open to works by writers resident in Scotland or Scots by birth, upbringing or inclination. During submissions window (1 May to 30 September), submit by post to *New Writing Scotland*, ASLS, 7 University Gardens, Glasgow G12 8QH. Guidelines at www.asls.arts.gla.ac.uk/NWSsubs.html. Usually responds within four to six months.

No feedback offered with rejection. Contributors are paid £20 per published page and receive a print copy and a discount purchase price on the magazine.

WE SAY: We looked at a digital extract from Issue 34: Talking About Lobsters. It presents an interesting and fascinating story about a Ukrainian woman on her way to Scotland, crossing borders. The pages are quite full, with justified text and long paragraphs. As the writer is a professor in Eastern Europe studies, it aims to introduce the world beyond the western borders. It also includes poetry and short fiction from Scotland-based award-winning authors and authors who are just beginning their careers.

See also: ASLS (poetry publisher p18 and prose publisher p91)

NORTHWORDS NOW

PRINT AND DIGITAL
Easter Brae, Culbokie, Dingwall, Ross-shire IV7 8JU
editor@northwordsnow.co.uk
www.northwordsnow.co.uk
Editor: Kenny Taylor
Established 2005. Mixed form. Available by post and email order; from selected/local chain bookshops and independent bookshops; at national and local literary events; from other bookshop websites; and at libraries, galleries and other outlets in Scotland. All online content is freely available to all.

GENRES: Literary fiction; poetry; short stories (strictly no novel extracts); biography and true stories; travel; literary essays.

SUBMISSIONS: Open to all. Submit by post to The Editor, *Northwords Now*, 6 Kippendavie Lane, Dunblane, Perthshire, FK15 0HL, or via the submission form at www.northwordsnow.co.uk (guidelines at the same address). Usually responds within four to six months. Rejections may occasionally include unsolicited feedback. Contributors are paid (a set rate and by negotiation) and receive a print copy of the magazine.

WE SAY: We looked at a PDF of this 32-page literary magazine, which is printed in newspaper format. A bold and striking cover announces the contents, which are laid out across four columns per page for prose, and three columns for poems. The effect is one of immediacy and freshness. Work appears in English and in Scottish Gaelic, and always embraces Scotland as landscape and culture.

NOTTINGHAM REVIEW, THE

DIGITAL AND E-ZINE
thenottinghamreview@gmail.com
www.thenottinghamreview.com
Editor: Spencer Chou
Established 2015. Mainly fiction, recently expanding to include poetry. All online content freely available to all.

GENRES: Literary. Strictly no non-fiction.

SUBMISSIONS: Open to all. Submit by email to thenottinghamreview@gmail.com. Guidelines at www.thenottinghamreview.com/submit. Usually responds within four weeks. Rejections may include occasional unsolicited feedback. Unpaid.

WE SAY: *The Nottingham Review* is a beautiful digital magazine available in multiple formats. The design is simple – professional and contemporary. There are no images in the inner pages, just text

with plenty of white space. The cover is uncluttered: one large, simple image. Where possible, there are live links to information on contributing writers, so readers can easily find out more. Each issue has a theme, and the stories are engaging nuggets of the everyday, followed by enthusiastic comments on the web-browser version.
See also: prose publisher p140

OGHAM STONE, THE
PRINT AND DIGITAL
School of Culture and Communication, University of Limerick
+353 21 202336
oghamstoneul@gmail.com;
oghamstone@ul.ie
www.theoghamstoneul.com
Editors: MA Students of Creative Writing and English
Established 2013. Mixed-form output. Some online content is freely available to all.
GENRES: Literary; visual.
SUBMISSIONS: Open to all, during submissions windows only. Submit via www.theoghamstoneul.com/submit/ (guidelines at the same address). Usually responds within four to six months. No feedback offered with rejection. Contributors receive print copies of the magazine.
WE SAY: We looked at a digital version of the Spring 2017 issue. A full-colour, painted cover image is taken from a Richard Smyth painting, which is shown in full in the inner pages. We feel the top-page margins of the inner pages run a little narrow, but the overall design is a pleasure, with the text regularly interspersed with beautiful colour illustrations in a range of styles, and the complete writer biographies on the final

page. The issue is closed with a final page featuring another extract from the cover painting.

PALM-SIZED PROMPTS
E-ZINE
palmsizedprompts@gmail.com
palmsizedprompts.wordpress.com
Editor: E.M. Killaley
Established 2015. Fiction. All online content available to all.
SUBMISSIONS: Open to all. Submit by email to palmsizedprompts@gmail.com. Guidelines at www.palmsizedprompts.wordpress.com/about. Usually responds within four weeks. All submissions to prompts are posted on the website. Unpaid.
WE SAY: The cleanly presented website divides work by month and year, as a new prompt is posted each month. Responses can be read by date, or by author; all contributors have the opportunity to send in a bio, which appears on the 'Our Writers' page as well as above the list of the writer's work. A complete list of the monthly posts can also be viewed under 'Prompts'.
See also: *Palm-Sized Press* (prose magazine p267)

PAPAYA PRESS
ZINE
www.papayapress.co.uk
Editor: Lauren Vevers
Established 2015. Mixed form. Publication available direct from publisher website.
GENRES: Experimental; literary; DIY.
SUBMISSIONS: Open to all. Also accepts submissions on a rolling basis for publication in the Papaya Press blog. Priority is given to female-identifying voices. Submit

by email to papayapressinfo@ gmail.com. Guidelines at www. papayapress.co.uk/#submissions. Usually responds within four to six months. Rejections may occasionally include unsolicited feedback. Contributors receive a free print copy.

WE SAY: The digital version of *Tender Bodies* from Papaya Press still retained the bohemian feel of an independent zine – the blend of photography, drawings and written pieces capture a mood of very different creatives drawing from a common theme. The style of written work varies – everything from traditional poetry, to prose poems, to flash fiction – and so form does not feel like a barrier to a successful submission.

PAPER AND INK
PRINT

paperandinkzine@outlook.com
www.paperandinkzine.co.uk
Editor: Martin Appleby
Established 2013. Mixed form. Available direct from the publisher website and from independent bookshops.
Longlisted for Best Magazine in the 2017 Saboteur Awards.
GENRES: Drama and criticism; literary fiction; poetry. No non-fiction.
SUBMISSIONS: Open to all. Submit by email to paperandinkzine@ outlook.com. Guidelines at www.paperandinkzine.co.uk/ submissions. Usually responds within one to three months. Rejections may occasionally include unsolicited feedback. Contributors receive a print copy of the magazine.

PENNILESS PRESS MAGAZINE
DIGITAL

10 Albert Road, Grappenhall, Warrington, Cheshire K1C 2X9
01925 602430
info@pennilesspress.com
www.pennilesspress.co.uk
Editors: Alan Dent, Ken Clay
Mixed form, publishing literary fiction; poetry; biography and true stories; history; society, education and politics and literary criticism.
See also: Penniless Press Publications (prose publisher) p146

PENNY DREADFUL, THE ☆
PRINT

Clonmoyle House, Coachford, Cork
The.P.Dreadful@Gmail.com
www.thepennydreadful.org
Editors: Marc O'Connell, John Keating
Mixed form. Annual subscription £26. Available direct from publisher website, selected/local chain bookshops, independent bookshops and at local literary events.
GENRES: Drama and criticism; graphic/comics; literary fiction; poetry; and reviews, specifically literary pieces that can include elements of biography.
SUBMISSIONS: Open to all. Submit through Submittable via www. thepennydreadful.org/index.php/ submit/ (guidelines in the same place). Usually responds within four weeks. Rejection may occasionally include unsolicited feedback. Unpaid.
WE SAY: A perfect-bound magazine, with a professional design on high-quality paper – and a particularly dark ethos. The issue we checked out (No. 5) had a cover featuring a woman with blank, black eyes, a knowing smile and a

red hood with horns – fair warning about the edgy, occasionally humorous writing inside. Contemporary, Irish and living up to its name, the work featured well-written stuff – but be warned: it's not a comfort read.

PEOPLE'S FRIEND, THE
PRINT
peoplesfriend@dcthomson.co.uk
www.thepeoplesfriend.co.uk
A very popular magazine for readers aged from around 30 to 'well over 80'. Accepts a range of work, including poetry, short stories and articles, all in a very distinctive style for popular readership. Clear guidelines are available on the website.

PLANET AND PLANET EXTRA
PRINT AND E-ZINE
PO Box 44, Aberystwyth, Ceredigion SY23 3ZZ
01970 611 255
submissions@planetmagazine.org.uk;
website@planetmagazine.org.uk
www.planetmagazine.org.uk
Publishes articles, poetry and reviews (with a focus on Wales, as this journal is 'The Welsh Internationalist'). Paid.

PLATFORM FOR PROSE
ONLINE SHOWCASE
editor@platformforprose.com
www.platformforprose.com
Established 2015. Mixed form: shorts, flash and poetry. Available direct from publisher website. Forthcoming anthologies (e-books) will be available from Amazon. Some online content freely available to all.
GENRES: Contemporary short fiction. No children's or young adult fiction, sci-fi or fantasy.

SUBMISSIONS: During submissions windows, submit by email to editor@platformforprose. com. Guidelines at www. platformforprose.com/submissions. Usually responds within four weeks. No feedback currently offered with rejections. Unpaid.
WE SAY: Despite the name, this showcase does include some poetry. It's an easy to navigate, good-looking site with a healthy mixture of short stories, flash fiction and poems. It also recently branched out into audio presentation and included comment sections under the content so that readers can express their pleasure at the work.

POPSHOT MAGAZINE
PRINT AND DIGITAL
hello@popshotpopshot.com
www.popshotpopshot.com
Editor: Laura Silverman
Established 2008. Fiction and poetry. Annual subscription £20 (for four issues) from 2018. Publication available direct from publisher website; in chain bookshops nationwide and from bookshop websites.
GENRES: Literary fiction; poetry. No non-fiction.
SUBMISSIONS: Open to all. Submit at www.popshotpopshot. com/submit (guidelines at same address). Usually responds within four weeks – no feedback unless requested. Contributors receive print copies of the magazine.
WE SAY: An A5, 64-page literary magazine printed on matt paper. We looked at Issue 14. The modern formula of contemporary illustration mixed with poetry, short stories and flash fiction feels fresh and original. Each illustration

is quirky and unique, specifically commissioned to appear alongside each piece of writing. Our favourite was 'Through the Flowers', a short story complemented by pop-art flowers with eyeballs at their centre. Wonderfully weird. The magazine has taken off in 18 countries around the world.

PORRIDGE MAGAZINE

E-ZINE AND PRINT
porridgemagazine@gmail.com
www.porridgemagazine.com
Editors: Georgia Tindale,
Nora Selmani, Kitty Howse
Established 2016. Mixed form.
All online content available to all.
Publication available direct from
publisher website.
GENRES: Literary; academic;
political; multimedia;
interdisciplinary.
SUBMISSIONS: Open to all. Submit
by email to porridgemagazine@
gmail.com. Guidelines at
www.porridgemagazine.com/
submissions/. Usually responds
within four weeks. Rejections may
occasionally include unsolicited
feedback. Unpaid.
WE SAY: We looked at the e-zine
aspect of *Porridge*, and read with
enjoyment several of the items
on offer, particularly 'Are You
Home?' by Isy Weller and 'For
You, After a Film' by Sadia Pineda
Hameed. It's a very modern-
looking, information-packed zine,
with many articles and stories side
by side from the top of the Home
page, and striking images – both
photographs and illustrations – to
match. The site is easy to navigate,
and gives the feeling of being
able to dip in and out of work you
find interesting. Once you pick a
piece to read, the text is on the
right-hand side of the page, with a
larger version of the image on the
left. As you scroll through the text,
the image is fixed in place, giving it
a feeling of significance.

PROLE ☆

PRINT AND DIGITAL
01204 497726
admin@prolebooks.co.uk
www.prolebooks.co.uk
Editors: Brett Evans, Phil Robertson
Established 2010. Mixed form.
Annual subscription £15 (three
issues). Publications available direct
from publisher website and by
direct mail and email orders.
Prole won the Saboteur award for
Best Literary Magazine in 2016.
GENRES: Literary; engaging;
accessible; challenging;
entertaining.
SUBMISSIONS: Open to all. Submit
by email to submissionspoetry@
prolebooks.co.uk or
submissionsprose@prolebooks.
co.uk. Guidelines at www.
prolebooks.co.uk/submissions.
html. Usually responds within four
weeks. Rejections may occasionally
include unsolicited feedback.
Contributors are paid royalties only.
**See also: Prolebooks (poetry
publisher p61 and prose publisher
p149)**

PUSH – THE WRITING SQUAD

ONLINE PLATFORM
steve@writingsquad.com
www.sqpush.com
Editor: Steve Dearden
Established 2001. Mixed form.
All online content freely available
to all.
GENRES: Literary fiction; poetry;
travel; new journalism.
SUBMISSIONS: Submissions from
members only or by invitation only.

WE SAY: An online magazine that features articles and creative writing for young adults. The design is contemporary, the colour scheme bright but not overwhelming, and the work is clearly laid out. Content includes poetry and prose, lyrical and contemporary.

READER, THE
PRINT
magazine@thereader.org.uk
www.thereader.org.uk/getinvolved/magazine

Editor: Philip Davis
Literary mix magazine, published quarterly since 1997. Showcases writing from well-known names and new voices side by side. Welcomes submissions of poetry, fiction, essays, readings and thoughts.

RIPTIDE JOURNAL
PRINT
Dept of English, Queen's University of Exeter, Exeter EX4 6QH
editors@riptidejournal.co.uk
www.riptidejournal.co.uk
Editors: Dr Virginia Baily, Dr Sally Flint
Established 2006. Mainly fiction, but includes poetry and life-writing. Available direct from publisher website; by post and email order; from independent bookshops; and at local literary events. Stockists listed on the website. Some content available online to all.
GENRES: Children's fiction; drama and criticism; erotica; fantasy/sci-fi; graphic/comics; horror; romance. No non-fiction.
SUBMISSIONS: Open to all, during submissions windows. Submit by email to editors@riptidejournal. co.uk. Guidelines at www. riptidejournal.co.uk/contribute. Usually responds within four to six months. No feedback offered. Contributors are paid a set rate and receive a print copy and discount purchase price on the magazine.
WE SAY: Only technically a journal, *Riptide* is a series of anthologies published as volumes as opposed to issues. Each volume contains a healthy amount of work (23 pieces in Vol 10: 'The Suburbs', which is the one we looked at), and has a gloss laminate cover and decent paper. The inside is pure book: (no illustrations, a prelims page, contents, thanks, and the work), but the cover design is very much that of a journal, with a single piece of art in a wide, white frame, and brief information about the contents below. This volume had an introduction from Michael Rosen, and some recognisable names in the contributors' list.
See also: Dirt Pie Press (poetry publisher p27 and prose publisher p107)

ROASTBOOKS
SHORT STORY COLLECTIONS AND ANTHOLOGIES
No 31 Peninsula Heights, 93 Albert Embankment, London SE1 7TY
0207 300 7293
info@roastbooks.co.uk
www.roastbooks.co.uk
Specialist short story and flash fiction publisher, with modern and beautiful designs.

SABLE
PRINT AND E-ZINE
editorial@sablelitmag.org
www.sablelitmag.org
Managing editor: Kadija Sesay
An established and important publication, *Sable* is a showcase

magazine for writers of colour, featuring work from internationally renowned and new writers. The magazine also offers training and support, and created the Writer's HotSpot: the first international creative writing residencies for people of colour. Originally solely a literary magazine, *Sable* has been recreated as a cultural magazine, 'underwritten by literary factors'. Types of work accepted include fiction, poetry, in translation, memoir, travel narratives (Blackpackers), essays, classic review and more. Online only slots include reviews, listings and microfiction.

SUBMISSIONS: Open to all writers of colour. Submit by email to editorial@sablelitmag.org. Full guidelines at www.sablelitmag.org/submissions.

SALOMÉ

DIGITAL AND PRINT
salomeliterature@gmail.com
www.salomelit.com
Editor: Jacquelyn Guderley
Established 2017. Mixed form. Annual digital subscription £13 (four issues); digital and print subscription £40 (four issues in both digital and print format). Print publication available direct from publisher website. While only subscribers/purchasers can read complete issues (in print and digital download formats), free samples of pieces from each issue are available online.

GENRES: Literary; feminist; mixed theme.

SUBMISSIONS: Open to self-identifying women only, during submission windows. Submit online at www.salomelit.com/submissions. Guidelines at www.

salomelit.com/submissions-guide. Usually responds within one to three months. Rejections include feedback for all work submitted during submissions windows. Contributors are paid a set rate and receive free print and digital copies.

WE SAY: A magazine for emerging female writers, *Salomé* Issues 1 and 2 both have cover art featuring paintings of strong women in bold colours and include a thoughtful, but galvanising editor's letter. The use of art continues within, gorgeous paintings set between each story and poem, usually challenging the convention of the 'model' woman. The font choice changes from sans serif in Issue 1 to serif in Issue 2 (which we prefer), but the text is laid out cleanly, un-cramped. Full biographies of both writers and artist appear in the last few pages. The writing is set to theme (e.g. 'Body') to a high standard and with an eye to including as many different voices as possible.

SARASVATI

PRINT
24 Forest Houses, Halwill, Beaworthy, Devon EX21 5UU
publishing@indigodreams.co.uk
www.indigodreams.co.uk
Editor: Dawn Bauling
Established 2008. Mainly poetry, some prose under 1,000 words. Subscription £17/year for four issues. Available direct from publisher website; and by post and email order.
Indigo Dreams editors won the Ted Slade Award for Services to Poetry 2015 (organised by Poetry Kit).
GENRES: All styles considered.
SUBMISSIONS: Open to all.

Submit by post (IDP, 24 Forest Houses, Halwill, Beaworthy, Devon EX21 5UU) or by email (publishing@indigodreams.co.uk). Guidelines at www.indigodreams. co.uk. Usually responds within four weeks. No feedback offered with rejection.
WE SAY: An A5 quarterly publication by Indigo Dreams,

SHOOTER LITERARY MAGAZINE ☆
PRINT
98 Muswell Hill Road, London N10 3JR
shooterlitmag@gmail.com
www.shooterlitmag.com
Editor: Melanie White

Established 2014. Mixed form: short stories, poetry and short non-fiction. Annual subscription £19.99 (UK); £34.99 (international) (for two issues). Available direct from publisher website; by post and email order; at selected/local chain bookshops (eg Foyles Charing Cross); and at national and local literary events. An e-book version of the magazine is made available when print editions sell out. *Shooter* was nominated for Saboteur Awards' Best Magazine 2015.
GENRES: Literary fiction; literary journalism (essays, memoir, reported/researched narrative pieces); poetry; satire; biography. Varies according to theme.
SUBMISSIONS: Open to all, during submissions windows – submissions must relate to the issue theme and be of a literary standard. Submit by email to submissions.shooterlitmag@gmail. com. See guidelines at www. shooterlitmag.com/submissions. Usually responds within one to three months. Due to volume of submissions, rejection emails are no longer sent; successful writers can expect a response before or soon after the submission deadline. Contributors are paid a set rate and receive a print copy of the magazine.
WE SAY: We looked at Issue 6 entitled 'Bad Girls', which was right up our street. The issue focuses on the concept of the 'nasty woman', imposing a politically driven rejection of the vilification of powerful women. The cover image resonates in the bold and assertive prose, poetry and non-fiction pieces that follow. A high-quality publication, equally strong in both physical material and narrative voice.

showcasing poetry and prose. Looking at Issue 45, most contributors have three or more pieces of writing featured, giving the sense of a series of mini collections. This allows each writer to display their style more clearly, making for a diverse as well as engrossing publication. The glossy full-colour design is appealing and vibrant, encasing a simple black and white interior.

For what They Say, see Indigo Dreams Publishing Ltd (poetry publisher) p43. See also *The Dawntreader* (mixed-form magazine p192) and *Reach Poetry* (poetry magazine) p251

SCRIBE

E-BOOKS / NOVELS / NON-FICTION
2 John Street, London WC1N 2ES
020 3405 4218
www.scribepublications.co.uk
Operating for nearly 40 years, and spanning the globe despite still being 'small', Scribe publishes local, international and translated fiction, and serious narrative and literary non-fiction.

SENTINEL LITERARY QUARTERLY

PRINT AND E-ZINE
www.sentinelquarterly.com
Published at the end of January, April, July and October, online and in limited print. Mixed form, it accepts poetry, short stories, novel extracts, reviews and interviews, plays and essays. Note that a different email address applies for each area of submission.

SNOW LIT REV

PRINT
14 Mount Street, Lewes, East Sussex BN7 1HL

www.abar.net/snow.pdf
Editors: Anthony Barnett, Ian Brinton
Established 2013. Mixed form. Publication available direct from publisher website; by direct mail and email orders; and from independent bookshops.
GENRES: Literary; music; art; photography; film.
SUBMISSIONS: Open to all, although few unsolicited contributions are accepted. Guidelines at www.abar.net/snow. pdf. Usually responds within two weeks. Rejections may occasionally include unsolicited feedback.
See also: Allardyce, Barnett, Publishers (poetry publisher p16 and prose publisher p88)

SOMESUCH STORIES

DIGITAL AND PRINT
Unit 2, Royle Studios,
41 Wenlock Road, London N1 7SG
suze@somesuch.co
www.somesuchstories.co
Editor: Suze Olbrich
Established 2015. Digital publication but also publishes essays and short stories in themed collection biannually. Publication available direct from publisher website; from selected chain retailers; from independent bookshops; and from other bookshop websites.
In 2016, *Somesuch Stories* was shortlisted for the Stack Awards for Best Fiction and Best Non-Fiction.
GENRES: Literary fiction; biographical non-fiction; arts and culture; society and politics.
SUBMISSIONS: Pieces are commissioned following editorial prompts. Publication history is generally required. Query by email at stories@somesuch. co. Usually responds within four

weeks. No feedback with rejection. Contributors are paid a flat fee.

WE SAY: These less-than-A5 eclectic magazines reflect their online origin with design choices such as a sans-serif font in Issue 3, and double-spacing between paragraphs rather than indenting in both Issues 2 and 3. But they are good quality publications; the paperback cover of Issue 2 is more inflexible than Issue 3, but its black print on a silver metallic background is eye-catching. Issue 3, which curls the press' name to form its issue number, features a contents page with titles and names scattered across the page.

SOUTHWORD JOURNAL ☆
E-ZINE
Munster Literature Centre,
Frank O'Connor House,
84 Douglas Street, Cork
+353 21 431 2955
munsterlit@eircom.net
www.munsterlit.ie/Southword/issues_
index.html
Editors: Patrick Cotter, Mary Noonan, Matthew Sweeney, Colm Breathnach
Established 2001. Mixed form. All online content available to all.
GENRES: Literary fiction; poetry; literary criticism; Litríocht as Gaeilge.
SUBMISSIONS: Submit via Submittable at southword. submittable.com/submit (guidelines at the same address). Usually responds within one to three months. No feedback offered with rejections. Contributors are paid a set rate.
WE SAY: Originally a print journal, *Southword* made the move to digital a few years ago. The website is not particularly attractive, but is very easy to

navigate. Issues are listed with images of the writers, and the contents are ordered by form and link straight through to the work – which is extremely high quality in both English and Irish. *Southword* also pays very well. Stories and poems are literary and ideally have some connection to Ireland.
See also: Southword Editions (poetry publisher) p71

SPARK YOUNG WRITERS MAGAZINE
DIGITAL
Writing West Midlands, Unit 204, The Custard Factory, Gibb Street B9 4AA
0121 246 2770
www.sparkwriters.org
Editor: Emma Freelove
Established 2013 (previously called 'WriteOn!'). Mainly fiction. All online content available to all.
GENRES: Children's fiction; fantasy/sci-fi; poetry; YA; teenage.
SUBMISSIONS: Open to young people aged 8-20 living or learning in the West Midlands. Submit by email to emma@writingwestmidlands.org. Guidelines at www.sparkwriters. org/get-involved.

SPONTANEITY
E-ZINE
ruth.mckee@gmail.com
www.spontaneity.org
Editor: Ruth McKee
Established 2013. Mixed form. All online content available to all.
GENRES: Literary fiction; poetry; creative non-fiction.
SUBMISSIONS: Open to all. Submit by email to editor@ spontaneity.org. Guidelines at

www.spontaneity.org/submit/.
Usually responds within four weeks.
Rejections may include occasional
unsolicited feedback. Unpaid.
WE SAY: The contents page of
Spontaneity's current issue is laid
out like a series of newspaper
articles, linking to work inspired
by art (visual and written) that has
previously appeared on the site.
It's easy to fall down a rabbit-hole
of reactions as you discover what
prompted each piece. It's a unique
approach to a literary magazine,
and the resulting work is intense,
lyrical, personal and experimental.
If you're a writer who likes to work
to prompts, this is one for you.

STAND ☆
PRINT AND DIGITAL
Stand, School of English,
University of Leeds, Leeds LS2 9JT
stand@leeds.ac.uk
www.standmagazine.org
Editors: Jon Glover, John Whale,
Elaine Glover
Established 1952. Mixed form.
Subscribe online at
www.standmagazine.org.
Single issues may be purchased
in selected bookshops or by
emailing stand@leeds.ac.uk.
SUBMISSIONS: Open to all.
Submit by post to *Stand*, School of
English, University of Leeds, Leeds
LS2 9JT (please include an s.a.e. if
within UK). Only subscribers may
submit by email. Usually responds
within one to three months.
Rejections may include feedback.
WE SAY: A long-established
magazine producing a variety of
poetry, fiction and criticism. The
horizontal book and full-colour
cover immediately stands out as
a unique publication. Stand acts
as a symbol of the need to 'Stand'

against oppression and injustice,
reflected by the powerful voices
it publishes. Most poets feature
multiple poems each, allowing
contributors an even wider
platform for their writing.

STEPAWAY MAGAZINE
E-ZINE
editor@stepawaymagazine.com
www.stepawaymagazine.com
Editors: Darren Richard Carlaw,
Elena Kharlamova
Established 2011. Poetry and flash
fiction. All online content available
to all. Winner of the Walking
Visionaries Award 2015 (Walk21).
GENRES: Literary fiction; poetry;
travel – literature that evokes the
sensory experience of walking in
specific neighbourhoods, districts
or zones within a city.
SUBMISSIONS: Open to all.
Submit by email to
submissions@stepawaymagazine.
com. Guidelines at www.
stepawaymagazine.com/about.
Usually responds within one to
three months, with feedback only if
requested. Unpaid.
WE SAY: This e-zine publishes
contents on a theme, particularly
featuring poetry and short stories
about walking and navigating
urban spaces, with a contemporary
lyrical aesthetic. The e-zine
homepage features the magazine
cover image for the current issue,
with the distinctive masthead
and an eye-catching image (the
previous covers are archived for
the curious). Clicking on the image
takes you to the issue contents
page, a straightforward list (Issue
24 was one essay and plenty of
poetry), with a separate page
displaying contributor biographies.

225

STINGING FLY, THE ☆

PRINT

PO Box 6016, Dublin 1, Ireland

stingingfly@gmail.com

www.stingingfly.org

Editors: Thomas Morris,
Declan Meade

Established 1997. Mainly fiction. Subscription €30/year. Available direct from publisher website, in selected/local chain bookshops and Independent bookshops and at local and national literary events.

GENRES: Literary fiction; poetry; essays; reviews.

SUBMISSIONS: Open to all, subject to submission windows. Submit via Submittable at stingingfly. submittable.com/submit. Guidelines at www.stingingfly.org/ submissions. Usually responds within one to three months. Rejections may occasionally include unsolicited feedback. Contributors are paid a set rate and receive a print copy and a discount purchase price on the magazine.

WE SAY: We looked at Issue 33/Vol 2 of this magazine, 'In the Wake of the Rising', which at 288 pages, resembles a hefty anthology. A matt laminate cover, with a striking graphic design of old photographs. The contents consist of critical and artistic responses to the Easter Rising, in the centenary year of the event, and so is politically and historically rooted. The work included is sometimes serious, sometimes experimental – one poem is entirely in tweets. The layout is clean and inviting – crucial when a magazine has as much to say as this one does. A great read.

See also: prose publisher p157

STREETCAKE MAGAZINE

DIGITAL

streetcakemagazine@gmail.com

www.streetcakemagazine.com

Editors: Nikki Dudley, Trini Decombe

Established 2008. Mixed form. All online content available to all.

GENRES: Experimental; crime/ thriller/mystery; fantasy/sci-fi; literary fiction; poetry. No nonfiction.

SUBMISSIONS: Open to all. Submit by email to streetcakemagazine@ gmail.com. Guidelines at www.streetcakemagazine.com/ submissions.html. Usually responds within one to three months. Rejection may include occasional unsolicited feedback. Contributors receive a digital copy. Unpaid.

WE SAY: A long-established digital magazine, *Streetcake* keeps its issues short and sweet. We looked at Issue 53. The cover is a simple, bright image: an artistic photo by Tony Rickaby with plenty going on; the contents, which consist of just seven poems in this particular issue, are cleanly laid out and leaning towards the experimental.

STRIX

PRINT

strixleeds@gmail.com

www.strixleeds.com

Editors: Ian Harker, Andrew Lambeth

A tall-format magazine 'ideally suited to longer poems (a sestina fits comfortably on a single page)'. Accepts poetry (up to 40 lines) and short fiction (up to 1,500 words). Printed three times a year.

STRUCTO

PRINT AND DIGITAL

editor@structomagazine.co.uk

structomagazine.co.uk

Editor: Euan Monaghan

Established 2008. Mixed form. Annual subscription £14 (two issues). Available direct from publisher website; from independent bookshops and newsagents; and on other bookshop websites.
All online content is available to all.
GENRES: Literary fiction; poetry; slipstream; literary interviews; essays.
SUBMISSIONS: Open to all. Submit via Submittable (guidelines and link at www.structomagazine.co.uk/submissions). Usually respond within six weeks. Rejections may occasionally include unsolicited feedback. Contributors receive print copy/ies and a discount purchase price on the magazine.
WE SAY: A striking cover image, overlaid by the *Structo* logo, which wraps from the front to back. The text layout uses plenty of white space, occasionally flipping sideways to accommodate the long lines of a poem. The content alternates, poetry and prose, with highlights such as an interview with Vera Chok, one of the contributors to the anthology *The Good Immigrant* edited by Nikesh Shukla.
See also: Structo Press (poetry publisher p72 and prose publisher p159)

SYNAESTHESIA MAGAZINE
DIGITAL
synaesthesiamagazine@gmail.com
www.synaesthesiamagazine.com
Editors: Annabelle Carvell, Carlotta Eden, Caroline Icke
Established 2013. Very mixed form (fiction, poetry, interview, articles, music). All online content available to all.
GENRES: Literary fiction; poetry;

art, fashion and photography; music, stage and screen; science, technology and medicine; travel – article subjects can be dependent on the issue theme.
SUBMISSIONS: Open to all, during submissions windows. Submit through Submittable at synaesthesia.submittable.com/submit. Guidelines at www.synaesthesiamagazine.com/#!submissions/ck0q. Usually responds within one to three months. Writer and artist contributors receive a small payment of £5.
WE SAY: Previously a 'flip-book' style digital magazine, *Synaesthesia* has more recently moved into a pure webpage approach – but it's still a feast for all senses. Bold edgy photographs and paintings compliment every piece of work; video and music are also incorporated into the design. This is a thoroughly modern magazine, and the writing is punchy, sharp and beautiful. Each issue has a different theme, with the archives available. The editors have also released their first print issue, 'We Are Women', which is as bold and sleekly designed as the digital issues.

TALES FROM THE FOREST
E-ZINE
talesfromtheforest.mag@gmail.com
www.talesfromtheforest.net
Editor: Rose Fortune
Established 2016. Poetry, prose, art. All online content available to all.
GENRES: Literary.
SUBMISSIONS: Open to all, but submissions are theme-based so check the guidelines at www.talesfromtheforest.net/

submissions. Submit by email to talesfromtheforest.mag@gmail.com. Usually responds within one to three months. Feedback on rejections only if requested. Unpaid.

WE SAY: *Tales from the Forest* is an incredibly visually striking site, with surreal and bold illustrations linking to each issue of the e-zine, plus another (also striking) smaller illustration leading to an author spotlight interview. Each issue features work by artists (not necessarily art that's similar to the type that illustrates the site). We particularly looked at Issue 5, with strong, emotional poetry and beautiful stories. The contents are listed by author name rather than piece title, which means a casual browser doesn't necessarily have a hint as to the content of what they are about to read.

TEARS IN THE FENCE

PRINT
Portman Lodge, Durweston, Blandford Forum, Dorset DT11 0QA
tearsinthefence@gmail.com
www.tearsinthefence.com
Editor: David Caddy
Established 1984. Mainly poetry, reviews and interviews. Annual subscription £25 for three issues. Available direct from publisher website; by post and email order; and at local literary events. Nominated for Best Poetry Magazine Pulitzer Award and nominated for Best Poetry Editor Pulitzer Award.
GENRES: Drama and criticism; poetry; art, fashion and photography; travel; literary fiction.
SUBMISSIONS: Open to all. Submit by email to tearsinthefence@gmail.com. Guidelines at www.

tearsinthefence.com/how-to-submit. Usually responds within one to three months, with feedback offered for a fee. Contributors receive a print copy of the magazine.

WE SAY: An internationalist literary magazine producing a range of forms, from poetry and fiction to critical reviews and essays. This glossy, simplistically styled publication contains a high quantity and quality of writing, including some experimental and between-genre pieces. We looked at Issue 65 in which the editorial note fiercely asserts the importance of independent publishing; proudly branding their publication as an outlet for alternative thought driven by human issues and concerns.

TEST CENTRE

PRINT
71 Oriel Road, London E9 5SG
admin@testcentre.org.uk
www.testcentre.org.uk
Editors: Jess Chandler, Will Shutes
Established 2012. Mixed form. Publications available direct from publisher website; from independent bookshops; and at local literary events.
Test Centre was nominated for Most Innovative Publisher at the Saboteur Awards 2015.
GENRES: Poetry; fiction.
SUBMISSIONS: During submission windows only. Submit by post (71 Oriel Road, London E9 5SG) or by email (admin@testcentre.org.uk). Guidelines at www.testcentre.org.uk/about/submissions. Usually responds within one to three months. Rejections may occasionally include unsolicited feedback. Contributors receive a

free print copy.
WE SAY: A4, 64 pages, with a stab-stapled spine. 'Test Centre Six' (the issue we looked at) has a heavy cardboard cover with monochrome artwork. Released in a limited edition series, *Test Centre* features fiction and poetry both from contributing writers, and from authors under the Test Centre book imprint.
See also: poetry publisher p74 and prose publisher p162

THREE DROPS FROM A CAULDRON
DIGITAL AND PRINT
www.threedropspoetry.co.uk
Editors: Kate Garrett, Amy Kinsman, Grant Tarbard, Becca Goodin
Established 2015. Mixed form. Digital magazine with five Season Specials a year in print. All online content available to all.
GENRES: Mythology; folklore; fairytales; literary; horror.
SUBMISSIONS: Open to all. Submit by email to threedropspoetry@gmail.com. Guidelines at www.threedropspoetry.co.uk/submissions/web-journal-submissions/. Usually responds within four weeks, with feedback only if requested. Contributors receive royalty share payment for seasonal specials. Digital journal contributions are unpaid.
WE SAY: The flip-book style digital issue ('Beltane 2017') that we looked at has a beautiful Rackham-style illustrated cover with a script font. The inner pages are plainer, allowing the writing to carry the elemental, fey feel of the magazine. The poetry featured is rooted in nature, very textural, with more than a few poems inspired by fairytales. We particularly enjoyed

the angry, heartbroken poem 'The Giant's Wife' by Wendy Mannis Scher, written from the point of view of the giant's wife in *Jack and the Beanstalk*, looking for her husband after he chased Jack.
See also: Three Drops Press (poetry publisher p74 and prose publisher p163)

TOKEN MAGAZINE
PRINT
tokenmagazine@gmail.com
www.tokenmagazine.co.uk
Editor: Sara Jafari
Established 2017. Mixed form. Publications available direct from publisher website and at select zine fairs.
GENRES: Literary, modern, experimental, commercial, life writing.
SUBMISSIONS: Open to all, focusing on those under-represented in the arts. Submit by email to tokenmagazine@gmail.com. Guidelines at www.tokenmagazine.co.uk/callforsubmission. Usually responds within one to three months. No feedback offered with rejections. Contributors receive a print copy.
WE SAY: We looked at a digital version of Issue 1, which has a colourful geometric design, the bright borders of the cover offset by a black and white line drawing. This is a well-designed magazine, with thoughtful choices of illustration and photography, and excellent use of colour in the background. The contents give voice to unheard writers, with strong writing and imagery exploring, for example, the Black experience and why 'nude' means peachy beige. Though no theme was planned, the editorial

note points out that many of the (beautifully written) pieces deal with feelings of isolation. This is a new publication, and clearly one to watch.

TRAFIKA EUROPE
DIGITAL
editor@trafikaeurope.org
www.trafikaeurope.org
Prints quality new fiction (short stories and novel excerpts) and poetry in English and English translation from across Council of Europe countries.

UNDER THE RADAR
PRINT
mail@ninearchespress.com
www.ninearchespress.com
Editors: Matt Merritt, Jane Commane
Established 2008. Mainly poetry, some short fiction. Annual subscription £18 (soon to be £22). Available direct from publisher website; by post and email order; at chain bookshops nationwide; at independent bookshops; at literary events; from Amazon; and through Inpress Books.
Winner of the 2014 Sabotage Award for Most Innovative Publisher.
SUBMISSIONS: Open to all, during submissions windows. Submit through Submittable at ninearchespress.submittable. com/submit. Guidelines at www. ninearchespress.com/magazine. html. Usually responds within one to three months. No feedback if rejected. Unpaid.
See also: Nine Arches Press (poetry publisher) p52

[UNTITLED] ☆
PRINT AND DIGITAL
untitledfalkirk@gmail.com
www.untitledfalkirk.co.uk
Editor: Craig Allan
Established 2012. Mixed form. Available direct from publisher website; by post and email order; at selected/local chain bookshops; at independent bookshops; and at local literary events. All online content is available to all.
GENRES: Crime/thriller/mystery; fantasy/sci-fi; graphic/comics; literary fiction; poetry; art, fashion and photography; society, education and politics.
SUBMISSIONS: [Untitled] now accepts national and international submissions. Submit only during submissions windows, by email to untitledfalkirksubmissions@gmail. com. Usually responds within four weeks. Rejections may occasionally include unsolicited feedback. Contributors receive a print copy of the magazine.
WE SAY: [Untitled] has unveiled a new website with a digital archive of the zine, so we were able to scroll through the past five issues, which brim with a range of art and writing. That the zine is 'artist-led' shows in the variations in illustration – the covers are visually stunning. The poetry and prose within are character-driven, energetic and nudge-wink at the reader. The text is cleanly laid out on the pages between adverts for local events, photography and more art. The print version is free, so each issue ends with a plea to pass it on to a friend.
See also: Untitled Falkirk (poetry publisher) p76

VISCERAL REALISM
PRINT
editorial@visceral-realism.co.uk
www.visceral-realism.co.uk

Editors: Victoria EM, Matthew Scholar, Lucy Simpson, Sean McGandy, Andrew Lawson, Wanda Dunham, Danielle Matthews, Matthew Adamson

Established 2016. Mixed form. Publication available direct from publisher website and by direct mail and email orders.

GENRES: Literary; art.

SUBMISSIONS: Open to writers living in Manchester at the time of publication, or otherwise at least having been in Manchester. Submit by email to submissions@visceral-realism.co.uk or online at www.visceral-realism.co.uk. Guidelines at www.visceral-realism.co.uk/submissions. Usually responds within one to three months. Feedback provided only if requested. Contributors receive a print copy.

VISUAL VERSE

DIGITAL / ONLINE ANTHOLOGY OF ART AND WORDS
visualverse@thecurvedhouse.com
www.visualverse.org
Editors: Preti Taneja, Kristen Harrison
Established 2013. Mixed form. All content available to all.

GENRES: Fantasy/sci-fi; historical fiction; literary fiction; poetry; art, fashion and photography. Welcomes all genres with a literary register.

SUBMISSIONS: Submit through the submissions form at www.visualverse.org/submit (guidelines at same address). Cannot respond individually with acceptance/rejections – if accepted, pieces appear on the site within one week. Editors sometimes edit in collaboration with the writer. Contributors receive extensive publicity and the opportunity to be published in related projects and other journals.

WE SAY: *Visual Verse* gives their writers a gorgeous monthly picture prompt and one hour to respond to it. The work is carefully curated and cleanly presented, and each month's selection shows an extraordinary breadth of imagination. The editors also promote their writers, and maintain an easy-to-search archive. *Visual Verse* is a unique publication with an extensive readership – a great way to challenge yourself and get your work read.

WALES ARTS REVIEW ☆

E-ZINE / DIGITAL
www.walesartsreview.org
Editor: Gary Raymond
Established 2012. Mainly non-fiction. All online content available to all. Some published fiction has been released as an anthology.

GENRES: Literary fiction; art, fashion and photography; music, stage and screen; society, education and politics.

SUBMISSIONS: Submit by email to gary@walesartsreview.org. Guidelines at www.walesartsreview.org/contact. Usually responds within four weeks. Rejections may include occasional unsolicited feedback. Unpaid.

WE SAY: *Wales Arts Review* is a professional e-zine, complete with eye-catching headlines, sliding images and daily updates. The focus is on reviews but creative writing and illustrations are also included – there's a handy link that take you straight to the stories, including work from some of Wales' best writers.

WASAFIRI MAGAZINE ☆
PRINT
Wasafiri, c/o School of English and Drama, Queen Mary University of London, Mile End Road, London E1 4NS
wasafiri@qmul.ac.uk
www.wasafiri.org
Editors: Susheila Nasta (founding editor), Rukhsana Yasmin (deputy editor)
Established 1984. Mixed form. Subscription approx £50, and can only be purchased via publisher Taylor and Francis. Single issues are also available by post and email order, and at independent bookshops and local literary events. Only subscribers/purchasers can access online content.
GENRES: Crime/thriller/mystery; drama and criticism; erotica; fantasy/sci-fi; graphic/comics; horror; historical fiction; literary fiction; poetry; romance; art, fashion and photography; biography and true stories; children and teenagers; history; society, education and politics; travel and literary criticism.
SUBMISSIONS: Open to all. Submit via email to wasafiri@open.ac.uk. Check submission guidelines at www.wasafiri.org/submissions. Usually responds in over six months. Rejections may include occasional unsolicited feedback. Contributors are paid a set rate, and receive a print copy and a discount purchase price on the magazine.
WE SAY: Perfect-bound, 100-page almost-A4 literary magazine, *Wasafiri* has a glossy, contemporary design that usually features photographic artwork on the cover. Chock full of international contemporary writing, the magazine opens with articles, interviews and art commentary (complete with full colour pictures), followed by short fiction and poetry. It ends with plenty of in-depth reviews of books from around the world. As befits an international magazine, plenty of the writing inside is translated. The issue we looked at had a particular focus on Brazilian culture.

WHITE REVIEW, THE
PRINT AND E-ZINE
editors@thewhitereview.org
www.thewhitereview.org
Mixed form, including poetry, short stories, criticism, features and essays, published as separate online and print issues. Shortly to launch a space for book and exhibition reviews online. Serious-minded but accessible work.

WIFIE
E-ZINE
hello@wifie.co
www.wifie.co
Editors: Rachel Morgan-Bruce, Stephanie Torrance
Mixed-form e-zine, looking for fiction, poetry, non-fiction, visuals (images or video from artists, photographers, performance artists etc), as well as experimental fiction, commentary, lyrics, reviews and other miscellany. The zine also promotes different cultural events.

WILDNESS
ONLINE JOURNAL
submissions@readwildness.com
www.readwildness.com
Editors: Michelle Tudor, Peter Barnfather
Established 2015. Mixed form. All online content available to all.

232

GENRES: Literary; poetry.
SUBMISSIONS: Open to all.
Submit by email to submissions@
readwildness.com. Guidelines at
www.readwildness.com/submit.
Usually responds within four
weeks. No feedback offered with
rejections. Unpaid.
WE SAY: The *Wildness* homepage
opens straight onto the most
recent issue, with plenty of white
space and in a large clear font,
with accents of green. The issue
is introduced with a pullquote,
and the contents divided into
two columns. Each content item
has a quote subhead, a small
picture of the author and a note
as to the type of writing you'll
be clicking through to. It's a
smart and effective layout. Once
through to the writing, more
is made of the space (no more
columns). It's easy on the eye, the
writing is a very high standard, and
this is a contemporary and pleasant
read.
**See also: Platypus Press (poetry
publisher p58 and prose publisher
p148)**

WINAMOP.COM
E-ZINE
editor@winamop.com
www.winamop.com
Established 2003. Mixed form.
All online content available to all.
GENRES: Drama and criticism;
historical fiction; literary fiction;
poetry; biography and true stories;
music, stage and screen.
SUBMISSIONS: Open to all. Submit
by email to editor@winamop.com.
Guidelines at www.winamop.com/
guidelines.htm. Usually responds
within four weeks. Rejections may
include occasional unsolicited
feedback.

WE SAY: *Winamop* is an
established, home-brew e-zine,
featuring work from a community
of regular contributors, which it is
actively looking to expand. The
design is somewhat old-fashioned,
but wins points for being easy to
navigate and read. The supportive
vibe and encouraging submissions
blurb ('if you think it's good
enough, likely so will we') make
it a very welcoming and inclusive
publication.

WORLD'S TONGUE, THE
E-ZINE
theworldstongue@gmail.com
www.theworldstongue.com
Editor: Charlea Harrison
Established 2017. Poetry, prose,
translation. Keen to support
unpublished and young writers
as well as established writers. All
online content available to all.
GENRES: Poetry; short/flash fiction;
translation; identity; experimental.
SUBMISSIONS: Open to all. Submit
by email to theworldstongue@
gmail.com. Guidelines at www.
theworldstongue.com/submit.
Usually responds within four
weeks. Rejections may occasionally
include unsolicited feedback.
Unpaid.
WE SAY: A new e-zine with a
simple yet attractive website
which is easy to navigate. The
website focuses on celebrating
identity and inclusivity, and this
is reflected in its submissions
criteria. Whilst predominantly
accepting poetry and prose,
the submissions guidelines also
seek experimental genres and it
welcomes non-fiction criticism on
the theme of identity.

YOUR ONE PHONE CALL
E-ZINE
youronephonecall@yahoo.co.uk
youronephonecall.wordpress.com
Editor: Dai Shotter
'Poetry with a knife edge'. A Wales-based literary zine, for the most part publishing 'top notch' poetry, but also occasionally flash fiction and short stories, on a rolling basis (no simultaneous submissions).

Poetry magazines and e-zines

These journals and magazines are all dedicated to poetry only – any prose they publish is strictly poetry-related, in the form of interviews, news, reviews or articles.

No matter what type of poetry you write, you should be able to find a home for it here. There is an astonishing range of style on display, from performance, to punk, to formal; here, poetry stalwarts jostle shoulders with scrappy zines and e-zines.

Poetry magazines and e-zines

ACUMEN LITERARY JOURNAL
PRINT
6 The Mount, Higher Furzeham Road,
Brixham, South Devon TQ5 8QY
01803 851098
info@acumen-poetry.co.uk
www.acumen-poetry.co.uk
Editor: Patricia Oxley
Established 1985. Annual
subscription £16. Available direct
from publisher website; by post
and email order; at local literary
events; and on Amazon.
Award-winning publication.
SUBMISSIONS: Open to all.
Submit by post or by email to
6 The Mount, Higher Furzeham
Road, Brixham, South Devon TQ5
8QY or patriciaoxley6@gmail.
com. Usually responds within four
weeks. Feedback only if requested.
Contributors receive a print copy.
WE SAY: acumen is one of our
leading poetry magazines,
combining poetry with reviews and
articles. A5 and perfect bound, it's
well designed, with sleek, eye-
catching covers and quality writing
that has the knack of being serious
but readable, inviting responses
to previous issues and opening
discussion through reviews and
essays. We looked at Issue 80,
in which Editor Patricia Oxley
describes the process of choosing
the included poems. Frequently
and fairly described as one of
the most wide-ranging, inclusive
poetry journals around, this should
be a prime target for any serious
poet.
**See also: acumen (poetry publisher)
p15**

AGENDA MAGAZINE
PRINT AND ONLINE BROADSHEETS
The Wheelwrights, Fletching Street,
Mayfield, East Sussex TN20 6TL
editor@agendapoetry.co.uk
www.agendapoetry.co.uk
Editor: Patricia McCarthy
Established 1959. Annual
subscription £28.
SUBMISSIONS: Open to all,
during submission windows.
Submit by email to submissions@
agendapoetry.co.uk. Usually
responds within one to three
months. Rejection may occasionally
include unsolicited feedback.
WE SAY: Agenda is a perfect-
bound publication with an
anthology aesthetic. Although
the page count varies, each issue
is book length and the title and
theme are chosen to reflect the
submissions. We looked at Vol 49,
No 1: 'Callings'. The matt cover
is usually the work of a chosen
artist (who is featured in the
publication and online) on a block-
colour background. The magazine
presents lyrical, accessible poems,
essays and reviews on cream
paper, and offers free supplements
as Broadsheets on its website.
**See also: Agenda Editions (poetry
publisher) p15**

ANIMA
PRINT
www.animapoetry.uk
Editor: Marcus Sly
Established 2014. Annual
subscription £15 (including
postage). Available direct from
publisher website.

GENRES: Spirituality and beliefs.
SUBMISSIONS: Open to all. Submit through Submittable at anima. submittable.com/submit. Usually responds within four to six months. Rejection may occasionally include unsolicited feedback. Contributors receive a print copy (but must contribute postage costs).
WE SAY: We looked at a PDF of the first issue of *Anima*. The print version of the 72-page A5 magazine is perfect bound, with a solid colour cover, and the title and butterfly logo embossed in white – a style that serves the publication well. The theme was spiritual, the poems curated and displayed in a way that takes the reader on a journey. There is a feeling of being offered stories in poetry form, compounded by the inclusion of 'epilogue' poems in their own section at the end. With very little information about the contributing poets, this is all about the poetry, and presenting it in such a way that it stands on its own.
See also: Anima Poetry Press (poetry publisher) p16

ANTIPHON

DIGITAL AND E-ZINE
editors@antiphon.org.uk
www.antiphon.org.uk
Editors: Rosemary Badcoe,
Noel Williams
Established 2011. Free access – all online content available to all. Includes recordings of poets reading their work on the blog.
SUBMISSIONS: Open to all. Submit through Submittable at antiphon.submittable.com/submit. Guidelines at www.antiphon.org. uk/index.php/submissions. Usually responds within one to three

months. Rejection may occasionally include unsolicited feedback. Unpaid.
WE SAY: This free online 61-page magazine publishes original poems, submitted through their website. The issues are designed to be downloaded in PDF format, and have a somewhat plain but nevertheless felicitous layout. We looked at Issue 21, which is set up as a theatre play with four acts, all containing seven to nine poems, plus reviews on the poets' first published book. Authors' biographies are displayed at the end of the magazine, which keep the poems clear from distracting information, displaying them in their full quality.

ARTEMIS POETRY ☆

PRINT
3 Springfield Close, E Preston, West Sussex BN16 2SZ
01903 783816
editor@poetrypf.co.uk
www.secondlightlive. co.uk
Editors: Dilys Wood and guest editors
Established 2002. Subscription £11 annual, including postage and packing. Back copies £5. Available by post and email order.
SUBMISSIONS: Open to women only. Submit by post to 3 Springfield Close, East Preston, West Sussex BN16 2SZ. Usually responds within one to three months, only to successful submissions. Unpaid.
WE SAY: Issues of *ARTEMISpoetry* are generally around 60 pages long, and the magazine features the work of new and established women writers only, and particularly that of older poets. The cover design is a little crowded (and has been relatively unchanged

for years) with the layout containing so much colour and so much text that at first glance it's not recognisable as a magazine cover. The contents count, though – publisher Second Light is a formidable organisation and *ARTEMIS* is packed with worthy essays and interviews alongside the poetry, again bringing much-needed attention to female poets.

BACKLASH JOURNAL
PRINT
www.backlashpress.com
Publisher: Gretchen Heffernan
Backlash Journal is the regular publication from Backlash Press, an independent publishing house dedicated to releasing work that narrates a contemplated resistance to obedience and trend. Looks for 'experimental, yet enduring' work. Send up to three poems.
See also: Backlash Press (poetry publisher p19 and prose publisher p93)

BLACKBOX MANIFOLD
E-ZINE
www.manifold.group.shef.ac.uk
Editors: Alex Houen, Adam Piette
Established 2008. All online content available to all.
GENRES: Experimental; literary; DIY.
SUBMISSIONS: Open to all. Guidelines at www.manifold.group.shef.ac.uk/issue1/submissions.html. Usually responds within one to three months. No feedback offered with rejections. Unpaid.
WE SAY: This e-zine was easy to navigate, with archives and submissions very clearly marked. The site has a clean bold aesthetic without the use of images so the only thing for a reader to focus on

is the work. Chosen submissions for each issue are organised by author, and interviews and reviews are listed separately.

BLACK LIGHT ENGINE ROOM, THE
PRINT
12 Harrogate Crescent, Middlesbrough TS5 6PS
theblacklightenginedriver@hotmail.co.uk
Editor: p.a. morbid
Established 2010. Poetry, prose. Subscription £18 (UK), £20 (Europe), £30 (rest of the world) for three issues per year. £30 (UK), £40 (Europe), £50 (rest of the world) for both *Black Light Engine Room* and Dark Matter chapbooks (see p239). Available by post and email order; and at local literary events.
SUBMISSIONS: Open to all. Submit by email to theblacklightenginedriver@hotmail.co.uk. Usually responds within one to three months. No feedback offered with rejection. Contributors receive a print copy.
WE SAY: A 17-page A4 stapled magazine, on slightly shiny paper, with a wildly eye-catching and colourful wrap-around cover design. We looked at Issue 13, where the front page showed an illustrated cat gazing out at the reader, and the back cover showed the back of the cat. The poetry within is intense, but each page contains around four poems, sometimes by different writers, which can make it difficult to focus on just the one poem.
See also: The Black Light Engine Room (poetry publisher) p239

BLITHE SPIRIT
THE BRITISH HAIKU SOCIETY
PRINT

blithespirit.editor@gmail.com
www.britishhaikusociety.org.uk/journal
Editor: Shrikaanth Krishnamurthy
Established 1991. Poetry. Annual
subscription costs £27 within the
UK. Issues available direct from the
publisher website; by direct mail
and email orders; and at national
literary events. Some online
content available to all.
GENRES: Haiku; tanka; haibun;
renku.
SUBMISSIONS: Open to members
of The British Haiku Society only.
Submit by email to blithespirit.
editor@gmail.com. Guidelines at
www.britishhaikusociety.org.uk/
journal. Usually responds within
four weeks. Rejections may include
occasional unsolicited feedback.
Unpaid.
WE SAY: We looked at a PDF
sampler of *Blithe Spirit*, which had
a plain black-and-white layout with
a serif font. The design makes
good use of the space, scattering
haiku (and senryu, tanka, haibun
and sequences) down the page so
the eye skips from one to the next,
allowing the images to settle. The
poetry included ranges from classic
haiku form to more experimental
approaches (we were particularly
struck by Chris Luck's home
intruder haiku).

BUTCHER'S DOG POETRY
MAGAZINE
PRINT

c/o New Writing North,
3 Ellison Terrace, Ellison Place,
Newcastle upon Tyne NE1 8ST
submissions@butchersdogmagazine.
com
www.butchersdogmagazine.com

Editors: Degna Stone, Luke Allan,
Sophie F Baker, Jake Campbell,
Amy Mackelden, Andrew Sclater
Established 2012. Poetry, reviews,
interviews. Subscription £11
per annum + p&p. Available
direct from publisher website, in
selected/local chain bookshops
and independent bookshops, and
at literary events.
Butcher's Dog was selected for The
Pushcart Prize 2016.
SUBMISSIONS: *Butcher's Dog*
is currently on hiatus while the
editorial team make plans. Keep
checking their website for further
news.
**See also: Butcher's Dog (poetry
publisher) p21**

COMPASS MAGAZINE, THE
E-ZINE

editors@thecompassmagazine.co.uk
www.thecompassmagazine.co.uk
Editors: Lindsey Holland,
Andrew Forster
Established 2015. Poetry, reviews,
poetics. All online content freely
available to all.
SUBMISSIONS: Submit by email
to editor@thecompassmagazine.
co.uk. Guidelines at www.
thecompassmagazine.co.uk/
submissions-2. Usually responds
within one to three months. No
feedback with rejection. Unpaid.
WE SAY: A stylish e-zine, *The
Compass* is a site that's been
designed from scratch to best suit
its purpose (as opposed to being
created from a simple template).
The range of content – reviews,
interviews, articles and poems –
means the home page is quite
crowded, but it's easy to navigate
and pleasant to look at. The content
is top-end: this is a poetry zine run
by poets for the poetry community.

CRUNCH, THE
E-ZINE, PODCASTS AND VIDEO
www.crunchpoetry.com
Editors: Richard James Jones,
Adam Sillman, Rhys Owain Williams
Established 2015. All online
content available to all.
SUBMISSIONS: By invitation only.
Unpaid.
WE SAY: *The Crunch* is a
multimedia poetry magazine.
Each issue takes up a single
page of the site and focuses
on a single featured poet. The
content includes a 'cover' image,
which includes the issue number
ensconced next to a carefully
considered editorial; the biography
of the featured poet and a photo;
a podcast interview with the poet;
and videos of the poet performing.
Despite the amount of content,
the approach isn't too crowded or
overwhelming, and it's a pleasure
to focus so wholly on the work of a
single writer.

CTRL+ALT+DEL
E-ZINE
Top Flat, 52 High Street, Bethesda
LL57 3AN
rhys.trimble@gmail.com
www.cad.trimbling.com
Editor: Rhys Trimble
Established 2008. All online
content is available to all.
GENRES: Experimental; minimalist;
vispo.
SUBMISSIONS: Submission usually
by invitation only, but 'if you think
you fit in, have a go'. Submit by
email (rhys.trimble@gmail.com).
Usually responds within one to
three months. Feedback offered
if requested. Unpaid (except for
glory).

DARK HORSE, THE
PRINT
www.thedarkhorsemagazine.com
Founded in 1995 by Scottish
poet Gerry Cambridge. Publishes
poetry – both free verse and in
metre and rhyme – alongside
essays, reviews, interviews.
Welcomes submissions (in
hard copy only) from new and
established poets.

DIAMOND TWIG
E-ZINE
9 Eversley Place,
Newcastle upon Tyne NE6 5AL
0191 276 3770
diamond.twig@virgin.net
Editor: Ellen Phethean
Primarily a book publisher, but
also publishes one poem a month
online.
**For fuller descriptions of this press,
see also poetry publisher p27 and
prose publisher p107**

ENVOI POETRY JOURNAL
PRINT
Meirion House, Tanygrisiau,
Blaenau Ffestiniog, Wales LL41 3SU
01766 832112
www.cinnamonpress.com
Editors: Jan Fortune, Kay Syrad
Established 1957. Poetry, reviews,
translations, interviews and
features. £16 for three-issue annual
subscription. Publication available
direct from publisher website; at
local literary events and via Inpress
Books.
GENRES: All poetry forms welcome
in *Envoi*.
SUBMISSIONS: During submissions
windows: please send in January
(for June); May (for October);
October (for February).
Submit by email only to
envoi@cinnamonpress.com.

Guidelines at www.cinnamonpress.com/index.php/envoi. Usually responds within one to three months. Standard email/letter rejection in most cases, but may offer feedback to those who have come close to publication.

WE SAY: A larger-than-A5 perfect-bound magazine with a matt cover. We saw Issue 177, which is divided into three sections: poetry, features and essays, and reviews. In the former, two poems by Harriet Parker were of note, personifying two experiences you might not have had a word for: 'Mamihlapinatapai' (a look between two who long to start something but are too scared) and 'Kilig' (the heady-sublime rush you feel right after something good happens).

For a fuller description of this press, including what They Say, see also Cinnamon Press (prose publisher p23 and poetry publisher p100)

ERBACCE
PRINT
erbacce@blueyonder.co.uk
www.erbacce-press.com
Editor: Dr Alan Corkish
Co Editor: Dr Andrew Taylor
Established 2004. Quarterly journal, available direct from publisher website; by post and email order; at independent bookshops; at national and local literary events; and from Amazon. Note: *erbacce* is a cooperative, all profits are used exclusively to produce new books.

SUBMISSIONS: Open to all. Submit by post (Dr Andrew Taylor, 5 Farrell Close, Melling, Liverpool L31 1BU) or by email (erbacce@hotmail.com). Guidelines on the website. Usually responds within 48hrs.

Contributors receive a copy of the journal and a discount on further copies.

WE SAY: *erbacce* is a 36-page journal printed on white paper. With a thin cover bearing a slight sheen, this saddle-stitched quarterly has a definite independent feel; the press is entirely owned and run by poets, and aims to present all submission and competition opportunities for free.

See also: erbacce-press (poetry publisher) p31

HIGH WINDOW, THE
E-ZINE
72 Welholme Avenue, Grimsby, North East Lincolnshire DN32 0BP
submissions@thehighwindow.uk
www.thehighwindowpress.com
Editors: David Cooke, Anthony Costello
Established 2016. All online content is available to all.
GENRES: Poetry; verse translations.
SUBMISSIONS: Open to all. Submit by email to submissions@thehighwindow.uk. Guidelines at www.thehighwindowpress.com/submissions. Usually responds within one to three months. No feedback offered with rejection.

WE SAY: A vibrant and professional website which is clear and easy to use. The poems are divided into those selected for each journal, a featured American poet and those which have been translated from other languages. The work is on trend with other contemporary publications such as *Agenda* and *POEM*.

See also: The High Window Press (poetry publisher) p40

IOTA POETRY
PRINT
58 Dale Road, Matlock, Derbyshire
DE4 3NB
info@templarpoetry.com
www.templarpoetry.com
Founded 25 years ago. Published
three times a year. Features around
25 poets per issue, plus features
and reviews. £1 admin fee for
submissions made by email, or
submit by post.
**See also: Templar Poetry (poetry
publisher) p74**

JOURNAL, THE
PRINT
38 Pwllcarn Terrace, Blaengarw,
Bridgend, South Wales CF32 8AS
01656 857483
smithsssj@aol.com
www.thesamsmith.webs.com
Editor: Sam Smith
Established 1996. Subscription £11
(UK only). Available direct from
publisher website; and by post and
email order.
SUBMISSIONS: Publication history
required. Submit by post (38
Pwllcarn Terrace, Blaengarw,
Bridgend, South Wales CF32 8AS)
or by email (smithsssj@aol.com).
Usually responds within four weeks.
No feedback offered with rejection.
Contributors receive a print copy.
WE SAY: The two digital issues we
looked at feature a wide variety
of poetry, as well as reviews
and an ongoing series of Norse
translations. There is a lot packed
into the pages of *The Journal*, with
multiple poems often appearing
together on the page. Experimental
and non-traditional formatting
seems to be welcomed, as well as a
wide variety of subjects.
**See also: Original Plus (poetry
publisher) p53**

LITTER MAGAZINE
E-ZINE
leafepress@hotmail.com
www.leafepress.com/litter
Editor: Alan Baker
Established 2000. Poetry, reviews,
interviews. All online content
available to all.
SUBMISSIONS: Solicited work
only. No feedback offered with
rejections.
**See also: Leafe Press (poetry
publisher) p46**

LONG POEM MAGAZINE
PRINT
20 Spencer Rise, London NW5 1AP
mail@longpoemmagazine.org.uk
www.longpoemmagazine.org.uk
Editors: Linda Black, Lucy Hamilton
Established 2007. Two issues per
year. Annual subscription £16.50
including P&P within the UK; £28
including P&P outside of the UK.
Publication available direct from
website.
GENRES: Poetry; essay on aspect
of long poems; online book
reviews (long poems only).
SUBMISSIONS: Open to all; only
accepts long poems or sequences
(must be at least 75 lines of poetry
but no book length poems). Two
submission months per year: June
and November. Submit by email
to mail@longpoemmagazine.
org.uk. Guidelines at www.
longpoemmagazine.org.uk/
submissions. Usually responds
within three months. No
feedback offered with rejections.
Contributors receive a print copy.
WE SAY: We looked at extracts
from *Long Poem Magazine*
available on the publication
website. The covers of the
magazine are striking in their use
of white space – only the top and

bottom of the cover contain any images, text or colour. The poems we read varied in form and style, and included translated works. Each poem includes a paragraph by the poet providing context and insight into how the poem was written or translated. The editorials – accessible for each issue – are equally in depth and thoughtful.

MAGMA ☆
PRINT AND DIGITAL
23 Pine Walk, Carshalton SM5 4ES
info@magmapoetry.com
www.magmapoetry.com
Editors: rotating editorship
Poetry and poetry-related features, in themed issues. Annual subscription £18.95 (including P&P). Available direct from publisher website; in selected/ local chain bookshops; and in independent bookshops. Online, only subscribers/purchasers can access full content, with some content available to all.
SUBMISSIONS: Open to all. Submit through Submittable at www. magmapoetry.com/contributions (guidelines available at same address). Usually responds within one to three months. Rejection may occasionally include unsolicited feedback. Contributors receive a print copy.
WE SAY: *Magma* is square – 74 large square pages, in fact – and this alone gives it an edge. The colour is full cover, and the inner pages are punctuated with greyscale images and large black headline boxes. We looked at the digital version, but could easily imagine the weight of the magazine in print: modern and hefty. The shape allows space for long lines and experimental,

concrete poetry to be displayed. The editors change for each issue, so the contents will vary, but whatever you send, you know it will look good in print.

MODERN POETRY IN TRANSLATION
PRINT
c/o The Queen's College, Oxford OX1 4AW
editor@mptmagazine.com
www.modernpoetryintranslation.com
Editor: Clare Pollard
Established 1965. Subscription £23/year for three issues. Available direct from publisher website; by post and email order; in selected chain and independent bookshops; and from Amazon. Some digital content is freely available to all.
GENRES: Poetry in translation.
SUBMISSIONS: Submit during submissions windows. Visit www. modernpoetryintranslation. com/submit for current calls for submissions. May take over six months to respond. Rejections may occasionally include unsolicited feedback. Contributors are paid a set rate.
WE SAY: This digital anthology (Issue No 2, 2017) contains several mini-collections from various authors, translated from their native languages. Each poet has a short introduction, written by the translator, and some have headshots included. The colour scheme of the anthology is very crisp and clean, with red being used for page numbers, poet names, and a very powerful mantra at the beginning of the anthology.

NORTH MAGAZINE, THE ☆
PRINT
0114 346 3037

office@poetrybusiness.co.uk
www.poetrybusiness.co.uk
Editors: Ann Sansom, Peter Sansom

Established 1986. Poetry,
reviews, critical articles.
Annual UK subscription £18
(£24 rest of the world). Available
direct from publisher website; by
post and email order; online at
Newsstand; at Salts Mill (Shipley),
Heffer's Bookshop (Cambridge),
Five Leaves Bookshop
(Nottingham), Magazine
(Brighton), and Blackwell's
Bookshop.
SUBMISSIONS: Open to all,
during submissions windows.
Submit by post to The Poetry
Business, Bank Street Arts, 32-40
Bank Street, Sheffield, S1 2DS.
Online submissions accepted from
overseas only. Usually responds
within one to three months.
No feedback with rejection.
Contributors receive a print copy
of the magazine.
**See also: smith|doorstop books
(poetry publisher) p69**

OPEN MOUSE, THE
E-ZINE
theopenmouse.wordpress.com
Editor: Colin Will
Established 1996. Single poems
(around 100 per year). All online
content available to all.
SUBMISSIONS: Open to all. Submit
by email to colin.will@zen.co.uk.
Guidelines at theopenmouse.
wordpress.com. Usually responds
within four weeks. No feedback
offered with rejection.
WE SAY: Self-described as 'a site
for poems', *The Open Mouse* is
developed from a basic WordPress
template, which means it's an easy
scroll through poems that are
added twice a week. The tastes of

the editor, and idiosyncrasies of the
site, mean that the poetry included
is accessible and fairly traditional
in style (no concrete poetry or
strange spacing), nothing requiring
footnotes and explanations. This
well-curated site is a pleasure to
read.

PENNINE PLATFORM
PRINT
Frizingley Hall, Frizinghall Road,
Bradford BD9 4LD
01274 541015
nicholas.bielby@talktalk.net
www.pennineplatform.co.uk
Editor: Nicholas Bielby
Established 1976. Annual
subscription £10.50 for two issues
in the UK; £14 in Europe and £16
worldwide. Publications available
direct from publisher website; by
direct mail and email orders; and at
local literary events.
SUBMISSIONS: Open to all.
Submit by post to Frizingley Hall,
Frizinghall Road, Bradford
BD9 4LD. Guidelines at
www.pennineplatform.co.uk.
Usually responds within four to
six months. Feedback is always
provided. Contributors receive a
free print copy.
**See also: Graft Poetry (poetry
publisher) p38**

PICAROON POETRY
DIGITAL
picaroonpoetry@gmail.com
picaroonpoetry.wordpress.com
Editor: Kate Garrett
Established 2016. All online
content available to all.
GENRES: Literary; gritty realism;
magical realism; absurdism.
SUBMISSIONS: Open to all.
Submit by email to
picaroonpoetry@gmail.com.

Guidelines at picaroonpoetry. wordpress.com/submissions. Usually responds within four weeks. Rejections may occasionally include unsolicited feedback. Unpaid.

WE SAY: The *Picaroon* website has a startling Jolly Roger logo and a dark background, which serves to highlight the circular issue 'cover' images – all of which are photo art. Clicking through takes you to a short introduction and the full cover image, which in turn takes you to the issue itself. Laid out cleanly, in a sans serif font, the names and titles of the poems emphasised with a line graphic.

PB MAG

PRINT
Co. Wicklow, Éire
+353 4022 3556
buspoems@gmail.com
thepoetrybusmag.wixsite.com/ change

Cover image credit: Steve Caldwell

Established 2010. Available from independent bookshops and direct from the publisher website. A poem from *PB$* ('Like That Raw Engine' by George Szirtes) was shortlisted for the 2016 Forward Prize for Best Single Poem, and included in the Forward Prize anthology.

GENRE: Urban-grit.

SUBMISSIONS: Open to all. During submissions windows, submit by email to buspoems@ gmail.com. Guidelines at thepoetrybusmag.wixsite. com/change/submissions. Usually responds within one to three months. Rejections may occasionally include unsolicited feedback. Contributors receive a print copy and a digital copy of the issue.

WE SAY: *Poetry Bus 5* (which we saw in PDF format) is a sizeable magazine, stretching to 126 pages of poetry and wonderful art: the contents cover four pages out of necessity. The poetry includes a range of styles, all presented with an eye for the space. Many of the textured images that feature every ten pages or so make use of words, and there's an extra surprise burst of colour around halfway through, with a four-page comic entry from David Timoney. Something for everyone, basically, but without feeling at all confusing for the reader. The final five pages feature short biogs of every contributor.

See also: PB Press (poetry publisher) p57

The contributors' biographies are on the main website. The poems in Issue 10 are memorable. I was a fan of the four-line 'What Blake didn't say about innocence' by Tristan Moss.
See also: Picaroon Poetry (poetry publisher) p58

PICKLED BODY, THE
E-ZINE
thepickledbody@gmail.com
www.thepickledbody.com
Editors: Dimitra Xidous,
Patrick Chapman
Themed poetry and art magazine, presenting 'work from the surreal to the sensual and points in between'.

PN REVIEW
PRINT
Carcanet Press, 4th Floor, Alliance House, 30 Cross Street, Manchester M2 7AQ
0161 834 8730
info@carcanet.co.uk
www.pnreview.co.uk
Editor: Michael Schmidt
A Carcanet Press publication, and one of the heavy-weights in terms of poetry publication. A top-tier magazine that includes poetry, and poetry related reviews, interviews and academic features.
SUBMISSIONS: Hard-copy submissions only (except for individual subscribers, who can submit electronically). Submissions no longer than ten pages of work. Decisions usually made within eight weeks. See the website for full guidelines.
See also: Carcanet Press (poetry publisher) p22

POEM
PRINT
www.tandfonline.com
Editor: Fiona Sampson
Subscription £30 for four issues. Includes poetry, essays, interviews, some reviews. Available from independent bookshops and direct from the publisher website. Some online content is available to all.
GENRE: English-language or translated world poetry.
WE SAY: We saw a digital version of Volume 5, Number 1, which included a photo of greenery wrapping the spine and reflected in the green of the back cover. The University of Roehampton publication includes an 'Aims and Scope' note at the beginning of the issue, explaining the content they print and how citations are tracked via Taylor & Francis online. This issue, the second in a pair featuring Romanian poets, in particular considered isolationism and exposure to different viewpoints through exposure to international writing.

POEMS IN WHICH
E-ZINE
poemsinwhich@gmail.com
www.poemsinwhich.com
Editors: Rebecca Perry, Alex MacDonald, Amy Key, Wayne Holloway, Nia Davies
Established 2012. All content is freely available to all. Winner of Best Magazine in the 2013 Saboteur Awards.
SUBMISSIONS: Open to all. Submit by email to poemsinwhich@gmail.com. Guidelines at www.poemsinwhich.com/about. Usually responds within one to three months. Rejection may occasionally include unsolicited feedback. Unpaid.
WE SAY: The design of *Poems in Which* is simple: no blaring colours

or images, easy-to-find contact details. The site's USP – that every poem must be a 'poem in which' something happens – means that the often experimental, sharply contemporary styles of the poems featured are grounded: there's always something for the reader to grasp. It also makes for some memorable titles. The magazine is edited by some of the UK's best up-and-coming poets.

POETRY LONDON ☆
PRINT
The Albany, Douglas Way, London
SE8 4AG
020 8691 7260
admin@poetrylondon.co.uk
www.poetrylondon.co.uk

POETRY IRELAND REVIEW ☆
PRINT
11 Parnell Square, Dublin 1, Ireland
+353 1 6789815
publications@poetryireland.ie
www.poetryireland.ie
Editor: Eavan Boland

Established 1981. Annual subscription €38/€42. Available direct from publisher website; by post and email order; at chain and independent bookshops nationwide; at literary events; and from Amazon and other bookshop websites.
GENRE: Literary.
SUBMISSIONS: Open to all. Submit by post to Poetry Ireland, 11 Parnell Square, Dublin 1, Ireland. Guidelines at www.poetryireland.ie/writers/submission-to-pir. Usually responds within four to six months. Rejection may occasionally include unsolicited feedback. Contributors are paid a set rate.
WE SAY: We looked at the online catalogue for this journal. We were struck by the artwork on the cover of the most recent issue (122). All the available covers are professional and eye-catching, but this one is a textured painting of two abstract beings – faces expressive in just a few strokes – holding hands. We hope this sort of craftsmanship appears in the published work, of which there are 121 pages, packed with poetry and essays (the website also lets us view the contents page). We recognised more than a few names in the list (Nessa O'Mahony, Eleanor Hooker and Chris Preddle, for example).
See also: Poetry Ireland (poetry publisher) p60

Editors: Jess Chandler, Ahren Warner, Sam Buchan-Watts, Martha Kapos
Established 1988. Poetry, reviews, interviews with poets. Subscription UK: £25/year; Europe: £33/year; outside Europe: £40/year. Available direct from publisher website and at chain bookshops nationwide.
SUBMISSIONS: Open to all. Submit by post or by email to Poetry London, The Albany, Douglas Way, London SE8 4AG or admin@poetrylondon.co.uk. Usually responds within one to three months. Rejection may occasionally include unsolicited feedback. Contributors are paid a set rate and receive a discount purchase price on the magazine.
WE SAY: One of the major titles in poetry publishing, *Poetry London* is as much about profile as poetry, judging from the portraits of poets it uses as cover images. It contains poetry from around the world, along with features and articles. It also boasts a comprehensive poetry listings section. It's a coup to get your work into this magazine.
See also: Poetry London (poetry publisher) p60

POETRY REVIEW, THE
PRINT AND DIGITAL
The Poetry Society,
22 Betterton Street, London
WC2H 9BX
info@poetrysociety.org.uk
www.poetrysociety.org.uk/publications-section/the-poetry-review
Editor: Emily Berry
The quarterly journal of The Poetry Society, this barely needs an introduction. Includes work by new and established poets, as well as interviews, articles on poetry, critiques and art. Wide readership, as it is distributed to every full member of The Poetry Society. Hard copy submissions only.

POETRY SCOTLAND
PRINT
91-93 Main Street, Callander, Scotland FK17 8BQ
sallyevans35@gmail.com
www.poetryscotland.co.uk
Editor: Sally Evans
A broadsheet magazine containing nothing but poetry, with a focus on Scottish writing. Open only to UK residents, and adamant that work is chosen on merit, not on previous publication history, so a good one for beginners to approach. Poems in English, Gaelic, Scots and occasionally Welsh and other languages all considered. The editor strongly emphasises the need for would-be contributors to read and adhere to the submission guidelines, which are available on the website.

POETRY SPACE SHOWCASE ☆
PRINT AND DIGITAL
www.poetryspace.co.uk
Editor: Susan Sims
Subscription ('Friend of Poetry Space') £15 per year. Available direct from publisher website and on Amazon. All online content is available to all.
SUBMISSIONS: Open to all. Submit by email to susan@poetryspace.co.uk. Usually responds within one to three months. Rejections may include occasional unsolicited feedback. Unpaid.
WE SAY: The *Poetry Space Showcase* is slightly hidden in the Poetry Space website (the link is part-way down the menu to the left) and is less showy than the name suggests: a single, easy-on-

the-eye web page, followed by the featured poems. But showiness isn't everything, and this is still a professional, understated site. A different photograph heralds the start of each new poem, which all share the virtues of striking imagery and memorable metaphors.

See also: Poetry Space (poetry publisher) p61

POETRY WALES ☆
PRINT AND DIGITAL
57 Nolton Street, Bridgend CF31 3AE
01656 663018
info@poetrywales.co.uk
www.poetrywales.co.uk
Editor: Nia Davies
Established 1965. Poetry, reviews, articles. Annual subscription £27. Available direct from publisher website; by post and email order; and at local literary events. Only subscribers/purchasers can access online content.
SUBMISSIONS: Open to all. Submit through Submittable at poetrywales.submittable. com/submit. Usually responds within four to six months. No feedback offered with rejections. Contributors are paid a set rate and receive a print copy of the magazine.
WE SAY: Perfect-bound 96-page magazine on thick quality paper. The copy we looked at (Vol. 51, No. 1) featured a landscape photo on the matt cover, and explored how Patagonia and Wales might imagine each other. The content included some translated poetry, as well as in-depth articles alongside the many poems, which ranged from strict structure to free-verse.
See also: Seren Books (prose publisher p155 and poetry publisher p66)

PULSAR POETRY MAGAZINE
E-ZINE
34 Lineacre, Grange Park, Swindon, Wiltshire SN5 6DA
pulsar.ed@btopenworld.com
www.pulsarpoetry.com
Editor: David Pike
Established 1994. Poetry and reviews. All online content freely available to all.
GENRES: Hard-hitting work with message and meaning. Not keen on religious or epic poems.
SUBMISSIONS: Open to all – up to three unpublished poems, but no simultaneous submissions. Submit by post or by email to Pulsar Editor, 34 Lineacre, Grange Park, Swindon, Wiltshire SN5 6DA or pulsar.ed@btinternet.com. Usually responds within four weeks. No feedback offered with rejection. Contributors receive exposure.
WE SAY: *Pulsar Poetry* has a simple, but unconventional, old-fashioned layout, on a yellow background with rather a small font. With drop-down menus and menu-bars now the norm, it's not easy to find the poems, but once found the content is clearly signposted. The poetry and discourse are modern and the zine works hard to promote its poets and other publications.

QUAIT
PRINT
114 Sandy Lane, Cholton, Manchester M21 8TZ
www.sinewavepeak.com
Managing Editor: Valgerður Þóroddsdóttir
Established 2011. Concrete and formal poetry – each issue dedicated to a different poetic form. Available direct from publisher website and at independent bookshops. Only

subscribers/purchasers can access online content.

SUBMISSIONS: Open to all. Submit by email to luke@sinewavepeak. com. Usually responds within four weeks. Rejection may occasionally include unsolicited feedback. Contributors receive a print copy and a discount purchase price on the magazine.

For a fuller description of this press, see sine wave peak (poetry publisher) p69

QUID
PRINT
www.barquepress.com/quid.php
As the website says, for this zine, 'Name = cost = image'. An occasional journal of 'poetics, criticism, invective and investigation'. Copies available online to download and print out.

See also: Barque Press (poetry publisher) p19

RAUM POETRY
PRINT
info@roomspoetry.com
www.raumpoetry.com
Keen to experiment with unconventional poetry as well as traditional forms, any form of good poetry or poetry in translation is welcomed. Submissions are accepted on a rolling basis.

REACH POETRY
PRINT
24 Forest Houses, Halwill, Beaworthy, Devon EX21 5UU
publishing@indigodreams.co.uk
www.indigodreams.co.uk
Editor: Ronnie Goodyer
Established 1997. A monthly publication. Subscription £51/year for 12 monthly issues or £4.50 single UK. Available direct

from publisher website; and by post and email order. Indigo Dreams Editors won the Ted Slade Award for Services to Poetry 2015.

GENRES: All styles considered and wide range in each monthly issue.

SUBMISSIONS: Open to all. Submit by post (IDP, 24 Forest Houses, Halwill, Beaworthy, Devon EX21 5UU) or by email (publishing@ indigodreams.co.uk). Guidelines at www.indigodreams.co.uk. Poetry, lively letters section, readers' votes. Usually responds within four weeks. Occasional feedback offered with rejection. Contributors receive a monthly monetary prize, shared by the top three as voted for by readers.

WE SAY: A5 monthly publication by Indigo Dreams which showcases both new and experienced poets. The perfect bound, full-colour design is attractive and the issue engages readers through interactive elements in which readers can vote for their favourite poems. Publishing around 500 poems each year, this magazine is a fruitful source of diverse forms, projecting a range of voices through high quality writing.

For what They Say, see Indigo Dreams Publishing Ltd (poetry publisher) p43. See also *The Dawntreader* p192 and *Sarasvati* p220 (mixed-form literary magazines)

RIALTO, THE ☆
PRINT
PO Box 309, Aylsham, Norwich NR11 6LN
info@therialto.co.uk
www.therialto.co.uk
Editor: Michael Mackmin
Assistant Editor: Fiona Moore
Established 1984. Poetry,

poetry news and views. Annual subscription £24 (overseas £24+£12 shipping; concessions £19). Available direct from publisher website and at a few selected/local chain bookshops and independent bookshops.

SUBMISSIONS: Open to all. Submit by post (*The Rialto*, PO Box 309, Aylsham, Norwich NR11 6LN) or Submittable (therialto.submittable. com/submit). Guidelines on the website. Usually responds within one to six months. Returns may include occasional unsolicited feedback. Contributors are paid a set rate.

WE SAY: Perfect-bound, 64-page A4 magazine with an artistic edge. The screamingly bright cover of Issue 83 featured a full-page illustration of reds, oranges and yellows, on a bold blue ground. Inside on thick white paper, poems are laid out with clear thought as to their shape and size, so there's no feeling of overcrowding, and even the title page has a couple of poems on it (Wordsworth and Hopkins).

See also: The Rialto/Bridge Pamphlets (poetry publisher) p63

SALON OF THE REFUSED
E-ZINE
refusedpoems@gmail.com
www.salonoftherefused.com
Editors: Jacqueline Saphra, Norbert Hirschhorn
Established 2017. All online content available to all.

SUBMISSIONS: Open to all. If the poet believes in their work and it has been rejected a minimum of four times, *Salon of the Refused* will publish it. Submit by email to refusedpoems@ gmail.com. Guidelines at www.

salonoftherefused.com/send-us-a-poem. Usually responds within four weeks. Unpaid.

WE SAY: *Salon of the Refused* is a simple site, with a basic menu to the side listing different issues, the contents of which are laid out as one long, scrollable page each. The banner image at the top of the site is a painting of traumatised-looking writer-type – appropriate for the presumably rejection-weary submitters to this zine – which made this reviewer laugh. Despite the required multiple rejections of the work featured, the poetry is nonetheless of a high standard, often rather experimental. We particularly liked the sensuality and texture of Fiona Moore's poem 'Honey from the Strawberry Tree'.

SHEARSMAN MAGAZINE
PRINT
50 Westons Hill Drive,
Emersons Green, Bristol BS16 7DF
editor@shearsman.com
www.shearsman.com/shearsman-magazine
Editor: Tony Frazer
Established 1981 (2003 in its current form). Poetry and literary criticism. Available direct from publisher website, by post and email order, at selected/local chain and independent bookshops and on Amazon and other bookshop websites.

SUBMISSIONS: Open to all, only during submissions windows. Submit by post (Shearsman Books Ltd, 50 Westons Hill Drive, Emersons Green, Bristol BS16 7DF) or by email (editor@shearsman. com), avoiding attachments. Full guidelines at www.shearsman.com/ shearsman-magazine-submissions. Usually responds in up to three

months. No feedback offered if rejected. Contributors receive two free copies of the magazine.
WE SAY: A 108-page A5 publication chock full purely of poetry. We looked at a PDF of *Shearsman*, so can't comment as to the quality of print materials, but the design is clean and effective. A single line draws attention to the poet's name and the poem title, the sans-serif font of which makes a nice comparison with the more traditional serif used for the poems.
See also: Shearsman Books Ltd (poetry publisher) p67

SKYLIGHT 47
PRINT AND DIGITAL
Skylight 47, Treanlaur, Maree, Oranmore, County Galway, Ireland
skylightpoets47@gmail.com
skylight47poetry.wordpress.com
Editors: Ruth Quinlan, Nicki Griffin, Bernie Crawford, Marie Cadden
Established 2013. Mixed form. Subscription €12.40/year within Ireland or €14.40/year outside Ireland for two issues. Publications available direct from publisher website; by direct mail and email orders; from independent bookshops; and at local literary events. Some online content available to all.
Skylight 47 was nominated for the Galway Cathaoirleach Community Awards in 2016.
GENRES: Literary.
SUBMISSIONS: Open to all, during submission windows. Submit by email to skylightpoets47@gmail.com. Guidelines at skylight47poetry.wordpress.com/submissions. Usually responds within one to three months. No feedback offered with rejections.

Contributors receive a print copy.
WE SAY: With a digital newspaper style, this 24-page magazine showcases a great deal of work in a short space, fitting multiple poems or prose pieces on each page. Illustrations compliment the poems, as does a beautifully designed cover, with one artist featured per issue.

SOUTH POETRY MAGAZINE
PRINT
PO Box 4228, Bracknell RG42 9PX
south@southpoetry.org
www.southpoetry.org
Editors: Patrick Osada, Anne Peterson, Chrissie Williams, Andrew Curtis, Peter Keeble
Established 1990, published twice annually. Poetry, reviews, profiles. Annual subscription £12 (or £22 for two years). Available by post and email order; and at the Foyle's Charing Cross and Royal Festival Hall branches in London.
SUBMISSIONS: Open to all. Submit by post to *South Poetry Magazine*, PO Box 4228, Bracknell RG42 9PX. Hard copies only, please, using the submissions form. Full guidelines at www.southpoetry.org/submissions. Individual responses not possible. Successful submitters' names are posted on the website eight to ten weeks after the deadline for that issue's submissions. Contributors receive a print copy.
WE SAY: *South Poetry* has stuck to the same format for years, including the use of a striking black-and-white cover photograph. Contents include a profile and sample work from an established poet, a wide selection of anonymously submitted new poetry, and reviews. We looked

at an online example so can't comment on the print layout, but the style of poems selected is wide-ranging.

SPILLING COCOA OVER MARTIN AMIS
E-ZINE
admin@spillingcocoa.com
www.spillingcocoa.com
Named in honour of Wendy Cope, this website is dedicated to the serious art of writing humorous poetry. Editor's referenced poets include Pam Ayres, Brian Bilston, Spike Milligan and more. Publishes a new poem roughly once a week.

STRIDE MAGAZINE
E-ZINE
editor@stridemagazine.co.uk
stridemagazine.blogspot.co.uk
Editor: Rupert Loydell
Established 1982. Poetry, prose poems, and reviews. All online content available to all.
SUBMISSIONS: Submit two or three pieces in the body of an email to editor@stridemagazine.co.uk. We do not require biographical or bibliographical information. Usually responds within four weeks. No feedback offered with rejections.
WE SAY: *Stride* is hosted on a straightforward blogspot site – not pretty, but it works. Submissions info is at the top of the homepage, and the poems appear in date order in your blogspot view of choice (a scrolling full-page view; tiles; extracts… you choose). Start clicking through to the articles and poetry, and it's clear that the focus for *Stride* is entirely on the work. No menus, nothing distracting – just a clear font and careful layout for each item. Reviews and articles are smart, opinionated and in-depth, and the poetry ranges from traditional to concrete (there are some beautiful shapes on the page).

THANK YOU FOR SWALLOWING
DIGITAL
thankyouforswallowing@gmail.com
thankyouforswallowing.wordpress.com
Editors: Cathleen Allyn Conway, Sarah Nichols
Established 2015. All online content available to all.
GENRES: Feminist; social justice/political; literary; experimental.
SUBMISSIONS: Open to all, during submission windows. Submit by email to thankyouforswallowing@gmail.com. Guidelines at thankyouforswallowing.wordpress.com/submission-guidelines. Usually responds within four weeks. Rejections may occasionally include unsolicited feedback. Unpaid.
WE SAY: We looked at Volume 2, Issue 5 (Nov/Dec 2016), which had a dark cover with a picture of Hillary Clinton 'leaning' on the title image. The layout is clean but interesting, off-setting sans-serif titles against serif, almost old-typewriter, body text. The contents are political – the first poem is titled 'I beg a photo of Hillary Clinton to win the election' – sometimes visceral, occasionally funny and wholeheartedly feminist. We found the whole issue galvanising.

WOLF, THE
PRINT
editor@wolfmagazine.co.uk
www.wolfmagazine.co.uk
Editor: James Byrne

Founded 2002, and quickly
became a leading poetry
magazine. Publishes international
translations, critical prose and
interviews. Poetry aesthetic
leans towards experimental over
mainstream, and serious over light
verse.

Prose magazines and e-zines

We define prose quite widely for this section: short stories, long short stories, flash fiction, creative non-fiction and more – even comics. Any magazine that publishes work that's literary, but not poetry, is included. However, the majority of these magazines focus on what we would normally think of as straight short stories. There are also some stunning publications for writers (and readers) of genre fiction.

AD HOC FICTION ☆
E-ZINE
helpdesk@adhocfiction.com
www.adhocfiction.com
Editor: John O'Shea
Established 2015. Fiction. All
online content available to all.
Ad Hoc Fiction was longlisted for
the Saboteur Awards, Wild Card
Category in 2016 and 2017.
GENRES: Micro-fiction.
SUBMISSIONS: Open to all. Submit
online at www.adhocfiction.com/
write. Usually responds within one
week. Feedback is not available.
The winning contributor of *Ad
Hoc Fiction*'s weekly contest is
rewarded with free entry to the
Bath Flash Fiction Award, worth £9.
WE SAY: *Ad Hoc Fiction* presents
all entries to its weekly competition
as a website-based, read-and-vote
e-book. It's a simple design: one
piece of flash fiction to a page
(there were 88 pages in the week
we looked at). The e-book is set to
perfectly fit a phone screen, and it
saves your last reading location. It's
a nifty set up, allowing for access
to a range of writing styles – but if
you only want to read the winning
stories, simply click the obvious tab
for the crowd-agreed best of the
best. This is an approach appealing
to both readers and writers.
**For a fuller description of this press,
see prose publisher p87**

AESOP MAGAZINE
PRINT AND DIGITAL
editor@aesopmagazine.com
www.aesopmagazine.com
Editor: Max Raku
Established 2015. Mainly fiction.

Free magazine. Print publication
available to all, via direct
distribution outside major central
London stations and in offices,
members' clubs and universities
in the City of London. Available
digitally by email.
GENRES: Crime/thriller/mystery;
drama and criticism; historical
fiction; literary fiction; romance;
biography and true stories;
humour.
SUBMISSIONS: Open to all. Submit
through the form at
www.aesopmagazine.com/
submissions.html (guidelines at the
same address). Usually responds
within one to three months,
with feedback only if requested.
Contributors receive a print copy
and a digital copy.
WE SAY: We looked at Issue 1. At
33-pages and A4 sized, *Aesop*
offers a selection of short stories
every month, against a bright
and charmingly colourful layout
of illustrations in a wide range of
styles that mean this free mag (of
which 60,000 copies in print and
digital are distributed each month)
will catch the eye of both children
and adults. Fonts and colours vary
story to story – a bold approach,
as this could look cluttered, but
Aesop's designers make it work,
and each story really stands out as
a result. The writing is for all ages,
too.

BLACK STATIC
PRINT, DIGITAL AND E-ZINE
5 Martins Lane, Witcham, Ely,
Cambridgeshire CB6 2LB
andy@ttapress.com

www.ttapress.com
Editor: Andy Cox
Established 1994 (under the title
The Third Alternative – renamed
in 2005). Mainly fiction. See www.
ttapress.com/shop for subscription
rates. Publication available direct
from the publisher website; by post
and email order; in chain bookshops
nationwide; in independent
bookshops; and at literary
events. All online content is freely
available to all. Winner of several
British Fantasy Awards and The
International Horror Guild Award.
GENRES: Horror and dark fantasy;
book reviews; film reviews;
interviews; comment.
SUBMISSIONS: Submissions open
to all. Stories of up to 10,000
words. Submit via Submittable
at tta.submittable.com/submit
(guidelines at same address).
Usually responds within four days.
Contributors receive money and a
copy of the magazine. Rejections
may occasionally include
unsolicited feedback.
WE SAY: We saw the digital
version of this slick-looking
horror magazine, which features
both fiction and articles about
the genre, as well as reviews of
both books and film. This issue
also includes a novella by Carole
Johnstone. The cover shows a
black and yellow figure resembling
a blindfolded Statue of Liberty,
and the issue is punctuated by
black-and-white artwork, mostly
photo manipulated. The fiction
in this issue is very subtle, literary
horror, and the magazine seems to
favour slightly longer works. A very
distinguished horror magazine –
well worth a look!
**See also: TTA Press (prose
publisher) p165**

BOHEMYTH, THE
E-ZINE
thebohemytheditor@gmail.com
www.thebohemyth.com
Editor: Alice Walsh
Established 2012. Mixed form. All
online content available to all.
Nominated for the Blog Awards
Ireland 2015.
GENRES: Crime/thriller/mystery;
fantasy/sci-fi; horror; literary fiction;
photography and ilustration;
non-fiction; humour; music, stage
and screen; travel.
SUBMISSIONS: During submissions
windows, submit by email to
thebohemytheditor@gmail.
com. Particularly interested in
receiving experimental writing
& submissions from women and
feminist writers, members of the
LGBTQ+ community, writers of
colour and writers from cultures
currently under-represented in
the publishing industry. Usually
responds within three months.
Rejection may include occasional
unsolicited feedback. Contributors
are unpaid.
WE SAY: *Bohemyth*'s home
page designs has changed from
displaying the contents of the
latest issue in a chart of green
circles with the writers' names in
them, to a more grid-like affair,
displaying images and names.
There's no clue as to whether you'll
be clicking through to fiction or
non-fiction, but this means readers
have the opportunity to discover
writing they might otherwise not
have been drawn to. It's a striking
and tidy design, free of adverts and
images apart from the *Bohemyth*
logo. The writing is evocative,
thoughtful and very, very good.

BOOKANISTA
E-ZINE
editors@bookanista.com
newvoices@bookanista.com
www.bookanista.com
Editors: Farhana Gani, Mark Reynolds

Welcomes general submissions from publishers and established writers for articles, interviews and short fiction. For open submissions, try their New Voices for short fiction.

CASKET OF FICTIONAL DELIGHTS, THE ☆
E-ZINE (ONLINE PUBLICATION)
Unit 5, Fort Horsted Business Centre, Primrose Close, Chatham, Kent ME4 6HZ
07553 131635
joanna@thecasket.co.uk
www.thecasket.co.uk
Editors: Joanna Sterling, Menna Bonsels and various visiting editors.

Established 2011. Fiction and multimedia. All online content available to all.
GENRES: Crime/thriller/mystery/literary fiction/romance.
No non-fiction.
SUBMISSIONS: By invitation only. *The Casket of Fictional Delights* holds an annual Flash Fiction competition from which new writers are drawn.
WE SAY: A bold and professional looking website. The stories are clearly marked not only by title and author, but by themes and style to enable easy browsing. The work included is of a high standard, with authors often widely published. There is also an audio section to enjoy where you can listen to a selection of the stories produced by a professional studio.

They say

Established in 2011 to showcase short stories and flash fiction when these genres were poorly represented in the UK. We publish writers from around the world and diverse backgrounds. We look for stories that will intrigue, amuse and provoke thought in the reader. Our stories are searchable by mood, author and type. Many of the short stories are recorded by professional actors or voiceover artists and published on iTunes, SoundCloud, TuneIn and Stitcher. We are consistently ranked in the top 20 of the short story category on iTunes. Our target readership is adults, mainly in the age range of 30-50.

CRIMEWAVE
PRINT
5 Martins Lane, Witcham, Ely,
Cambridgeshire CB6 2LB
andy@ttapress.com
www.ttapress.com
Editor: Andy Cox
Established 1999. Short stories.
Published irregularly – see
www.ttapress.com/shop for
subscription rates. Publication
available direct from the publisher
website; by post and email order;
in chain bookshops nationwide;
in independent bookshops and at
literary events. All online content
is freely available to all. Award-
winning stories.
GENRES: New modern crime and
mystery.
SUBMISSIONS: Submissions open
to all. Stories of up to 10,000
words. Submit via Submittable
at tta.submittable.com/submit
(guidelines at same address).
Usually responds within four
days. Rejections may occasionally
include unsolicited feedback.
Contributors receive money and a
copy of the magazine.
**See also: TTA Press (prose
publisher) p165**

DOPPELGÄNGER
PRINT
submissions@doppelgangermag.com
www.doppelgangermag.com
Editor: James Hodgson
A new magazine, published twice
a year. *Doppelgänger* strictly prints
three realist short stories and three
magical realist short stories in each
issue. Story-driven literary fiction
preferred.

DUBLIN REVIEW, THE
PRINT
PO Box 7948, Dublin 1, Ireland
order@thedublinreview.com
www.thedublinreview.com
Editor: Brendan Barrington
Established 2000. Mixed form:
fiction and non-fiction. See www.
thedublinreview.com/subscribe for
subscription information. Available
direct from publisher website; by
post and email order; and from
Amazon.
GENRES: Literary fiction; essays;
memoir; travel writing; criticism;
reportage.
SUBMISSIONS: Open to all.
Submit by email to submissions@
thedublinreview.com. Guidelines
at www.thedublinreview.com/
submissions. Usually responds
within one to three months. No
feedback offered with rejection.
Contributors are paid a set rate
and receive a discount purchase
price on the magazine.

EAST OF THE WEB
E-ZINE
submissions@eastoftheweb.com
www.eastoftheweb.com/short-stories
Fiction – short stories across
multiple genres, rates by age and
length for easy browsing. Receives
about half a million unique visitors
per month, and the site offers the
chance to easy reader feedback.

ELLIPSIS ZINE
DIGITAL AND PRINT
www.ellipsiszine.com
Editor: Steve Campbell
Established 2017. Fiction.
Publication available direct from
publisher website. All online
content available to all.
SUBMISSIONS: Submit by email
to ellipsiszinesubs@gmail.com.
Guidelines at www.ellipsiszine.
com/submissions. Contributors
receive print copies and a share

of the royalty fee.

WE SAY: Though we didn't see a print version of the zine, we did look at the online content. The website uses a simple but stylish template to present a range of short fiction, with a new piece added every few days. Each story is illustrated with a photographic image appropriate to the tale. The writing featured is striking, packing a punch in few words – as the best short fiction should.

ELSEWHERE JOURNAL
PRINT AND DIGITAL
paul@elsewhere-journal.com
www.elsewhere-journal.com
Editor: Paul Scraton
Accepts submissions for both the print journal (when subs window is open) and for the blog. 'Dedicated to involved and intelligent writing about place', which should also be combined with the current Issue theme.

FICTION POOL, THE
E-ZINE
thefictionpool@gmail.com
www.thefictionpool.com
Editor: Jo Simmonds
Established 2016. Fiction. All online content available to all.
GENRES: Experimental; literary; realist; surrealist; quirky.
SUBMISSIONS: Open to all. Submit by email to thefictionpool@gmail.com. Guidelines at www.thefictionpool.com/submit. Usually responds within four weeks. Rejection may occasionally include unsolicited feedback. Unpaid.
WE SAY: The homepage of this zine is stacked with colour-rich, moody photographic images drawing the eye to the corresponding story title overlaid on the pictures. It's a little like scrolling through the spines of books on a shelf. *The Fiction Pool* seems to have a propensity for interesting titles. The stories are laid out clearly, in a large font, and the content of them is often visceral, cleverly told, and unflinching. Take, for example, 'Twenty-First Century Mr Chips' by Michael Bloor, which lays out the tale of a paedophile investigation in the form of answer-phone messages.

FLASH: THE INTERNATIONAL SHORT-SHORT STORY MAGAZINE ☆
PRINT
Department of English, University of Chester, Parkgate Road, Chester CH1 4BJ
01244 513152
flash.magazine@chester.ac.uk
www.chester.ac.uk/flash.magazine
Editors: Peter Blair, Ashley Chantler
Established 2008. Mainly fiction. Subscription £11/year. Available direct from publisher website.
GENRES: Literary fiction of up to 360 words, with reviews and literary criticism.
SUBMISSIONS: Open to all. Submit by email to flash.magazine@chester.ac.uk. Guidelines at www.chester.ac.uk/flash.magazine/submissions. Usually responds within six weeks, no feedback with rejection. Contributors receive a print copy of the magazine.
WE SAY: Perfect-bound 111-page magazine that includes flash fiction, essays and reviews. The cover is matt, with a photographic image on the front and appropriately flashy silver spine and back. Reasonable quality white paper inside, and no illustrations, but

plenty of very short fiction. After the original fiction, there's a section called 'Flash presents', which presents classic work (Virginia Woolf, in the issue we looked at – Vol. 7 No. 2), followed by an essay on her work. Then several reviews and advertisements thoughtfully kept to the last few pages.

FLIGHT JOURNAL
E-ZINE
www.flightjournal.org

Publishes bold, short fiction. A journal born of Flight 1000, a Spread the Word Associates scheme. Spread the Word is the London writer's development agency, which identifies and supports talented writers from a diversity of backgrounds.

GHASTLING, THE
PRINT AND DIGITAL
editor@theghastling.com
www.theghastling.com

FICTIVE DREAM
E-ZINE
fictivedream@gmail.com
www.fictivedream.com
Editor: Laura Black

Established 2016. Fiction. Online content available to all.
GENRES: Literary fiction; general fiction.
SUBMISSIONS: Open to all. Submit by email to fictivedream@gmail.com. Guidelines at www.fictivedream.com/submissions-guidelines/. Usually responds within four weeks. Rejections may occasionally include unsolicited feedback. Unpaid.
WE SAY: This e-zine is easy on the eye, with a dusky blue header, sans-serif fonts and a clear menu to follow. We looked at a number of the stories available. All of them are formatted with the title, followed by an appropriate image, the date of publication and the name of the writer. The biogs appear at the end, next to the

They say

We're interested in stories that focus on those moments that change people's lives. Stories with a distinctive voice, clarity of thought and precision of language. They may be on any subject. They may be challenging, dramatic, playful, exhilarating or cryptic. Above all, they must be well-crafted and compelling.

handy tagging options (should you wish to find more stories about e.g. slime / eggs / vinyl). To the left is a list of the most recent titles to be published, and beneath that, the archive sorted by month. Of the stories, we particularly loved Thomas McColl's *Tell me what it means*, which address the standard teen rebellion through music, but in a fresh way, and Sandra Arnold's *The Passion Tree* made us shudder.

Editor: Rebecca Parfitt
Established 2014. Fiction.
Print available on Amazon and via the publication website; all online content available to all.
GENRES: Graphic/comics; horror; literary fiction; the macabre and peculiar. No non-fiction.
SUBMISSIONS: During submissions windows, submit by email to editor@theghastling.com. Usually responds within one to three months. No response by indicated time means a rejection. Unpaid at the moment.
WE SAY: *The Ghastling* calls itself a 'modern-day pennydreadful', but its production values are far higher than that implies. Slightly smaller than A4, with a page count that varies depending on the contents (it started out at 54 pages and has climbed from there), this magazine is perfect bound, using quality materials with a design that harks back to woodcut prints, but with touches of colour and contemporary art mixed in. The cover images so far have been unnerving – and that sense of slowly unveiled horror perfectly invokes the stories within.
See also: The Ghastling Press (prose publisher) p118

GREEN BOOK, THE
PRINT
brian@swanriverpress.ie
www.swanriverpress.ie
Editor: Brian J. Showers
Established 2013. Non-fiction commentaries, articles, reviews. Available direct from publisher website; by post and email order; from independent bookshops and online book dealers; and at national literary events and local literary events.

GENRES: Literary criticism and history based around Irish gothic, supernatural and fantastic. No fiction.
SUBMISSIONS: Open year-round. Usually responds within four weeks. Rejection may occasionally include unsolicited feedback. Contributors receive a print copy.
WE SAY: 108 pages, perfect bound, with a glossy cover that always features white text against a background of green, with a photo image in the middle, *The Green Book* is a scholarly affair, simple and well put together. It contains a mixture of new and old writing (Rudyard Kipling appears in the issue we looked at), with reviews appearing last.
See also: Swan River Press (prose publisher) p159

HALO LIT MAG
DIGITAL
submissions@halolitmag.co.uk
www.halolitmag.co.uk
Editor: Lorrie Hartshorn
'Illuminating fiction by women'. Publishes flash fiction on a theme (up to 1,000 words) accompanied by visual art. Provides prompts for themes. Strictly no genre fiction, non-fiction or poetry.

INTERZONE
PRINT, DIGITAL AND E-ZINE
5 Martins Lane, Witcham, Ely, Cambridgeshire CB6 2LB
andy@ttapress.com
www.ttapress.com
Editor: Andy Cox
Founded 1982, and taken over by TTA Press in 1994. Fiction, interviews, reviews. See www.ttapress.com/shop for subscription rates. Publication available direct from publisher website;

by post and email order; in chain bookshops nationwide; in independent bookshops; at literary events; and from Amazon, Apple, and Weightless Books. All online content freely available to all. Winner of British Science Fiction Association award and British Fantasy Award; nominated many times for the Hugo Award.

GENRES: Sci-fi and fantasy; book reviews; film reviews; interviews; comment.

SUBMISSIONS: Submissions open to all. Stories of up to 10,000 words. Submit via Submittable at tta.submittable.com/submit (guidelines at same address). Usually responds within four days. Rejections may occasionally include unsolicited feedback. Contributors receive money and a copy of the magazine.

WE SAY: The cover of the digital copy we saw of this sci-fi/fantasy magazine is a photo manipulation of a woman, with red and blue light obscuring some of her face. The look is 90's futurism – but stylishly done. The art inside also includes hand-drawn illustrations. The issue itself features articles, fiction and reviews of sci-fi and fantasy media, as well as interviews with authors. The work itself is innovative, almost literary sci-fi – a very interesting read.

See also: TTA Press (prose publisher) p165

LONG STORY, SHORT JOURNAL
E-ZINE
longstoryshortjournal@gmail.com
longstoryshort.squarespace.com
Editor: Jennifer Matthews
Established 2012. All online content available to all.

GENRES: Literary fiction. No non-fiction.

SUBMISSIONS: Open to all, but stories must be 4,000 words or longer. No upper limit. Submit by email to longstoryshortjournal@gmail.com. Guidelines at longstoryshort.squarespace.com/submissions. Usually responds within one to three months. Rejection may occasionally include unsolicited feedback. Unpaid.

WE SAY: One lengthy short story each month appears on the simple professionally designed site. The contents page displays a photo and an introduction to each story; the stories themselves run down the page unimpeded by adverts. If you'd prefer a PDF to print out, *Long Story, Short* welcomes requests by email for that format. With its descriptive and engaging content, this e-zine encourages readers to sit down and take their time to read good writing.

NECESSARY FICTION
E-ZINE
editor@necessaryfiction.com
www.necessaryfiction.com
Editors: Steve Himmer,
Michelle Bailat-Jones (translations),
Helen McClory (fiction),
Susan Rukeyser (reviews)
Book reviews, short stories, 'Research Notes' and occasional interviews and essays, updated throughout the week. Particularly supportive of independent publishers in their reviews, and all areas of writing are open to submissions.

NUMBER ELEVEN MAGAZINE
E-ZINE
numbereleveneditor@gmail.com
www.numberelevenmagazine.com

Editor: Graham Connors
Quarterly publication for short stories, flash fiction, graphic novel artwork and illustrations. Looks for 'edgy and arresting prose' so good that the editors are 'jealous that [we] didn't write [it] ourselves'.

OPEN PEN
PRINT, PODCAST AND BLOG
info@openpen.co.uk
www.openpen.co.uk
Editor: Sean Preston
Established 2011. Fiction. Annual subscription £10 for four issues. Publication available direct from publisher website and from independent bookshops.
In the 2016 Saboteur Awards, *Open Pen* was shortlisted for Best Magazine and Best Anthology.
GENRES: Literary; hipster; urban-grit; humour.
SUBMISSIONS: Open to all. Submit by email to submissions@openpen. co.uk. Guidelines at www.openpen. co.uk/submit. Usually responds within one to three months, with feedback only if requested. Contributors receive free print copies.

PALM-SIZED PRESS
PRINT
palmsizedpress@gmail.com
palmsizedprompts.wordpress.com
Editor: E.M. Killaley
Established 2017. Mainly fiction. Publication available direct from publisher website.
SUBMISSIONS: Open to all, during submission windows and in accordance with specified theme. Submit by email to palmsizedpress@gmail.com. Guidelines at palmsizedprompts. wordpress.com/press. Usually responds within one to three

months. No feedback with rejection. Unpaid.
WE SAY: We saw a sneak peek of the first zine, *Retrospective*. With a white matt, perfect bound cover, the small square book features the line drawn work of one artist. After a section at the front compiled of new submissions, the second presents an anthology of selected works from the previous three years of prompt responses from the e-zine.
See also: *Palm-Sized Prompts* **(mixed-form magazine p215)**

PARAGRAPH PLANET
E-ZINE
www.paragraphplanet.com
A creative writing website that publishes one 75-word paragraph every day. Going since 2008, it accepts a range of writing, including 'a mixture of twist-in-the-tale flash fiction, evocative short, short fiction, openings of published novels or brief moments captured'.

PYGMY GIANT, THE ☆
E-ZINE
thepygmygiant@gmail.com
www.thepygmygiant.com
Editors: Mel George, Sarah Dawkins, Tom Carlisle
Established 2007. All online content available to all.
GENRES: Literary fiction; humour; non-fiction.
SUBMISSIONS: Open to all UK-based writers. Submissions must be 800 words or fewer. Submit by email to thepygmygiant@gmail.com. Guidelines at www.thepygmygiant. com/submissions/submission-guidelines. Usually responds within one to three months. Rejections

may include unsolicited feedback. Unpaid.

WE SAY: The website for this e-zine is straightforward: a banner image at the top, simple to navigate archive down the right-hand side, along with a search bar, and the option to browse by category. The editors make an effort to promote their writers – the page we particularly looked at was a selection of their favourite flash in honour of Flash Fiction Day. The stories were all sharply observant of human behaviour – glimpses into lives. We loved the wry humour of *The Art of War* by Jamie Thunder. The site also includes a section devoted to friends and books.

REFLEX FICTION ☆
E-ZINE
16 Glyme Close, Abingdon OX14 3SY
dave@reflexfiction.com
www.reflexfiction.com
Editor: David Borrowdale
Established 2016. Fiction. All online content available to all.
GENRES: Literary.
SUBMISSIONS: Open to all. Submit online at www.reflexfiction.com/flash-fiction-submissions-entry-form. Guidelines at www.reflexfiction.com/flash-fiction-competition-rules. Usually responds within one to three months. The top three contributions from each quarter win a cash prize.
WE SAY: We looked at the online publication of the most recent *Reflex Fiction* flash winners. 'Barely Casting a Shadow' by Alicia Bakewell is displayed in a framed space on the page, with an image above the title – frankly a very spooky image, that

looks like someone struggling to breathe through cloth stretched over their face. The fiction is (as flash fiction should be) a whole vivid world, complete with broken relationships, in just a few words. High quality and evocative writing.

RIFE
ONLINE JOURNAL
byl@watershed.co.uk
www.rifemagazine.co.uk
Magazine made by the young people of Bristol, for the young people of Bristol. Covers arts, culture, social issues, politics, music film through lists, videos, essays, articles and many gifs. Looking for submissions and pitches.

SCOOP
PRINT
Studio 3, The Print House, 18-22 Ashwin Street, London E83DL
hello@scoopthemag.co.uk
www.scoopthemag.co.uk
A monthly magazine for ages 8+ that includes original fiction and non-fiction and promises 'never to talk down to [its] readers'.

SHIFT_
E-ZINE
Twitter: @Shift_Zine
www.shiftthezine.co.uk
'A magazine about YA literature.' Looks for non-fiction (book reviews, articles, film reviews, interviews) up to 1,500 words. Articles must focus on issues relating to YA. Fiction (500-5,000 words) should be suitable for a YA audience.

SHORELINE OF INFINITY ☆
PRINT, DIGITAL AND E-ZINE
0131 208 1900
editor@shorelineofinfinity.com
www.shorelineofinfinity.com

Editor: Noel Chidwick
Established 2015. Mainly fiction. Available direct from publisher website, post and email order. Only subscribers/purchasers can access online content.

GENRES: Fantasy/sci-fi; reviews; commentary on science fiction related topics.

SUBMISSIONS: Open to all, during submissions windows. Submit via the online manager at www.shorelineofinfinity.com/submissions (guidelines at same address). Usually responds within one to three months. Standard rejection may occasionally include unsolicited feedback. Contributors are paid a set rate and receive a digital copy of the magazine.

WE SAY: This magazine continues to go from strength to strength. The digital copy of Issue 8 that we looked at comes in at a whopping 134 pages, complete with multiple high-quality illustrations on different styles, a graphic novel section, title pages for stories, drop caps galore and an eye-catchingly illustrated cover. As well as stories, *Shoreline* includes interesting reviews of sci-fi novels (so many that the magazine publishes the rest on the website). Noel Chidwick's editor's letter, gently humorous and also illustrated, points out that the theme that has emerged is people whose humanity is being tested.

SHORT FICTION ☆
PRINT
editor@shortfictionjournal.co.uk
www.shortfictionjournal.co.uk
Editor: Tom Vowler
Established 2007. Short fiction. Available direct from publisher website and at national and local literary events. All online content available to all.

GENRES: Literary. No non-fiction.

SUBMISSIONS: Open to all, during submissions window only. Submit by email to shortfiction2010@gmail.com. Guidelines at www.shortfictionjournal.co.uk/?page_id=29. Usually responds within one to three months, but only to writers whose work is being accepted. Contributors receive a print copy of the magazine.

WE SAY: 164-pages of thick, slightly shiny, paper; perfect bound, with a David Shrigley picture on the cover (we looked at Issue 9), *Short Fiction* is a heavyweight of short story publishing. The contents read like a guide to established short story writers whose work you should be paying attention to (think Alison Moore, Rhoda Greaves, Toby Litt, Alex Preston...). Subtitled 'The Visual Literary Journal', this issue is filled with black-and-white images alongside the text, plus a full-colour art supplement. There's a playfulness in the layout of the text as well: bolds, italics, font size variation and speech bubbles are all welcome additional to the rather experimental stories.

SOUTH CIRCULAR, THE
DIGITAL
hello@thesouthcircular.com
www.thesouthcircular.com
Editor: Aoife Walsh
Established 2011. Short stories. Quarterly. Only purchasers can access content (€3 per issue, PDF and ePub).

Award-nominated: Danielle McLaughlin's story *Five Days to Polling Day* (Issue 8, December 2013) was nominated for the 2014 writing.ie Short Story of the Year Award as part of the Bord Gais Irish Book Awards.

GENRES: Literary. No non-fiction.
SUBMISSIONS: Open to all, during submissions windows. Submissions welcome from anywhere in the world, but must be English language. Submit by email to submissions@thesouthcircular.com. Guidelines at www.thesouthcircular.com/submit. Responds within one to three months to successful submissions only. Contributors are paid a set rate and receive a digital copy of the magazine.
WE SAY: We looked at Issue 5: 40 pages of simple and effective design. The cover image is from Irish-Swedish design duo, M&E Design, and is eye-catching and rather beautiful. That the magazine only features four stories means they can use the space to display the text properly. Each story has a title page, and has been laid out with care. A lattice effect image bookends them. The contributors to this magazine are usually emerging writers, so this is a good submission opportunity for less-established writers.

SPELK
E-ZINE
spelkfiction@gmx.com
www.spelkfiction.com
Editor: Gary Duncan
Established 2014. Flash fiction. All online content available to all.
GENRES: Crime/thriller/mystery; literary. No non-fiction.
SUBMISSIONS: Open to all. Submit by email to spelkfiction@gmx.com. Guidelines at www.spelkfiction.com/submit-2. Usually responds within four weeks. Rejection may

occasionally include unsolicited feedback.
WE SAY: *Spelk*'s layout is a simple template. The homepage features the most recent published story, a basic menu and an alphabetical list of contributors linking to their featured stories, so you can hunt for your favourite writers. The browse function is a bit awkward – if you click on the archives, only the last story posted in the month appears, giving the false impression that *Spelk* only updates once a month. In fact, it's more like once a week, so readers keep coming back for a regular hit of sharp flash fiction – and the fiction is edgy, packing a punch in 500 words or fewer.

STORGY MAGAZINE ☆
DIGITAL AND E-ZINE
www.storgy.com
Editors: Tomek Dzido, Anthony Self, Ross Jeffery, Alice Kouzmenko
Established 2013. Fiction. All online content available to all.
GENRE: Literary. No non-fiction.
SUBMISSIONS: Open to all. Submit by email to submit@storgy.com. Guidelines at www.storgy.com/touch-us. Usually responds within one to three months. No feedback offered with rejection. Contributors receive a digital copy.
WE SAY: *Storgy* is a prime example of what an e-zine can be. The fonts are clear, the site is slick and the home page is loaded with images, but not overwhelming. We get the impression that a lot of thought has gone into making the reading experience a pleasant one: *Storgy* has nearly 6,000 Likes on Facebook, so this e-zine clearly has readers. One thing we do miss is a comprehensive archive list, but you

could argue that this just gives the new work a sense of immediacy.
See also: Storgy (prose publisher) p158

UNIFORMAGAZINE
PRINT
info@uniformbooks.co.uk
www.uniformbooks.co.uk
Established 2014. Non-fiction. Publications available direct from publisher website; by direct mail and email orders; and from independent bookshops.
GENRES: Visual and literary arts; cultural geography and history; music and bibliographic studies.
SUBMISSIONS: Open to all. Usually responds within four weeks. Rejections may occasionally include unsolicited feedback. Contributors receive print copies.
See also: Uniformbooks (poetry publisher p76 and prose publisher p166)

WORMWOOD
PRINT
Coverley House, Carlton, Leyburn, North Yorkshire DL8 4AY
01969 640399
markl.valentine@btinternet.com
www.tartaruspress.com
Editor: Mark Valentine
Established 1990. Mainly publishes non-fiction. Available direct from publisher website; by post and email order; and in independent bookshops.
Wormwood was nominated for a World Fantasy Award in 2012.
GENRES: Supernatural; decadent; fantastic.
SUBMISSIONS: Open to all. Submit by email to markl.valentine@btinternet.com. Guidelines at www.tartaruspress.com/wormwood.html. Usually responds within four weeks. No feedback offered with rejection. Contributors receive a print copy of the magazine.
See also: Tartarus Press (prose publisher) p160

Part 3:
Script publishers
and producers

Script submissions: an introduction

Script writing can be a difficult genre to crack, partly because where prose and poetry writers need only submit to an editor, scriptwriters often need to convince a whole production team that their work is worth investing in and taking to the next level. Then there are all the different genres to consider. A script that's suitable for radio, where there are no costumes to consider, might be far too expensive to produce in the theatre or on film. A script that involves a lot of subtle action and not much dialogue would be hopeless in the vocal medium of radio.

Working with local theatre groups, perhaps approaching university theatre groups and film makers, and of course working through various online forums are all viable ways to get your work produced. Then are also specialist script publishers, as well as theatres and production houses with teams actively looking for new work. The world of script is relatively small, so if you submit something a director likes, but which doesn't quite fit the bill, they may well remember your name.

In our research, we discovered that every script producer or publisher has a unique approach to working with writers: different guidelines for would-be collaborators to follow; different preferred genres. Indie publishers are usually more socially aware and engaged than their commercial counterparts; indie theatres and film-makers are the same, often looking for scripts with a political edge that makes all that work they will put in seem worthwhile.

This section includes some of the companies and presses that produce and/or publish scripts, whether for film, audio, TV or stage. There are larger companies out there too, of course (BBC, anyone?), but these producers and publishers actively want playwrights and scriptwriters to approach them and to work with them. As with submissions to book and magazine publishers, remember that these people are probably juggling a multitude of responsibilities beyond reading your script so: follow the guidelines, be patient, be polite. And don't forget to check out the mixed-form magazine section (p179) to uncover some mags that also taken accept scripts.

AURORA METRO ☆
PRINT SCRIPTS;
THEATRE PRODUCTION
67 Grove Avenue, Twickenham
TW1 4HX
020 3261 0000
submissions@aurorametro.com
www.aurorametro.com
Editor: Cheryl Robson

Established 1989. Stage. Also publishes prose (see p92). All scripts can be read in full on the publisher website; by direct mail and email orders; from selected/local chain bookshops; from independent bookshops; at local literary events; and from Amazon and other bookshop websites. All productions can be viewed in national and local theatres. Aurora Metro production *Combustion* by Asif Khan was shortlisted in 2017 for the Stage Début Award in playwright category; the Off West End Award and the Eastern Eye Award for Best Play.

GENRES: BAME; socio-political of particular interest.

SUBMISSIONS: Submissions open to all. Submit by post (67 Grove Avenue, Twickenham TW1 4HX) or by email (submissions@aurorametro.com). Guidelines at www.aurorametro.com/newsite/contact-us/submit-your-work. Usually responds within one to three months. Rejections may occasionally include unsolicited feedback. Successful playwrights receive monetary payment by negotiation, print and digital copies of the publication and are offered a discount purchase price on further copies. Free to submit.

WE SAY: *Southeast Asian Plays* is a selection of short plays by Southeast Asian playwrights: 'eight plays from seven very different nations in a region connected mainly by geography', as the fulsome introduction explains. Following the introduction, the plays are left to speak for themselves (though each is followed by a biography of the playwright and the translator). The layout is clear and easy to follow, and we'd say this is an important work, giving English speakers insight into and access to contemporary Southeast Asian theatre.

See also: prose publisher p92

BABYJANE PRODUCTIONS
FILM/TV PRODUCTION;
PRINT BOOKS (SCREEN)
+353 9145 6891
info@babyjaneproductions.com
www.babyjaneproductions.com
Executive producer: Emma Owen

Established 2015. Screen. Productions can be viewed on national and local television, and on online-only TV and film channels.

GENRES: Thriller; action; crime; biography; documentary.

SUBMISSIONS: Submissions are by invitation or from agents only. Submit by email to info@babyjaneproductions.com. Guidelines are at www.babyjaneproductions.com/get-in-touch. Usually responds to

278

submissions within one to three months. No feedback offered if rejected. Successful screenwriters receive payment (at either a set rate or a negotiated rate).

BREAD & ROSES THEATRE, THE ☆
THEATRE PRODUCTION
68 Clapham Manor Street, London SW4 6DZ
020 8050 3025
info@breadandrosestheatre.co.uk
www.breadandrosestheatre.co.uk
Established 2012. Stage production. Productions take place at local theatres. The Bread & Roses Theatre won the ICWP 50/50 Applause Award in 2015 and 2016.
SUBMISSIONS: Submissions are only accepted during specific callouts, which are listed at www.breadandrosestheatre.co.uk/playwriting. Usually responds in one to six months. Feedback is not usually offered if rejected. Successful writers may receive a set monetary payment, print publication, the production and performance of their script, and complete feedback on their script – but please be aware that not all of these apply to all submissions.

CRESSRELLES PUBLISHING COMPANY LIMITED
PRINT SCRIPTS; THEATRE PRODUCTION
10 Station Road Industrial Estate, Colwall, Worcestershire WR13 6RN
01684 540154
simon@cressrelles.co.uk
www.cressrelles.co.uk
Editor: Simon Smith
Established 1972. Focus on stage scripts. Publications available by direct mail and email order; from chain bookshops nationwide; from independent bookshops; amazon.com and other online bookshops.
GENRES: Drama; comedy
SUBMISSIONS: Submissions are open to all. Submit post (10 Station Road Industrial Estate, Colwall, Worcestershire WR13 6RN) or by email (simon@cressrelles.co.uk). Usually responds to submissions within four to six months. Rejections may occasionally include unsolicited feedback. Successful playwrights are paid a set rate, receive print copies of the publication and are offered a discount purchase price on further copies.

ENCOMPASS PRODUCTIONS
THEATRE AND FILM/TV PRODUCTIONS
liam@encompassproductions.co.uk
www.encompassproductions.co.uk
Creative producer: Liam Fleming
Established 2010. Predominantly stage production. Productions take place at local theatres, and can be seen on an online only television/film site. Encompass production *Chummy* was shortlisted for the 2017 Off West End Awards.
GENRES: Drama; comedy; sci-fi; thriller; psychological.
SUBMISSIONS: Submissions are open to all. Submit by email (thinktank@encompassproductions.co.uk). Guidelines are available at www.encompassproductions.co.uk/writerswanted. Usually responds in one to three months. Feedback is not offered if rejected. Successful writers will have their script produced and performed. If a full-length play is produced, they are paid and receive a share of profits.

GALLERY PRESS, THE
PRINT PUBLICATION
Loughcrew, Oldcastle, County Meath, Ireland
+353 49 854 1779
gallery@indigo.ie
www.gallerypress.com
Originally established in 1970 to publish the work of young Irish poets, with many of those poets becoming established, leading figures. Now also accepts plays, but only plays that have received a professional production. Submit hard copy only, and ensure you are familiar with previous publications.
See also: poetry publisher (p37)

JONATHAN WOODHOUSE
PUBLICATION
press@encompassproductions.co.uk
www.encompassproductions.co.uk
Creative producer: Liam Fleming
Established 2010. The publishing branch of Encompass Productions (p278). Publications are available from the publisher on request.
GENRES: Drama; comedy; sci-fi; thriller; psychological.

LAZY BEE SCRIPTS
PRINT BOOKS (STAGE); DOWNLOADABLE SCRIPTS (STAGE)
www.lazybeescripts.co.uk
Established 2000. Stage. All scripts are can be read in full on the publisher website, and productions can be viewed in local theatres. Accepts one-act plays, full-length plays, short plays, and sketches.
GENRES: All genres, including youth drama and pantomimes.
SUBMISSIONS: Submissions open to all. In first instance, query via the online form at www.lazybeescripts.co.uk/Publishing/Default.aspx. If the idea is approved, writers will receive an invitation to submit, subject to terms and conditions. Usually responds within four weeks. Successful playwrights receive royalty payments for sales and performance rights. Free to submit. Writers looking for feedback should approach via the paid script appraisal service, which is separate from the submission process.

MANTLE LANE PRESS
PRINT SCRIPTS (STAGE)
Mantle Arts, Springboard Centre, Mantle Lane, Coalville LE67 3DW
01530 830811
matthew@red-lighthouse.org.uk
www.mantlelanepress.co.uk
Established 2015. Stage. All scripts can be read in full on the publisher website; at local literary events; and from Amazon. Productions can be viewed in local theatres and through online-only radio.
GENRES: Contemporary stage plays on any subject; comedy; writing by/for young people.
SUBMISSIONS: By invitation only. Submit online at www.greensubmissions.com/537/mantle-lane-press/index.php?. Guidelines at www.greensubmissions.com/537/mantle-lane-press/terms.php?. Usually responds within one to three months. Rejections may occasionally include unsolicited feedback. Successful playwrights receive monetary payment at a set rate, as well as print and digital copies of the publication.
See also: prose publisher p133

PAINES PLOUGH
THEATRE PRODUCTION
4th Floor, 43 Aldwych, London WC2B 4DN
020 7240 4533

office@painesplough.com
www.painesplough.com
Artistic Directors: James Grieve,
George Perrin
Established 1974. Stage.
Productions take place at national
and local theatres, and on national,
local and online-only radio
stations. Paines Plough doesn't
publish scripts, but does work with
publishers including Nick Hern
Books. Winner and nominee of
more than 35 awards, including
Off West End, Scotsman Fringe
First and Manchester Theatre
Awards, most recently winning
the Scotsman Fringe First Award
for Growth by Luke Norris, and
nominated for Welsh Theatre
Awards' Best Playwright in the
English Language (Alan Harris,
Love, Lies and Taxidermy).
GENRES: Any (see FAQs at www.
painesplough.com/project/big-
room/send-us-your-play).
SUBMISSIONS: Submissions are
open to all. Submit via the online
form at www.painesplough.com/
project/big-room/send-us-your-
play (guidelines available at the
same address). Usually responds to
all submissions within four weeks.
Unsuccessful writers will receive a
phone call. Successful submissions
may be produced.

PAPATANGO ☆
THEATRE PRODUCTION;
PRINT BOOKS (STAGE)
360 Kingsland Road, London E8 4DA
scripts@papatango.co.uk
www.papatango.co.uk
Artistic Director: George Turvey
Producer: Chris Foxon
Established 2010. Stage.
Productions take place at national
and local theatres. Publications are
available direct from the publisher

website; from chain bookshops
nationwide; at national and local
literary events; and on Amazon.
Winner of the 2016 Alfred Fagon
Audience Award.
GENRES: New writing.
SUBMISSIONS: Submissions
are open to all. Submit by
email to scripts@papatango.
co.uk. Guidelines available at
www.papatango.co.uk/literary-
guidelines. Usually responds to
submissions within one to three
months. Rejections include a letter
containing personal feedback from
readers. Successful playwrights
receive payment (set rate),
complete feedback on the script,
and the script is produced and
performed.

QUIDS IN THEATRE COMPANY
THEATRE PRODUCTION;
RADIO/AUDIO
07793 607804
info@quidsintheatrecompany.com
www.quidsintheatrecompany.com
Production manager: Annie Begg
Established 2014. Stage.
Productions take place at local
theatres. Nominated for the
Aberdeen Business Awards 2017.
GENRES: Drama; experimental;
historical; new writing; monologue.
SUBMISSIONS: Submissions are
open to all. Submit by email to
info@quidsintheatrecompany.com.
Usually responds to submissions
within four weeks. Will provide
free feedback with rejections on
request. Successful playwrights
receive payment (set rate).

SMITH SCRIPTS
THEATRE AND FILM/TV
PRODUCTIONS; RADIO/AUDIO
PO Box 121, Wellington, Somerset
TA21 1BW

0844 997 1000
info@smithscripts.co.uk
www.smithscripts.co.uk
Editor: Paul Smith
Established 2016. Predominantly
stage production. Productions
take place at local theatres,
and online-only radio stations;
and scripts can be bought direct
from the publisher website, or by
direct mail and email order.
GENRES: Pantomime; drama;
comedy; historical; thriller.
SUBMISSIONS: Submissions are
open to all. Submit by email
(info@smithscripts.co.uk).
Guidelines are available at
www.smithscripts.co.uk/script-
submissions. Usually responds
within four weeks. Rejections may
occasionally include unsolicited
feedback. Successful writers are
paid by sales of downloaded
scripts and performance fees.

STAGESCRIPTS LTD

PRINT BOOKS (STAGE);
THEATRE PRODUCTION
0345 686 0611
admin@stagescripts.com
www.stagescripts.com
Established 2007. Stage-ready
scripts. Publications are available
direct from the publisher website,
and by post and email order.
Productions take place at local
theatres.
SUBMISSIONS: Playwrights must
have a publication/production
history to submit work. Submit
via shop.stagescripts.com/pages/
submissions.html (guidelines
available at the same address).
Usually responds in four to six
months. Feedback is not offered
if rejected. Successful writers
are paid a percentage rate:
the publishers sell scripts and
licence productions and take a
percentage, with the rest going to
the writer.

Part 4:
Competitions

the Bridport Prize

poems | short stories | flash fiction | novels

Raising funds for Bridport Arts Centre

CLOSING DATE
31ST MAY
EACH YEAR

Poems | 1st prize £5000
Max. 42 lines

Short Stories | 1st prize £5000
Max. 5,000 words

Flash Fiction | 1st prize £1000
Max. 250 words

Novel Award | 1st prize £1000
Plus up to a year's mentoring from
The Literary Consultancy (worth £2,340)
Max. 8,000 words from opening chapters

enter online | www.bridportprize.org.uk
or request a postal form at
PO Box 6910, Bridport, Dorset, DT6 9BQ

The Bridport Prize is a competition organised
to raise funds for the benefit of Bridport Arts Centre

Conquering competitions

Entering writing competitions can feel like casting your precious words into an abyss, only to watch them drop out of sight without so much as a faint splash. Nevertheless, it can be a worthwhile endeavour.

For winners, there is the actual prize money, of course, plus the glow of achievement and validation, and the notch on your CV. But even if you don't win, there's the camaraderie on social media amongst people who have entered, and the flurry of anticipation when the longlists are announced. More importantly, there is the insight that can be gained from reading the winners' work and critically applying that same eye to your own work. And bear in mind that when the competition is run by a small press or magazine, the entrance fees play a vital part in helping the press to survive.

Here are a few tips to improve your chances of winning:

- We've said it before, but please (please) read the rules carefully, and stick to them. If they call for anonymous entries, make sure your name is confined to a cover sheet only. If they call for entries by post rather than email, then post your work. If the competition is for unpublished work only, make sure your story hasn't appeared anywhere – if you win, you will be found out and disqualified. Managing a competition is hard work; don't give the organisers and judges any reason to exclude you.
- Don't go for the obvious idea. Try stepping out of your comfort zone of gender, sexuality, setting. Judges will be reading hundreds of entries so it helps if there is something (other than your brilliant writing) that makes your entry stand out.
- Avoid rushing to finish an original poem or story just minutes before the deadline. Give yourself time to step away from it for a few days – the longer the better – and edit it at least once more before you submit.
- Check that your story is actually telling a story and that your poem has something to say. Judges often comment that story entries read like an extract from a longer manuscript; or that a poem doesn't seem to have a point.
- Cut the padding. Start your story as late as possible in the narrative. With poems, ask yourself whether you really need that opening stanza. Judges, far more than normal readers, need to be ensnared by your very first line.
- Obviously you will check carefully for typos and punctuation mistakes, but look out for clichés and obvious word pairings too.

Clichés leap off the page for sifters and judges, so spend time identifying and rewriting each one.

And if the results come through and your entry isn't on the longlist?

- Don't take it personally. Remember that when there's a panel of judges, the winners are often the result of argument and compromise. With a single judge, individual taste plays a part, too.
- Don't abandon the work. Reread it critically. Could you make it stronger? If so, redraft it and try again. If it's already as good as it can be, try again with a different competition – or submit it to one of the many magazines we've helpfully listed in this book for that purpose.

Good luck!

A3 REVIEW, THE
www.TheA3Review.com
Themed monthly contest.
CATEGORIES: Poetry; flash fiction; graphic stories; comics. No more than 150 words; no larger than A6 panel.
ENTRY FEE: $5 (approx £3) per submission.
PRIZES: £175 first prize; £100 second prize; £75 third prize.

AD HOC FICTION
www.adhocfiction.com
CATEGORIES: Flash fiction.
PRIZES: Free entry to the Bath Flash Fiction Award, worth £9.

AESTHETICA MAGAZINE
www.aestheticamagazine.com/
creative-writing-award
CATEGORIES: Poetry (up to 40 lines per poem); short fiction (up to 2,000 words).
ENTRY FEE: £15+VAT for two poems or one story. Multiple entries allowed.
PRIZES: £500 (poetry winner); £500 (short fiction winner); publication in the Aesthetica Creative Writing Anthology; a selection of books from Vintage and Bloodaxe Books; one-year print subscription to Granta; full membership to The Poetry Society (poetry winner); consultation with Redhammer Management (short fiction winner); a complimentary copy of the Anthology.

ALMOND PRESS
www.dystopianstories.com/terms-and-conditions
CATEGORIES: Short stories (under 5,000 words).
PRIZES: £100 first prize; shortlisted works published in electronic and print format; visibility.

AMBIT MAGAZINE
www.ambitmagazine.co.uk
CATEGORIES: Poetry; short fiction (no more than 1,000 words).
ENTRY FEE: £6 per poem; £8 per story.
PRIZES: Each category £500 first prize, £250 second prize, £100 third prize; publication; invitation to read at launch party.

A NEW ULSTER
www.anuanewulster.wixsite.com
Occasional competition offering free editing and formatting services for novels and first-time collections.
CATEGORIES: Single poem; novel.
PRIZES: Professional feedback and mentoring.

ARACHNE PRESS LIMITED
Solstice Shorts Festival Competition
www.arachnepress.com
CATEGORIES: Poetry; short story; songs.
PRIZES: Publication/performance; selection of books; badge.

ARTEMIS POETRY / SECOND LIGHT PUBLICATIONS
www.secondlightlive.co.uk
CATEGORIES: Long poems (over 50 lines, no upper limit); short poems (up to 50 lines).
ENTRY FEE: £6 per long poem; £4 per short poem (or £9 for

three/£14 for eight).

PRIZES: Each category £300 first prize, £100 second prize, £50 third prize, book prize for commended; publication.

AURORA METRO
The Virgina Prize for Fiction
www.aurorametro.com/newsite/
virginia-prize
Open to women fiction writers, writing in English.
CATEGORIES: Novel, any genre.
PRIZES: £1,000 and conditional offer of publication.

BARE FICTION
www.barefictionmagazine.co.uk
CATEGORIES: Poetry (max 40 lines); short story (max 3,000 words); flash fiction (max 500 words); début poetry collection (between 16 and 20 pages).
ENTRY FEE: £5 per poem (£3 subscribers); £6 per flash fiction (£4 subscribers); £8 per short story (£6 subscribers); £20 per poetry collection.
PRIZES: Poetry, flash fiction and short story: £500 first prize, £200 second prize, £100 third prize, £25 highly commended; publication. Poetry collection: first prize £1,000, plus collection publication and 50 complimentary copies; second and third prizes pamphlet publication and 30 complimentary copies.

BIRD'S NEST BOOKS
www.birdsnestbooks.co.uk/short-
story-competition-2017
CATEGORIES: Short story.
PRIZES: £75 plus publication.

BLACK PEAR PRESS
www.blackpear.net
CATEGORIES: Short story (up to 1,500 words).

ENTRY FEE: £5 per story.
PRIZES: First prize £75; second prize copies of two BPP publications; longlist and other selected stories published in anthology.

BREAD & ROSES THEATRE PLAYWRITING AWARD, THE
www.breadandrosestheatre.co.uk/
playwriting-award.html
CATEGORY: Full-length script.
PRIZES: Winner receives £500; professional feedback/mentoring; and full production or a rehearsed reading. 2x runners-up receive appraisal; feedback; and mentoring.

BRITTLE STAR
www.brittlestar.org.uk/competition
Runs bi-annually.
CATEGORIES: Poetry (no longer than 60 lines); short fiction (no longer than 2,000 words).
ENTRY FEE: £5 for first entry, £3.50 subsequent entries.
PRIZES: Each category £250 first prize, £50 second prize, £25 third prize; publication; invitation to launch and prize-giving.

CASKET OF FICTIONAL DELIGHTS, THE
www.thecasket.co.uk
Launched to coincide with Get Creative, a nationwide series of events celebrating and supporting everyday creativity.
CATEGORIES: Flash fiction.
DATES: 2018 dates: 17 March to 31 May. Longlist announced in August. Winning stories published in October.
ENTRY FEE: £5 per flash fiction.
PRIZES: Winner receives £150; top three entries published on the website; top ten entries

professionally recorded and broadcast as a special audio podcast on iTunes, SoundCloud, TuneIn and Stitcher.

CATERPILLAR, THE
www.thecaterpillarmagazine.com
CATEGORIES: *The Caterpillar* Poetry Prize (no line limit; entry fee €12 per poem); *The Caterpillar* Story for Children Prize (stories up to 1,500 words; entry fee €12 per story).
PRIZES: Poetry: €1,000, publication. Short story: €500 first prize plus two-week stay at *The Moth* Retreat, €300 second prize, €200 third prize, publication.

CINNAMON PRESS
www.cinnamonpress.com/index.php/
competitions/our-awards
CATEGORIES: Début poetry collection (10 poems up to 40 lines each); poetry pamphlet (15-25 poems up to 50 lines each); début novel/novella (first 10,000 words); short story (2,000-4,000 words) and mini competitions (see website).
ENTRY FEE: £10 for pamphlet prize; £12 per entry for novels, stories, and full poetry collections; £4 mini competitions.
PRIZES: Novel/novella: a year of mentoring/100 copies plus publishing contact. Poetry collection: a year of mentoring/100 copies plus publishing contact. Poetry pamphlet: publishing contract plus 30 copies of pamphlet x3. Short story: a year of mentoring/residential writing course + publication and other prizes for runners up.

COMMA PRESS
www.commapress.co.uk
New writer showcase.
CATEGORIES: Short story (between 2,000 and 6,000 words).
PRIZES: Paid publication.

COMMA PRESS
The Dinesh Allirajah Prize for Short Fiction
www.commapress.co.uk/resources/
prizes
CATEGORIES: Short story (between 2,000 and 6,000 words).
PRIZES: £500 to the winner, shortlist published in Comma e-book.

CUCKOO CHRONICLE
Cuckoo Young Writers Awards
www.chronicle.cuckoowriters.com
Part of the Northern Writers Awards.
CATEGORIES: Prose, poetry or creative non-fiction (writers aged 14-18).
PRIZE: £300.

DAHLIA PUBLISHING
www.leicesterwrites.co.uk/2017/01/
18/rules
CATEGORIES: Short story.
PRIZES: Monetary prize; publication.

DEMPSEY & WINDLE
The Brian Dempsey Memorial Prize
www.dempseyandwindle.co.uk/
competition.html
CATEGORIES: Single poem.
PRIZES: First prize: £50 and publication of winner's pamphlet including 10 free copies; second prize £25; third prize £10. Longlisted poems published in an anthology, with a free copy for each contributor.

DOG HORN PUBLISHING
www.doghornpublishing.com
CATEGORIES: Poetry (single poem);
poetry (collection/pamphlet);
novel; short story; flash fiction.
PRIZES: Publication; professional
feedback/mentoring; introduction
to agent/publisher.

EARLYWORKS PRESS
www.earlyworkspress.co.uk/
Competitions.htm
CATEGORIES: Short story, flash
fiction and poetry held annually.
Occasional novel and poetry
collection competitions.
PRIZES: Minimum of £100 for first
place in short story competitions,
others vary. Complimentary copy
of the anthology for shortlisted
authors, plus opportunity to join
the Earlyworks Press writers' club
and/or join in further publication
projects.

EYEWEAR PUBLISHING
www.eyewearpublishing.com
The Sexton Prize; The Melita Hume
Prize; The Fortnight Prize; The
Beverly Prize; The Best New British
and Irish Poets.
CATEGORIES: Single poem
(Fortnight, and Best New British
and Irish Poets); poetry collection
(Sexton and Melita Hume);
complete work of fiction, non-
fiction, collection of poetry, or
criticism (Beverly Prize).
PRIZES: Sexton: $1,000 and
publication; Melita Hume: £1,500
and publication; Fortnight: £140;
Beverly: TBA; Best New British and
Irish Poets: anthology publication.

FAIR ACRE PRESS
www.fairacrepress.co.uk/competitions
CATEGORIES: Poetry (collection/
pamphlet).

PRIZES: Publication; launch event
alongside the judge at a poetry
festival.

FAR HORIZONS PRESS
farhorizonsmagazine.wordpress.com
CATEGORIES: Short story.
PRIZES: Books.

FISH PUBLISHING
www.fishpublishing.com
CATEGORIES: Poetry (up to 300
words); YA novel (5,000 words
or first chapter); short story (max
5,000 words); flash fiction (max 300
words); short memoir (max 4,000
words).
ENTRY FEE: Fees vary, according
to whether entering online or by
post, and whether or not entrants
include critiques. See website.
PRIZES: Poetry: first prize €1,000;
second prize week-long residency.
YA novel: publication. Short story:
first prize €3,000 and week-long
fiction writing workshop; second
prize week-long retreat plus travel
expenses; third prize €300. Flash
fiction and short memoir: first prize
€1,000; second prize Fish online
writing course. Ten stories from
each short category appear in the
prize anthology, with published
authors receiving five copies each
and invitations to read at West
Cork Literary Festival.

FITZCARRALDO EDITIONS
The Fitzcarraldo Editions Essay
Prize
www.fitzcarraldoeditions.com/prize
CATEGORIES: Book-length essays
(submit a proposal of up to 5,000
words for an essay that will be
minimum 25,000 words).
PRIZES: £3,000; writing retreat;
publication; introduction to agent/
publisher.

FLASH
National Flash Fiction Youth Competition
www.chester.ac.uk/flash.fiction/youthcompetition
CATEGORIES: Flash fiction.
PRIZES: Up to £100.

FROGMORE PRESS, THE
The Frogmore Poetry Prize
www.frogmorepress.co.uk
CATEGORIES: Poetry (no longer than 40 lines).
ENTRY FEE: £3 per poem.
PRIZES: First prize £250 and two-year subscription to The Frogmore Papers; first runner-up £75 and one-year subscription; second runner-up £50 and one-year subscription. Shortlisters receive a selection of books.

GALLEY BEGGAR PRESS
www.galleybeggar.co.uk
CATEGORIES: Short story (up to 6,000 words).
ENTRY FEE: £10 per submission.
PRIZES: Winner chooses between £1,000 or year-long editorial support for a writing project; each shortlisted writer receives £150; each longlisted writer receives £50 of book tokens and a four-book subscription to Galley Beggar Press.

HAPPENSTANCE PRESS
www.happenstancepress.com/index.php/poetry-submission/monthly-competition
CATEGORIES: Poetry (single poem); short quizzes/fun competitions.
PRIZES: Books.

HOLLAND PARK PRESS
www.hollandparkpress.co.uk
CATEGORIES: Poetry (single poem); short story.

ENTRY FEE: Free.
PRIZES: £200 and publication.

INDIGO DREAMS PUBLISHING
www.indigodreams.co.uk
CATEGORIES: Poetry (collection/pamphlet) and single poem.
PRIZES: Publication.

INK SWEAT & TEARS
www.inksweatandtears.co.uk
In association with Café Writers Commission.
CATEGORIES: Poetry pamphlet (12 page plus a proposal).
ENTRY FEE: £10.
PRIZES: £2,000 and publication, plus 100 copies of the pamphlet.

INTERPRETER'S HOUSE, THE
Open House
www.theinterpretershouse.com/competition
CATEGORIES: Poetry (50 lines max).
ENTRY FEE: £3 for single poems, £10 for three poems.
PRIZES: £500 first prize; £150 second prize; £100 third prize; seven highly commended; publication.

JOTTERS UNITED LIT-ZINE
www.jottersutd.wix.com/jotters-united
CATEGORIES: Poetry; short story (max 2,000 words).
PRIZES: Publication; selection of books.

LINEN PRESS
www.linen-press.com
CATEGORIES: Short story; first novel chapter.
PRIZES: Professional feedback and mentoring; choice of Linen Press books.

LONDON MAGAZINE, THE
www.thelondonmagazine.org/category/tlm-competition

292

CATEGORIES: Poetry (up to 40 lines); short story (up to 4,000 words, no flash fiction).
ENTRY FEE: £7 first poem; £5 per subsequent poem. £10 per story.
PRIZES: Poetry £300 first prize, £200 second prize; £150 third prize. Short story £500 first prize, £300 second prize, £200 third prize. Publication.

MAGIC OXYGEN

www.magicoxygen.co.uk/molp4
Plants a tree in Boré, Kenya, for every entry received.
CATEGORIES: Single poem (up to 50 lines); short story (up to 4,000 words).
PRIZES: across each category: 1st prize £1,000; 2nd prize £300; 3rd prize £100; highly commended x2 £50.

MOTHER'S MILK BOOKS

www.mothersmilkbooks.com/index.
                        php/writing-prize
www.mothersmilkbooks.com/index
                        .php/pamphlet-prize
CATEGORIES: Poetry (pamphlet); poetry (single poem); prose.
PRIZES: Money; publication.

MOTH, THE

www.themothmagazine.com
CATEGORIES: *The Moth* Poetry Prize (no line limit; entry fee €12 per poem); *The Moth* Short Story Prize (stories up to 6,000 words; entry fee €12 per story); *The Moth* Art Prize (portfolio of 5-10 2D artworks; entry fee €20 per portfolio).
PRIZES: Poetry €10,000 first prize, €1,000 runner-up x3, publication. Short story €3,000 first prize, writing retreat second prize (w/€250 stipend), €1,000 third prize, publication. Art two-week retreat with €1,000 stipend.

MSLEXIA

www.mslexia.co.uk/competitions
Women writers only.
CATEGORIES: Novel (first 3,000 words for book of at least 15,000 words); short story (up to 3,000 words); flash fiction (up to 300 words); novella (tba); poetry (tba).
ENTRY FEE: £25 per novel entry; £10 per short story; £5 per flash fiction. Poetry and novella tba.
PRIZES: Novel: £5,000 for the winner. Short story: first prize £2,000; second prize £500; third prize £250; three finalists £100; publication for all. Flash fiction: first prize £500; three finalists £50; publication for all. Poetry and novella TBA.

NEW WELSH REVIEW/READER

The New Welsh Writing Awards
www.newwelshwritingawards.com
CATEGORIES: Non-fiction long-form essay (5,000 to 30,000 words).
ENTRY FEE: Free.
PRIZES: First prize: £1,000, e-book publication; professional feedback/mentoring; introduction to agent/publisher. Second prize: writing retreat (week). Third prize: residential weekend. All three receive a year's subscription. Runners-up: considered for publication.

NINE ARCHES PRESS

Primers – with The Poetry School
www.campus.poetryschool.com/
    primers-guide-your-poems-into-print
CATEGORIES: Poetry pamphlet (initial six poems; further 14 if shortlisted).
ENTRY FEE: £14 per submission.
PRIZES: Publication; professional feedback/mentoring.

NORTH MAGAZINE, THE
The Poetry Business Book & Pamphlet Competition; and The Wordsworth Trust Single Poem Prize
www.poetrybusiness.co.uk/
        competition-menu/competition
CATEGORIES: Collection/pamphlet (20-24 pages of poems; full-length manuscript if shortlisted).
ENTRY FEE: £28.
PRIZES: Main competition: equal share of £2,000; pamphlet publication x3; book publication x1; launch readings; magazine publication. Single Poem Prize: £1000, £300 and £200 prizes; launch readings.

NOTTING HILL EDITIONS
The Notting Hill Editions Essay Prize
www.nottinghilleditions.com/essay-
        prize-intro
CATEGORIES: Essays (between 2,000 and 8,000 words on any subject).
ENTRY FEE: £20 (includes a copy of previous competition winners book).
PRIZES: £20,000 first prize; £1,000 runners-up x5. Publication.

OUEN PRESS
www.ouenpress.com
CATEGORY: Short story (theme changes annually).
PRIZES: First prize £300; 2x runners up receive £100.

PAPATANGO
www.papatango.co.uk/literary-
        guidelines
CATEGORY: Script.
PRIZES: Winner receives approximately £8,000 in commission and royalties; publication; professional feedback and mentoring; an introduction to an agent/publisher; and production of the script.

PAPER SWANS PRESS
www.paperswans.co.uk
CATEGORIES: Poetry (collection/pamphlet), single poem and flash fiction.
PRIZES: Publication.

PEIRENE PRESS
www.peirenepress.com
CATEGORIES: Flash fiction.
PRIZES: Books.

PENNY DREADFUL, THE
www.thepennydreadful.org/index.
        php/novellaprize
CATEGORIES: Novella (between 15,000 and 35,000 words).
ENTRY FEE: €10 per manuscript, maximum two manuscripts per entry.
PRIZES: €2,000 and publication.

PENNYSHORTS
www.chiplitfest.com/short-story-
        competition-rules
Sponsors ChipLitFest Short Story competition.
CATEGORIES: Short stories (not exceeding 3,000 words).
ENTRY FEE: £5 per submission.
PRIZES: £500 first prize, £100 second prize, £50 third prize.

POETRY IRELAND
Trócaire Poetry Ireland Poetry Competition
www.poetryireland.ie/education/
        trocaire-poetry-ireland-poetry-
        competition
CATEGORIES: Single poem.
PRIZES: Money; tickets to a writing retreat; and professional feedback/mentoring.

POETRY LONDON
www.poetrylondon.co.uk/competition
CATEGORIES: Poetry (up to 80 lines).
ENTRY FEE: £7 per poem (£3 for subscribers).
PRIZES: £1,000 first prize; £500 second prize; £200 third prize, and publication in magazine. commendations £75 and online publication x4.

POETRY SPACE
www.poetryspace.co.uk/poetry-space-competition
CATEGORIES: Poetry (up to 40 lines).
ENTRY FEE: £5 per poem.
PRIZES: £250 first prize; £100 second prize; £50 third prize. Publication for top twenty poems, plus complimentary copy for poets.

POETRY WALES
www.poetrywales.co.uk
CATEGORIES: Poetry pamphlet (20-24 pages long).
PRIZES: Up to £250 and publication.

PROLEBOOKS / PROLE
www.prolebooks.co.uk/poetry%20competition.html
CATEGORIES: Poetry (collection/pamphlet), single poem and short story.
PRIZES: Monetary prize; publication.

PYGMY GIANT, THE
www.thepygmygiant.com/competitions
CATEGORIES: Flash fiction.
PRIZES: Book tokens and low-level fame.

REFLEX FICTION
www.reflexfiction.com/flash-fiction-competition-rules
CATEGORIES: Flash fiction.
PRIZES: 1st place £1000; 2nd place £500; and 3rd place £250.

RIALTO, THE
Nature and Place Poetry Competition
www.therialto.co.uk
Working with the RSPB, BirdLife International and the Cambridge Conservation Initiative.
CATEGORIES: Poetry (single poem); poetry (collection/pamphlet).
ENTRY FEE (SINGLE POEM): £6 for first poem, £3.50 for subsequent poems.
PRIZES (SINGLE POEM): £1,000 first prize, £500 second prize; writing retreat worth £550 third prize; plus a personal tour with Mark Cocker (East Anglia), and a personal tour with Nick Davies (Wicken Fen).

SHOOTER LITERARY MAGAZINE
www.shooterlitmag.com
Annual short story and poetry competitions.
CATEGORIES: Short story (any theme) and poetry (any theme, up to 125 lines long).
DATES: Short story 2018: opens January with April deadline. Poetry 2018: opens August with November deadline.
ENTRY FEE: Short story: £7 per story. Poetry: £3 per poem, or £8 for three poems. All entrants of both competitions receive an e-copy of the magazine issue featuring the winning writing.
PRIZES: 2017 prizes: first prize £150, runner-up £30. Short story 2018: prize pot of £500. Poetry 2018: prize pot of £150. All winners are published in print and online, runners-up are published online.

SHORELINE OF INFINITY
www.shorelineofinfinity.com
CATEGORIES: Short story.
PRIZES: £80; publication.

SHORT FICTION
www.shortfictionjournal.co.uk
CATEGORIES: Short fiction (up to 6,000 words).
ENTRY FEE: £7 per story.
Prizes: £500 plus publication for first prize; £100 plus publication second prize; place in masterclass third prize.

SMITH|DOORSTOP BOOKS
The Poetry Business Book & Pamphlet Competition; and The Wordsworth Trust Single Poem Prize
www.poetrybusiness.co.uk/
        competition-menu/competition
CATEGORIES: Collection/pamphlet (20-24 pages of poems; full-length manuscript if shortlisted).
ENTRY FEE: £28.
PRIZES: Main competition: equal share of £2,000; pamphlet publication x3; book publication x1; launch readings; magazine publication.
Single Poem Prize: £1000, £300, and £200 prizes; launch readings.

SOUTHWORD JOURNAL/ EDITIONS
www.munsterlit.ie
CATEGORIES: Gregory O'Donoghue Poetry Prize; The Seán Ó Faoláin Short Story Competition; The Fool for Poetry Chapbook Competition.
PRIZES: Poetry: first prize €1000, a week's residency, publication and a trip to Cork, Ireland; second prize €500 and publication; third prize €250 and publication. Ten runners-up are paid a €30 publication fee. Poetry pamphlet: first prize €1000; second prize €500. Both receive 50 complimentary copies of their chapbook. Short story: first prize €2,000, publication and week-long residency; second prize €500 and publication; four shortlisted writers receive a publication fee of €120.

STAND
www.standmagazine.org
CATEGORIES: Runs occasional competitions; see website for details.

STINGING FLY, THE
The Davy Byrnes Short Story Award
www.stingingfly.org
Run every five years.
CATEGORIES: Short story.
PRIZES (AS OF 2014): €15,000 first prize; €1,000 for five runners-up; publication.

STORGY
www.storgy.com
CATEGORIES: Short story (max 5,000 words). Check website for updates.
ENTRY FEE: £5 (check website for details).
PRIZES: Varying prizes, e.g. £500 first prize; £25 book vouchers for runners-up x2; publication; signed book.

[UNTITLED] / UNTITLED FALKIRK
untitledfalkirk.blogspot.co.uk
CATEGORIES: Poetry (single poem); poetry (collection/pamphlet); short story.
PRIZES: Publication; writing opportunities.

WALES ARTS REVIEW
www.walesartsreview.org
CATEGORIES: Short story; flash fiction; non-fiction.
PRIZES: Various prizes.

WASAFIRI MAGAZINE
www.wasafiri.org/wasafiri-new-writing-prize.asp
Open to anyone without a complete book in the category entered.
CATEGORIES: Poetry; fiction; life writing. 3,000 word limit or five poems max.
ENTRY FEE: £6 (one category); £10 (two categories); £15 (three categories).
PRIZES: £300 for the winner of each category; publication.

WAYWISER PRESS, THE
The Anthony Hecht Poetry Prize
www.waywiser-press.com/hechtprize.html
US-based office.
CATEGORIES: Book-length poetry collection.
ENTRY FEE: $27.
PRIZES: $3,000; publication; invitation to read.

WRECKING BALL PRESS
www.wreckingballpress.com
CATEGORIES: Poetry collection/pamphlet).
PRIZES: Publication.

We hope this guide will be useful for you during your publishing journey. If you know of a publisher that should have been included (or one that has closed down since the publication of this book), please contact us so that we can include/omit them from the next edition.
indiepressguide@mslexia.co.uk

With special thanks to...

All those writers and editors who alerted us about additional presses to include – or defunct ones to omit. Your help is so appreciated.

All the indie press editors, assistants and publicity directors who helped us compile this guide by filling out forms, answering questions, sending sample copies and spreading the word. We hope that some great writers will use these pages to discover you.

All those writers who also helped us discover presses by sharing their work on social media.

The Mslexia team – Kay Hadden, Martha Lane and Emily Owens – and volunteers Lisanne Buijze and Emma Whitehall, for their unflagging enthusiasm in the face of piles of publication samples, and for their hard work in reviewing them.

Last, but absolutely not least, Charlea Harrison, who worked her way calmly and efficiently through literally hundreds of proofs, survey responses and word documents, collating and checking information – and without whom this Second Edition would probably still not be finished.

Index

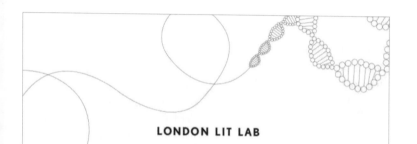

LONDON LIT LAB

If you're a writer, at some point you'll probably need some help. You might be struggling to find new ideas, want support completing or honing a story, or need a trusted eye to check your beloved manuscript. London Lit Lab's Zoe Gilbert and Lily Dunn are both published authors with years of teaching and mentoring experience, and a friendly and open attitude.

Courses
Our popular courses include:
- ➤ Write & Edit a Story in a Weekend (London)
- ➤ Continuing to Write Post-MA (London & Bristol)
- ➤ Beginner's Intensive One-day Workshop (London)
- ➤ Folk Tales in New Fiction (London)

Find more about our courses at **www.londonlitlab.co.uk**

Critique and Mentoring
We can design a package for you, at competitive prices. Get in touch at **info@londonlitlab.co.uk**

'Lily and Zoe offer teaching and coaching at the highest level. Their workshops have a reputation for encouraging excellence and creativity in a supportive environment. I am always recommending them.' Julia Bell, Course Convenor, MA Creative Writing, Birkbeck.

'Very clear, instructive and informative. The course opened my eyes to so many possibilities.' Mary, Continuing to Write.